Maintenance engineering and management

A guide for designers, maintainers, building owners and operators, and facilities managers

CIBSE Guide M

CIBSE

© February 2008 The Chartered Institution of Building Services Engineers London

Registered charity number 278104

ISBN 978-1-903287-93-4

Typeset by CIBSE Publications Department

Printed in Great Britain by Page Bros (Norwich) Ltd., Norwich, Norfolk NR6 6SA

Foreword

Publication of this document as CIBSE Guide M demonstrates how operation and maintenance has gained importance and recognition within the industry. Clients in particular are becoming more aware of the need to ensure that the many engineering services within their buildings, on which they rely to continue their businesses, will continue to function reliably and safely.

The skills needed to run the many different types of buildings, ranging from relatively simple such as those in the domestic sector to the complex such as hospitals and data centres, are now being recognised as a profession with defined levels of competency. Such skills are the key elements in the armour of the property and estate operator when demonstrating diligent management of the services that provide the environment in which we all live and work. Failure to maintain these services can result in contravention of health and safety and other legislation, reduced plant life and increased plant breakdowns affecting both business and staff performance.

Since the previous version of this document (published as *Guide to ownership, operation and maintenance of building services*), issues such as the environment, climate change and carbon management have all risen significantly up the political agenda. Clients are not only aware of these issues but wish to be seen to be actively addressing them, due in part to the realisation that the UK building stock uses some 50% of UK's energy.

This Guide is the result of the continuing work of the CIBSE Maintenance Task Group. It is intended to be an authoritative and valuable tool for those involved in the operation and maintenance of building services. It is also intended to be an important source of reference for designers, manufacturers, installers and professional advisors.

I would like to record my thanks to all those who have generously provided their time and shared their knowledge during the preparation of CIBSE Guide M.

John Armstrong
CIBSE President 2007–2008

CIBSE Maintenance Task Group

J H Armstrong (Chairman)
R Farman (Jones Lang LaSalle)
A Garside (Royal Bank of Scotland)
A Green (Faithful and Gould)
M Griffiths (Laing plc)
P Hastings (BSRIA/Cofathec)
P Hiddleston (Dalkia)
S Hunter (Dalkia)
R Jeeves (Jeeves Associates)
P Kee (Hurley Palmer Flatt)
G Keller (HVCA)
Hseih-Min Loy (Faithful and Gould)
A Martin (Knowledge Based Management)
D R O'Bryan (ASTM GBC Consultancy)
G Prudence (Essex County Council)
A G Saville (Armville Consultancy)
M Smith (BSRIA)

Acknowledgements

The Institution wishes to acknowledge Building Life Plans for providing some plant life data and the Building Cost Information Service (BCIS).

Editor

K J Butcher

CIBSE Director of Information

J Balian

Note from the publisher

This publication is primarily intended to provide guidance to those responsible for the design, installation, commissioning, operation and maintenance of building services. It is not intended to be exhaustive or definitive and it will be necessary for users of the guidance given to exercise their own professional judgement when deciding whether to abide by or depart from it.

Contents

1 Introduction

Summary

This chapter provides a general introduction to the Guide and outlines its scope and contents.

Building services engineers provide the internal environmental conditions that enable business processes to function at an optimum level while providing comfort conditions for occupants to achieve their maximum performance potential. This is reflected in the CIBSE's motto: 'For the greater comfort of mankind'. The engineering services that provide this comfort need to be properly operated and maintained throughout their lifespan, which could extend to more than 30 years, to ensure that they continue to perform efficiently and viably.

This guidance is a continuation of work by the CIBSE Maintenance Task Group and is intended for the benefit of all those involved in the operation and maintenance of engineering services. It is an update of the original version of this document which was published in 2000 as *Guide to ownership, operation and maintenance of building services*[1]. Principal areas of revision relate to legislation that has occurred since the first edition, the impact of climate change and subsequent need to address energy use and building performance. A list of definitions has been included as section 1.2. Chapter 6 has been rewritten, based on CIBSE Guide F: *Energy efficiency in buildings*[2]. Chapter 7 has been expanded to include information from CIBSE Knowledge Series KS4: *Understanding controls*[3] and CIBSE Guide H: *Building control systems*[4]. Chapter 10 has been developed further on O&M Manuals. A more detailed consideration of risk assessment and risk management has been provided in chapter 11. Chapter 12 now contains a more comprehensive list of indicative maintenance and utilities costs. Additional information and revisions to the table of plant life expectancies in chapter 13 make it more comprehensive and useable. Chapter 16 covers the wide range of legislation applicable to building operation.

The Task Group has tried to avoid duplicating information that is available elsewhere. Where information already exists, the reader is provided with a comprehensive reference rather than repeating the work of others.

The intention has been to identify current good practice and address topics of particular interest and relevance to those involved at all levels in engineering services maintenance. This includes designers, manufacturers, installers, maintainers, building owners, occupiers and operators, professional advisers and specialist providers. It is not expected that the reader will read the publication from cover to cover; rather that it will be used for reference and guidance as needs arise.

Maintenance of engineering services within the UK represents an annual business value conservatively estimated at some £7 billion. Maintenance is not the most glamorous aspect of engineering and much of it is focused on preventing failure rather than creating something tangible. It is, however, becoming more analytical and numerically based, including dealing with failure probabilities, management of resources, determining redundancy within systems and minimising risk.

This document is intended to bring maintenance into a sharper focus by helping building and property operators become more aware of their responsibilities and duties. It will also help services designers to appreciate their role in providing installations that are safe, economic to maintain and operate, and capable of giving satisfactory performance over their full lifespan.

1.1   Scope and structure

The scope of each chapter of this Guide is summarised as follows:

—   Chapter 1: *Introduction* describes the objectives of maintenance and outlines the scope and content of the Guide. A list of definitions is provided.

—   Chapter 2: *Guidance for building services designers* is particularly aimed at designers and identifies the areas that need to be taken into account from the earliest concept stage. Clients should also read this section as it emphasises matters that will need to be resolved and may need their commitment. Trouble free use of the engineering services is a key objective of any property operator both in terms of economic, reliable performance and ensuring that legislation is complied with. The needs of the client are also discussed and emphasis is given to the importance of the designer fully understanding what the client expects to achieve.

—   Chapter 3: *Maintenance techniques and their applications*: some of the techniques of maintenance have become complex and sophisticated, although opportunities for applying the full range within engineering services are often limited. This section gives an overview of the techniques to provide a general introduction and basic understanding of terminology and application.

— Chapter 4: *Maintenance contracts* looks at the contractual aspects of maintenance, covering types of contract, their content, legal details that influence which option to select, and how occupiers and property operators can ensure that the contract intent is being achieved.

— Chapter 5: *Maintenance strategy and inspection frequencies*: the maintenance strategy influences design decisions and therefore needs to be established before the start of detailed design. When the property and its services become fully operational, the maintenance strategy must be implemented and any revisions carefully assessed to determine the impact of any such changes on original design decisions. The section discusses this and the ongoing control of maintenance.

The provision of regular servicing and maintenance will sustain the operating efficiency and prolong the effective life of the engineering plant. The chapter covers optimising the frequency, sources of detailed work schedules, statutory requirements and adjusting the frequency of attendance.

— Chapter 6: *Energy efficiency and maintenance* provides guidance on energy efficiency aspects of operating and maintaining, based on information in CIBSE Guide F: *Energy efficiency in buildings*[1].

— Chapter 7: *Controls for building services*: the performance of any engineering installation will be directly related to the equipment that regulates and controls its operation. Chapter 7 provides a source of reference and guidance to this specialist area, including the purpose of controls, maintenance requirements, BMS and upgrading control systems.

— Chapter 8: *Commissioning and testing*: immediately following installation, a crucial stage is commissioning and testing; this ensures that the design intent is, or can be, achieved in practice. Procedures that need to be implemented for this to be successful are described.

— Chapter 9: *Handover procedures* addresses the handover of a fully functional, completed installation to the client. It identifies the point when the client accepts responsibility for security, insurance, operation and maintenance, and other contractual obligations triggered at that time. Also listed is information to be passed to the client and which forms part of the Health and Safety File.

— Chapter 10: *Operation and maintenance information*: having put the services into operation, a key element towards long-term satisfactory performance is the availability of detailed and comprehensive operation and maintenance information. The importance of such information has been reinforced by the Construction (Design and Management) Regulations 2007[5] and the subsequent requirement for such information in the Building Regulations[6]. Information on the content, preparation and updating of the documentation is provided.

— Chapter 11: *Risk assessment and management procedures*: part of any system design, installation and operation is the acknowledgement that there will be areas of risk, extending up to the final disposal stage. This is addressed, and the section includes a comprehensive assessment of how different risk activities relate to the risk categories of business, design, operation and disposal. It also addresses dependency modelling and system redundancy.

— Chapter 12: *Owning and operating costs* gives a detailed introduction to all aspects of cost management including types of cost data, bench marking, levels of information, cost prediction, budget control and investment appraisal. Indicative costs for maintenance and utilities for a range of buildings is provided

— Chapter 13: *Economic life factors and end of economic life*: possibly the most frequent question related to engineering plant and equipment is 'how long will this last?' or 'how long should this last?' The answers will depend on criteria such as the standard of maintenance, the severity of use and the degree of reliability required. Chapter 13 provides guidance and includes a comprehensive table of plant and equipment with details of life expectancies.

— Chapter 14: *Maintenance audits*: having accepted the installation, produced a maintenance contract, agreed service frequencies and identified the full cost of ownership, the property operator or occupier may require that the performance of the maintenance provider be assessed. Chapter 14 offers a standard approach using objective criteria that, for example, can give a year-on-year comparison.

— Chapter 15: *Condition surveys*: at any time during the life of a property it can be useful to assess the condition of the building or its engineering services. The chapter covers the types of survey techniques including thermal imaging and methods of recording information.

— Chapter 16: *Legislation, compliance and good practice*: the legislation applicable to the operation of buildings and their engineering services continues to expand and ensuring compliance is a growing concern to building operators. This section attempts to identify and summarise the current position. However with the constantly changing situation as more requirements are established, this can only provide an overview of key legislation relevant to building services, it cannot be fully comprehensive and is not intended to identify every item of legislation or code of good practice.

— Chapter 17: *Health and comfort* considers the relationship between the internal environment of a building, the health, safety and welfare of its occupants, and how the engineering services influence these factors. The guidance concentrates on air quality and thermal conditions, but also covers other aspects of occupant comfort.

— Chapter 18: *Training*: it is essential to ensure that maintenance engineers keep their skills up to date, continue to be aware of safety and health matters, develop individuals to maximum potential and help promote participation, ownership and belonging in a job that can be remote from the direct employer. Chapter 18 provides comprehensive information, including identification of needs, budgets, methods of provision and certification.

Given the potential interest of this Guide to all involved in building operation and maintenance, it is difficult to define the expected readership. Table 1.1 gives a general indication of where particular readers may find information of most value.

Table 1.1 Guide to relevance of chapters

Readership	Chapter/section
Property owners, occupiers and operators	All chapters
Designers	2, 3, 6–11, 12, 15, 16, 17
Installers	5, 6–10, 12, 16, 17
Manufacturers	2, 5–9, 10, 11, 12, 13, 16, 17
Commissioning engineers	2, 6, 7, 8–10, 16, 17
Maintenance providers/specialists	All chapters
Professional advisers	All chapters

1.2 Definitions

Benchmarking

The process of measuring performance (including price) of facilities services and comparing the results internally or externally (BS EN 15221-1[7]).

Beneficial occupation

Also referred to as 'partial possession'. The term given to early occupation of the works by the client where the contract does not include a specific provision for this.

Breakdown maintenance

The operation of restoring an item to fulfil its original function after failure in its performance.

Budget

A plan expressed in money terms, prepared and approved prior to the budget period and may show income, expenditure and the capital to be employed.

Buildability

The extent to which the design of a building and its engineering services facilitates ease of construction.

Business focused maintenance

The prioritisation of maintenance aligned to the core business activities taking into account business risk, resilience and performance of plant installations to ensure that the function of the business is optimised.

Capital expenditure (CAPEX)

The cost of acquiring, producing or enhancing fixed assets.

Chartered engineer (CEng)

A member of a chartered engineering institution who is concerned with the progress of technology through innovation, creativity and change; who is competent by virtue of appropriate education, training and relevant experience; who is able to analyse and develop solutions to engineering problems; who makes contributions to the development of engineering science and assumes personal responsibilities as the occasion demands for specific engineering matters.

Client

The person responsible for the running and maintenance of a building who has responsibilities under the CDM Regulations[5], who may or may not be the legal owner; the legal owner's agent or representative; or the building occupier. The client will be the person to whom a professional advisor will report, and who will be able to order maintenance works to be carried out, or:

An organisation that specifies needs and procures facilities services by means of a facility management agreement. *Note*: the client has a general and/or key function in all stages of the relationship with the service provider (BS EN 15221-1[7]).

Commissionability

The extent to which the design and installation of the building services facilitates capability of commissioning, or:

The ability of a system to be commissioned satisfactorily (CIBSE Commissioning Code M[8]).

Commissionable system

A system designed, installed and prepared to specified requirements in such a manner as to enable satisfactory commissioning to be carried out (CIBSE Commissioning Code M[8]).

Commissioning

The advancement of an installation from static completion to working order according to specified requirements.

Commissioning engineer

The person undertaking the commissioning procedure (CIBSE Commissioning Codes B[9] and M[8]).

Commissioning management

The planning, organisation, co-ordination and control of commissioning activities (CIBSE Commissioning Codes B[9], M[8], R[10], W[11]).

Commissioning specialist

The person responsible for setting the installation to work, and regulating and balancing it to achieve the specified performance, or:

The firm (or person) appointed to carry out specified duties in connection with commissioning engineering services in accordance with a commissioning specification (CIBSE Commissioning Code M[8]).

Competent person

A person who has sufficient training and experience or knowledge and other qualities to enable him/her properly to assist in devising and applying preventive and protective measures to control the risks presented by the business (Management of Health and Safety at Work Regulations 1999[12]), or:

A person who, by virtue of training and experience, can perform specified tasks satisfactorily and safely (BS 3811[13]).

Condition based maintenance

Preventive maintenance initiated as a result of knowledge of the condition of an item from routine or continuous monitoring.

Condition monitoring

The continuous or periodic measurement and interpretation of data to indicate the condition of an item to determine the need for maintenance (BS 3811[13]).

Condition survey

The subjective assessment of the present condition of an individual component or complete system, or:

The compilation of data referring to the state of repair of a building and its engineering services.

Consumable item

Maintenance material that is not item specific and not repairable (BS EN 13306[14]).

Consumable stock

Expendable materials (e.g. oils, lubricants, packing) that are held available for maintenance purposes (BS 3811[13]).

Corrective maintenance

Maintenance carried out after a fault intended to put an item into a state where it can perform a required function in a safe and efficient manner (BS 3811[13]).

Customer

Organisational unit that specifies and orders the delivery of facilities services within the conditions of a facilities management agreement (BS EN 15221-1[7]).

Defects liability period

The period following completion of the project during which the supplier will be liable for defects in their work and obliged to compensate the client for them.

Designer

A suitably qualified and experienced person or body appointed to design the engineering services and to specify the plant and equipment which will satisfy the client's requirements

Economic life

The estimated number of years until that item no longer represents the least expensive method of performing its function.

Emergency maintenance

Maintenance that is necessary to be put in hand immediately to avoid serious consequences (BS 3811[13]).

End user

Persons receiving facilities services in a permanent or temporary way (BS EN 15221-1[7]).

Energy manager

A person charged with the task of controlling the economical use of energy. The energy manager should be consulted whenever maintenance policies or programmes are discussed, particularly with regard to monitoring energy consumption (CIBSE TM19[15]).

Energy sources

All fuels and forms of motive power supplied to the system (CIBSE Commissioning Code M[8]).

Engineering services

The plant and equipment that provide comfort conditions and other facilities within the built environment such as communications, fire protection and security.

Facilities management

The integration of multi-disciplinary activities within the built environment and the management of their impact upon people and the workplace (British Institute of Facilities Management), or:

An integrated process to support and improve the effectiveness of the primary activities of an organisation by the management and delivery of agreed support services for the appropriate environment that is needed to achieve its changing objectives (British Institute of Facilities Management).

Failure modes, effects and criticality analysis (FMECA)

A method for establishing all potential failure modes in a system, and the possible effects of these failures on the system. The criticality analysis plots the probability of failure against the severity of the consequences. The results of the criticality analysis highlight failure modes with high probability and severe consequences allowing remedial actions to be prioritised.

Fine tuning

Local adjustment to the system where usage and system proving have shown such a need. This may also include re-assessment of control set points and values to achieve optimum performance (CIBSE Commissioning Codes M[8] and W[11])

Installer

The person or organisation responsible for installing, commissioning and handing over the completed engineering services to the client.

Log book

The permanent record of calibration settings and performance test results that are initiated by commissioning engineers and maintained thereafter by responsible persons (CIBSE Commissioning Code M[8])

Key performance indicator

Clients' measures that provide information about performance of facilities service delivery (BS EN 15221-1[7]).

Maintainability

The ability of a product under stated conditions of use, to be retained in or restored to a specified condition when maintenance is performed by personnel having specified skill levels under stated conditions and using prescribed procedures and resources (Def. Stan. 00-49[16]).

Maintenance

The combination of all technical and associated administrative actions intended to retain an item in, or restore it to, a state in which it can perform its required function (BS 3811[13]).

Maintenance contractor

The organisation whose primary function is maintenance of building services plant and equipment. The organisation may also be responsible for operating plant and equipment.

Maintenance management

The organisation of maintenance within an agreed policy (BS 3811[13]).

Maintenance policy

A written statement issued by, or on the authority of, the client and acceptable to the owner of the building or the nominee (see section 5.2.2).

Maintenance specialist

An individual or organisation whose specialism is the maintenance of building services and can offer advice on its planning and execution.

Occupants

Management and employees of the owner or tenants and all persons legally entitled to be on the premises. In general, this will be all those who benefit from the engineering services.

Operational risk

The risk of loss, resulting from inadequate or failed internal processes, people and systems, or from external events

Operating expenditure (OPEX)

Expenditure on the supply and manufacture of goods and the provision of services charged in the accounting period in which they are consumed. This includes repairs and depreciation of the fixed assets as distinct from the provision of those assets.

Operating instructions

The document that describes in detail the methods of starting up, running, shutting down, controlling and monitoring the system under all foreseeable conditions.

Owner

The person or body having a legal interest in the building. This includes freeholders, leaseholders and those holding a sublease which bestows a legal right to occupation and gives liabilities in respect of safety or building condition.

Planned maintenance

Maintenance organised and carried out with forethought, control and the use of records to a predetermined plan (BS 3811[13]).

Preventive maintenance

Maintenance carried out at predetermined intervals or corresponding to prescribed criteria and intended to reduce the probability of failure or the performance degradation of an item (BS 3811[13]).

Professional advisor

A suitably qualified and experienced person or body appointed by the client to provide independent advice on requirements for the design, operation and maintenance of the engineering services.

Risk based maintenance

The prioritisation of maintenance following a FMECA study. Focuses maintenance effort to achieve optimal benefit whether this is equipment reliability improvement or maintenance cost reduction, according to the priorities of the organisation.

Scheduled maintenance

Preventive maintenance carried out in accordance with an established schedule, e.g. time interval, number of operations, mileage.

Service level agreement

Agreement between the client/customer and the service provider on performance and conditions of facilities service delivery (BS EN 15221-1[7]).

Service provider

An organisation that manages and/or delivers facilities services as specified in a facilities management agreement. *Note*: the service provider can be internal or external to the client organisation (BS EN 15221-1[7]).

System

A collection of equipment or appliances connected together or associated to form a complex unity, placed in position and set up for use within a built environment.

Tasking

The identifiable elements of maintenance requirements for specified plant or equipment.

Testing

The measurement and recording of system parameters to assess specification compliance.

Whole life costing

The continuous process of forecasting, recording and managing costs throughout the life of an equipment, with the aim of optimising whole life costs and military output.

References

1   *Guide to ownership, operation and maintenance of building services* (London: Chartered Institution of Building Services Engineers) (2000) (out of print)

2   *Energy efficiency in buildings* CIBSE Guide F (London: Chartered Institution of Building Services Engineers) (2004)

3   *Understanding controls* CIBSE KS04 (London: Chartered Institution of Building Services Engineers) (2005)

4   *Building control systems* CIBSE Guide H (London: Chartered Institution of Building Services Engineers) (2000)

5   The Construction (Design and Management) Regulations 2007 Reprinted March 2007 Statutory Instruments 2007 No. 320 (London: The Stationery Office) (2007)

6   The Building Regulations 2000 Statutory Instruments 2000 No. 2531, as amended by The Building (Amendment) Regulations 2001 Statutory Instruments 2001 No. 3335 and The Building and Approved Inspectors (Amendment) Regulations 2006 Statutory Instruments 2006 No. 652 (London: The Stationery Office) (dates as indicated)

7   BS EN 15221-1: 2006: *Facility management. Terms and definitions* (London: British Standards Institution) (2006)

8   *Commissioning management* CIBSE Commissioning Code M (London: Chartered Institution of Building Services Engineers) (2003)

9   *Boilers* CIBSE Commissioning Code B (London: Chartered Institution of Building Services Engineers) (2002)

10   *Refrigeration* CIBSE Commissioning Code W (London: Chartered Institution of Building Services Engineers) (2002)

11   *Water distribution systems* (London: Chartered Institution of Building Services Engineers) (2003)

12   The Management of Health and Safety at Work Regulations 1999 Statutory Instruments 1999 No. 3242 (London: The Stationery Office) (1999)

13   BS 3811: 1993: *Glossary of terms used in terotechnology* (London: British Standards Institution) (1993)

14   BS EN 13306: 2001: *Maintenance terminology* (London: British Standards Institution) (2001)

15   *Relationships for smoke control calculations* CIBSE TM19 (London: Chartered Institution of Building Services Engineers) (1995)

16   *The UK Ministry of Defence Standard for Reliability and Maintainability Guide to Terminology Definitions* Def Stan 00-49 (London: Ministry of Defence) (date unknown)

2 Guidance for building services designers

Summary

This section is primarily aimed at building services designers, but contains information of interest to all those involved in the management, installation, commissioning, operation and maintenance of engineering services within buildings.

It outlines the wide variety of aspects that designers should take into account when preparing their designs and highlights those issues that should be considered to ensure that a building services installation can be practically installed, efficiently maintained and will meet the client's written and implied aspirations in the short-, medium- and long-terms.

The section does not cover the normally accepted tasks of preparing calculations and drawings of the building services designs; these are identified in other CIBSE Guides.

A client's exact requirements with respect to the operation and maintenance of engineering services may vary but the primary interest in almost every case will be to achieve trouble-free usage of the accommodation or premises. While there will be a general acceptance that engineering services need to be operated safely and efficiently there will also be an expectation that such operation is within the scope of staff who are trained and competent and will not require a proliferation of specialists. Similarly, clients will not expect the maintenance demands to infringe unduly on their usage of the premises.

Operating costs will typically be understood to include energy, maintenance and replacing minor plant items, with major plant replacement programmed and budgeted for separately. Client attitudes to running costs, however, may be more varied. At one end of the spectrum, a client may view running costs as being marginal when assessed against accommodation costs and staff wages, and simply accept operating and maintenance expenditure. At the other end of the spectrum, a client may challenge even modest running costs in order to keep these under continuing review and to seek cost-effective means of improving efficiency and reducing expenditure.

The environmental impact of a building and its engineering services is another area where client attitudes may vary significantly. The attitude of some clients may be simply to ensure that they 'stay on the right side of the law'. Others may be committed to a formal environmental policy which could include third-party assessment and certification[1-4]. Current Government guidance on corporate social responsibility (CSR) and changing legislative requirements are aimed at maximising the benefits and minimising the downsides of the environmental impacts of a business; the designer should play a significant role in this important arena.

The *BRE Environmental Assessment Method*[5] (BREEAM) offers a comparative and quantitative means of assessing environmental aspects of particular design features.

2.1 Designers' responsibilities

In addition to the general responsibilities of designers to consider all aspects of the installation, there is a specific obligation under health and safety legislation and The Construction (Design and Management) Regulations 2007[6] (CDM Regulations) to ensure that the designs can be safely installed and maintained, and to identify areas of abnormal risk related to these activities.

Designers have a key role in the performance of building services systems as a whole and, whether dealing with the overall concept design for large systems or preparing detailed drawings for a small part of an overall system, they should begin by addressing a range of questions which may include those given in Table 2.1. It is the responsibility of the designer to be aware of these aspects and to ensure that the installation meets its objectives.

The wide range of design responsibilities requires the design engineer to have a sound understanding of other construction disciplines and to be aware of the potential benefits of sharing ideas with other specialists. Wherever possible, designers should aim to present their proposals to installers, commissioning specialists and maintenance engineers, and to seek their input at an early stage before design proposals become too entrenched. This could help to facilitate later stages of the development and implementation of the design.

As shown in Figure 2.1, the ability of the designer to make cost-effective changes to the design, which may also influence life cycle costs, is most significant at the earliest stages of design. As the process moves to detail design and eventual construction, the costs of making changes rises dramatically.

A useful source of first-hand experience about the operation and maintenance implications of the plant and equipment within buildings is the facilities manager (FM).

Table 2.1 Typical questions to be addressed by designers

Task	Question
Briefing	Do I clearly understand my role and responsibility for the installation?
	Do I really know what the client wants and what the brief is?
	Have I examined all the options?
	What redundancy is required (i.e. what standby facilities in case operating units fail)?
Materials	Have I thought about the materials to be used and their suitability and life expectancy?
	Have I selected materials that are safe to work with?
Installation and commissioning	Have I thought about how practical it is to install my designs?
	Do I have the necessary information to make that judgement?
	Will the installation be easy to commission?
	Can tolerances on design parameters be relaxed?
Operation and maintenance	Will my design work consistently and reliably to achieve the design objective under a wide variety of conditions?
	Can the installation be operated and maintained safely by personnel with normal skill levels?
Costs	Have I established the client's requirements in respect of:
	— first costs?
	— operating costs (including energy and maintenance)?

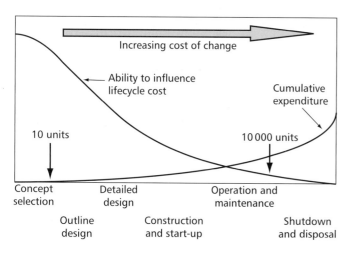

Figure 2.1 The ability to influence life cycle costs and the cost of changes at the various stages of a building's existence

For projects within an existing building feedback should be sought from the FM. For new developments, it may be possible to identify locations with similar requirements and discuss the design implications with the FM.

'Private Finance Initiative' (PFI) projects typically utilise specialist consultants (operating on behalf of the financial institution) to identify improvements that will reduce long term running costs and improve the profitability of projects/reduce the risk of project costs not being able to be paid back.

Appendix 2.A1 provides a design guide to maintainable buildings and could be used as a checklist to ensure that each stage and item is identified and addressed.

2.2 Advising and guiding the client

A client may seek advice and guidance on operation and maintenance aspects as outlined above or on related matters at any stage of the design process. In responding to such requests, building services designers should bear in mind the particular requirements and interests of the client and ensure that full account is taken of these.

In presenting the required guidance the designer should:

— use simple, straightforward language and terminology

— offer options for action wherever possible and outline disadvantages as well as advantages

— recommend a favoured option and state reasons for this choice

— provide indicative costings, both capital and running, for each favoured option.

2.3 Clients' requirements

2.3.1 Establishing the requirements

It is important for engineering services designers to ensure that they fully understand a client's requirements at an early stage of the design. In principle, the requirements should be relatively easy to define but most clients will have a limited understanding of operation and maintenance matters. This makes it important for designers to develop a detailed understanding in conjunction with the client and to ensure that all aspects are clarified at an appropriate stage of the design development (see Appendix 2.A1). Where this is not achieved, there may be a subsequent need for design changes with adverse effects on both the programme and costs.

An effective means of targeting and clarifying client requirements is the use of a questionnaire. Clearly, the questionnaire needs to be particular to the project but certain core questions will be generally applicable. These may include, but not be limited to, those listed in Table 2.2. However, designers should develop their own in-house questionnaires or checklists geared to the way they operate their design procedures. These approaches will help to ensure a more purposeful approach to particular design development.

As with all documentation, user feedback is essential to ensure that the questionnaire or checklist remains relevant and fully effective. The content of such documen-

tation should, therefore, be reviewed regularly, account being taken of previous experience. As noted above, facilities managers can play an important role at this stage.

In addition to establishing client understanding of and attitudes to operation and maintenance matters, building services engineers should acquaint themselves with the level of understanding by other members in the design team. In some instances it may be necessary for the building services engineer to take the lead in such matters on behalf of the team.

2.3.2 The brief

The key to success in any designer's activity is to understand the brief fully. Designers should not assume that they know the client's brief through either previous experience or knowledge of similar projects; they should interrogate the client and any representatives in an organised way. This can be carried out by a series of meetings or by a questionnaire (e.g. as Table 2.2). At a later stage it is essential to explain the completed engineering designs fully and clearly to the client and to ensure that the designs meet the requirements and aspirations.

Table 2.2 Establishing the client's requirements

Core questions to be asked

1 Is the client to be the building user? If not, is the building user known?

2 Does the client wish to operate on a total facilities management basis? If so, what are the responsibilities of each design discipline within the overall strategy?

3 Does the client have a maintenance policy?

4 Will the client employ a maintenance engineer/premises manager/facilities manager?

5 Will the maintenance engineer/workforce be in-house or engaged under contract?

6 Does the client have a maintenance budget in mind?

7 Will the engineering services be operated:
   (a) continuously?
   (b) intermittently for a 5-day week multi-shift operation?
   (c) intermittently for a 5-day week single-shift operation?
   (d) using other operational patterns?

8 What would be the feasible/preferred timing for routine servicing or monitoring attention on daily, weekly, monthly and quarterly bases (e.g. time of day; day of week; etc.)?

9 What would be the most demanding response time for emergency servicing in event of breakdown? To what parts of the building or services installation would this apply?

10 Is total contract maintenance to be applied to any plant items or parts of the building engineering services installations (i.e. where a contractor takes responsibility for the operation, maintenance and programmed replacement of plant or systems for a projected period of time)?

11 Is any part of the building required to be kept free from entry by maintenance personnel?

12 Does the client have preconceived views of economic life of plant and equipment? What is the investment programme for eventual plant replacement? (See sections 12 and 13.)

13 Ascertain any preferred (or not preferred) manufacturers or suppliers.

14 Does the client intend to establish and maintain an asset register for plant and equipment items? (Design data schedules can take account of this and be compiled in an appropriate format.)

15 Ascertain client in-house policies or requirements and the level of client understanding of:
   (a) health and safety
   (b) climate change
   (c) energy use
   (d) other environmental considerations
   (e) quality
   (f) refrigerants
   (g) water hygiene
   (h) energy efficiency
   (j) other aspects.

Where there are design options that balance capital cost against life expectancy, running costs, maintenance costs and reliability, these should be carefully analysed so that the client has the opportunity to consider these issues and contribute to decisions on the options.

If the brief is not defined by the client, the designer should clearly outline a brief and explain the assumptions and the design parameters to the client and obtain the client's agreement (preferably with a formal agreement and some form of sign-off). This particularly applies to the degree of redundancy associated with the various engineering elements of a scheme (see chapter 11, *Risk assessment and management procedures*). It is for the client, not the designer, to decide the amount of standby capacity, the redundancy built into systems and the acceptability of likely rectification times in the event of failure. Designers, however, have a duty of care to advise the client of these decisions.

2.3.3   Specifying materials and components

The selection of systems and choice of equipment are as important as the basic calculations required in designing the system. The true test of a designer's ability is whether, ultimately, the systems and installation meet the client's brief and not simply whether the calculations are correct.

Designers must consider the suitability and life expectancy of materials being proposed in the light of the client's brief. The solution, for example, in a retail outlet where life expectation may be five years could be substantially different to an office development where lease and dilapidation requirements may stretch over 30 years. Clear guidance on these matters is important and, where appropriate, designers should carry out whole life costing studies. (See chapter 13, *Economic life factors and end of economic life*).

The reliability of any system is only as good as the weakest part. Designers must be careful, therefore, to avoid specifying or allowing minor elements to be used that could have an adverse effect on the overall system performance.

Under the CDM Regulations[6], the responsibility lies clearly with the building services designer to ensure that the designs can be safely installed and maintained. The safety implications of materials and components, both in the short and the long-term, is important and designers should carry out their duties under the CDM Regulations with care and diligence to ensure that any potential hazards or risks are identified and controlled (see chapter 16). This analysis should include any intrinsic or environmental dangers the designer is aware of, together with any risks associated with installation of systems and any safety issues associated with maintenance.

Where designers are encouraged to test the market, seek alternatives or write a performance specification, they should ensure that their requirements are properly specified and carefully detailed. This is essential to allow the materials offered by the installation contractor to be checked to ensure that they meet the performance specification, and do not cause dangers or difficulties which have not previously been considered. It is the designer's

responsibility to ensure that the installation contractor has sufficient information to make an informed choice when alternatives are sought.

2.4   Installation

Engineering systems are an important part of the overall construction process and must be practical to install. The buildability of the installation (i.e. the extent to which the design of the building facilitates ease of construction, subject to the overall requirements for the completed building) and its maintainability should be considered fully by designers when preparing the outline and detailed designs, as improvements are much simpler to implement at this stage. For instance, the equipment should be safely accessible and special tools or access platforms provided as necessary to ensure ease of access.

It is important that designers ask for, and obtain, information on decisions being taken on other constructional elements during the design process to ensure that the services design can be installed. Questions to be asked include:

— What is the type of structure?

— Are holes for services distribution systems to be pre-cut or formed *in situ*?

— How are items to be suspended from the structure?

— What is the permissible floor loading of the plant rooms?

— How is the equipment to be hoisted into position?

— Is there a site restraint on dimensions or weight?

— What are the delivery times?

— When is the equipment required on site in the construction process?

— Are the procurement lead times sufficient?

Designers need to resolve all these and many other issues at the specification stage. It is also important that the designed and specified installation is robust and will operate under the variety of conditions likely to be experienced during its operational life.

2.5   Design parameters

Building services designers have the responsibility to ensure that equipment and systems are capable of being operated in accordance with the design parameters and can be efficiently and safely maintained. As part of this, the written procedures provided to fulfil operational and maintenance requirements should be easily understandable and achievable.

Designers should also ensure that, either by specification or written recommendation, they set out general requirements for maintenance of their installation. This may be by reference to recommended standards or procedures set out in this Guide and in other publications, such as the HVCA's *Standard maintenance specification for building services*[7], to ensure that all important maintenance issues are fully considered. The preparation of particular, detailed maintenance procedures may be a separate responsibility.

In many instances, the designer's involvement with operation and maintenance does not extend beyond specifying and reviewing the content of operation and maintenance manuals for delivery to the client at handover. The CDM Regulations[6] require the content of these manuals to form part of the Health and Safety File for the project, the requirements of which are covered in principle by the Approved Code of Practice[8]; see also chapter 16. The actual content of the manual will depend on the specification (usually prepared by the designer). It should also be noted that under Part L2 of the Building Regulations[9] there is a requirement to provide information to enable building users to operate buildings in an energy efficient manner, this obligation could also extend to the designer.

In most instances, the maintenance manual is not suitable as a basis for equitable, competitive tendering for an operation and/or maintenance service. In tendering, every effort must be made to ensure comparability of offers; for this reason, tenders need to be based on precise and definitive details of the maintenance procedures to be applied and their frequency. It is equally important for a maintenance specification to define the standard of technician or craftsman required and their competence to undertake the work as well as outlining some form of bench mark to cover the quality of the work carried out.

2.6 First-year operation and maintenance requirements

In the first year of usage of a new installation it is typical contractual practice to require installers, as a form of warranty of their work, to be formally responsible for any equipment, component or operational defects that may arise or become apparent. While designers are not directly implicated in this liability, their professional duty of care usually leads to an involvement in some way. This may be limited to identifying the true cause of any problem and providing an independent opinion on the apportionment of responsibility for a defect. In the case of more fundamental defects, the designer's input may entail a review of the design itself and, in extreme cases, the recommendation of design changes.

Details of all such defects should be fed back to the design team for formal review. This approach helps designers to work towards a 'right first time' approach and to filter out plant, equipment or design features that could lead to potential problems.

It is stressed that the contractual or warranty responsibilities for defects in the first 12 months after formal completion have nothing to do with, and do not include responsibilities for, routine maintenance.

It should also be noted that the need for maintenance attention does not lessen because the installation is new. Indeed, it may be argued that the need for maintenance attention during the running-in period is greater than under normal circumstances.

A possible option for first-year operation and maintenance is to enter into a short-term (12 month) contract with the installer. This question is more of a contractual than a design nature but designers should be prepared to outline the pros and cons of the option to the client. Where this course is contemplated, it is important for the designer/specifier to arrange for first-year operation/maintenance to form part of the actual installation tender; this ensures true competitiveness for both elements and the overall package.

This approach has the advantage that responsibility for first-year defects and for routine operation and maintenance are vested in the same organisation. In addition, there may be advantage to be gained from the knowledge of the installation held by the installer's organisation. It is not uncommon, however, for liaison between the maintenance and installation divisions of an organisation to be limited so that any potential benefit may not apply in practice.

In the event of a defect arising where the first-year operation and maintenance service is provided by an organisation independent of the installer, there is scope for the installer to argue that maintenance attention (or lack of it) was contributory to the problem. Therefore, this could be deemed to invalidate the installer's warranty. For this argument to be acceptable, it would be necessary to demonstrate that the applied operation and maintenance techniques were not in accordance with the instruction manual provided and that the installation did suffer damage as a direct result of this. Conclusive demonstration, one way or the other, may be difficult.

References

1   BS EN ISO 14001: 2004: *Environmental management systems. Requirements with guidance for use* (London: British Standards Institution) (2004)

2   BS ISO 14004: 2004: *Environmental management systems. General guidelines on principles, systems and supporting techniques* (London: British Standards Institution) (2004)

3   BS 8555: 2003: *Environmental management systems. Guide to the phased implementation of an environmental management system including use of environmental performance evaluation* (London: British Standards Institution) (2003)

4   BS EN ISO 19011: 2002: *Guidelines for quality and environmental management systems auditing* (London: British Standards Institution) (2002)

5   *BREEAM: BRE Environmental Assessment Method* (website) (Garston: Building Research Establishment) (http://www.breeam.org) (accessed March 2008)

6   The Construction (Design and Management) Regulations 2007 Reprinted March 2007 Statutory Instruments 2007 No. 320 (London: Her Majesty's Stationery Office) (1994)

7   *Standard maintenance specification for building services* (electronic database) HVCA SFG20 (London: Heating and Ventilating Contractors Association)

8   *Managing construction for health and safety: Construction (Design and Management) Regulations 1994* Approved Code of Practice HSE L54 (London: Health and Safety Executive) (1995)

9   The Building Regulations 2000 Statutory Instruments 2000 No. 2531, as amended by The Building (Amendment) Regulations 2001 Statutory Instruments 2001 No. 3335 and The Building and Approved Inspectors (Amendment) Regulations 2006 Statutory Instruments 2006 No. 652 (London: The Stationery Office) (dates as indicated)

Appendix 2.A1: Design guide to maintainable buildings

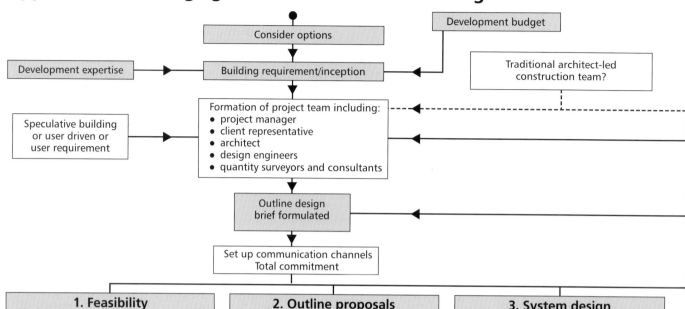

1. Feasibility		**2. Outline proposals**		**3. System design**	
Location of building		Minimise services requirement		Verify outline proposal report and integrate with all design team members	
Weather/climate		Simplify those deemed necessary			
Air/noise quality required		Highlight essential services		Ensure facilities representative included (if not previously appointed on design team)	
Microclimate for broad assessment of A/C requirements and possible options		Incorporate changes to feasibility brief			
Effect of weather on services equipment located outdoors		Future use of building, change of use, service capacity		Firm up envisaged maintenance regime, initiate selection of staff/contractor if possible (i.e. management organisation)	
Electrical/heat/cooling load (estimates)		Plantroom locations			
Sustainability options/concepts		Focus on daylight, max/min temperatures		Design systems to user-agreed specification:	
Types of systems and equipment available		Specific space/weight requirements		• HV electrical distribution	
Possible services (essential)		Plantroom/riser sizes		• LV system	
Reliability/availability requirements		Services required/specialists?		• generators	
Associated maintenance requirements		Business systems, IT/telephones etc.		• UPS system	
Cost implications		Shell and core — fit out?		• IT power distribution	
Services life cycle/building lifespan		Integration of services		• lighting systems	
Buildability of services		Specific use of floor/spaces		• lifts/escalators	
Adaptability		Lighting and power requirements		• cooling systems	
Local issues affecting service designs (e.g. transport/access to site)		Fresh air requirements		• heating systems	
		Water system options and consumption		• water systems/public health	
Feedback from previous buildings of same type		Control systems for services		• air systems	
		Risk analysis/contingencies		• acoustic provision	
Sick building syndrome considerations		Waste removal/disposal		• handling systems	
Highlight/weed out rogue options		Legislation/statutory requirements		• fuel/energy systems	
Consider maintenance resources required and integrate with user preference (i.e. on-site/remote, in-house/contracted)		Environmental considerations		• fire systems	
		Energy categorisation		• building management system	
		Access to plant areas and systems		• occupant controls?	
Report containing possible options, main services requirements, maintenance, reliability and costs to design team		Closer investigation of possible services		Reconsider possible maintenance implications	
		Reliability/availability, maintainability			
		Standardisation of services		Reconsider:	
Health and safety plan		Assist architect in glazing choice (possible manufacturers/spares)		• reliability/availability	
				• maintainability	
		Possible maintenance resource/costs		• access	
		Are sufficient skills available to maintain equipment which is deemed necessary?		• manufacturers/types available	
				• availability of spares/services	
		Facilities support on board with proposals to date?		• alternatives considered	
				• compliance of systems with legislation	
		Keep it simple		• integration/coordination between systems and other project disciplines	
				• identification of plant	
				Access for maintenance/replacement	
				O&M documentation requirements	
				Standardisation of services	
				Life cycle costing	
				Risk assessments/contingencies	
				Commissionability/retests	
				Avoid overspecification	
				Report to design team/client	
				Flexibility/growth capacity	
				Energy performance rating	

Early appointment of management commissioning team to test commissionability of evolving services design

Constant feedback to client or known specifier of options, reliability, maintainability and direct/long-term/alternative costs.

Continuous awareness to provide an energy efficient, environmentally considered solution

| Multidisciplined design/ project team? | Design consultant or contractors? | Client and occupier |

Operations and maintenance/facilities expertise: interface communication or member of design team?

Use of building, occupants (number and times), operational culture, workspace use?
How will it be handed over/operated?
What form of O&M documentation will be required?
(Accuracy is important: a poor or loose brief can be disastrous later in project)

4. Detailed design

Review options to date	
Include feedback from client	
Detail design/specification of all services of system design	
Practical application of:	
• reliability	
• maintainability	
• standby/duplication	
• access	
• standardisation	
Maintenance regime:	
• on site	
• remote	
• in-house	
• contract	
Specialist contractors requirement	
Operational competency required	
Legislation and testing possible	
Energy Performance in Buildings Directive:	
• environmental impact	
• opportunities to utilise renewables	
Availability of service	
Manufacturers/types	
Are components available?	
Avoid 'specials'	
Will design conditions always be met?	
How often will they not? What is inconvenience/cost?	
Frequency/convenience of plantroom access	
'Design out' problems and excess maintenance	
Prefabrication/construction efficiencies	
Outline O&M documentation:	
• planned preventive maintenance	
• breakdown maintenance	
• corrective maintenance	
• condition-based maintenance	
Computerised maintenance required?	
Isolation points — test facilities	
Coordination of services and disciplines for best overall solutions	
Specific service levels identified	
Future expansion	
Plant renewal implications	
Complete services life costs	
Keep it simple!	
Final solutions report to project team	
Is client fully aware of what will he/she be getting and overall costings?	
Scope — how/who will manage?	

5. Production information

Tender/contract information	
Specifications	
Precise O&M documents	
Form of handover (guide etc.)	
Bill of quantities	
Work stages/CDM Regulations	
Method of installation	
Commissioning specification and programme	
Expected results of commissioning?	
Training requirements and staff available for training	
O&M regime identified	
Operational and energy regulations	
Control and retention of site information and O&M documents	
Operational procedures	
Spares requirement	
Highlight associated legislation, codes of practice and guides	
Clarify performance service levels	
Full support of facilities team	
Develop service risk management plan	
Identify O&M cost separately	
Adequate retention specified?	
Penalties for poor maintenance	
Complete tender documents	

6. Tender

| Tender evaluation | |
| Presentations to ensure contractors fully committed to specification including service level, maintainability, energy and environmental requirements | |

7. Pre-construction

| Method statements to ensure compliance with CDM Regulations and all other requirements | |

8. Construction

Ensure installation is as design drawings to include valves, drain points and access	
Manufacturers specified are actually used	
Adequate on-site control	
Commissioning team on site to see installation process	
Allow adequate time for commissioning	
Facilities/operational staff presence on site	
Draft O&M documentation handed over early in construction	

9. Commissioning

Full test of operations to design spec.	
Maintainability	
All site documentation controlled and offered at handover	
Facilities team involved with commissioning	
CBM/vibration techniques used to check equipment to standards and specification	
Early completion of final handover documentation	
'Stave off' occupation until thoroughly commissioned	
All defects remedied	
Facilities team training complete	
Equipment labelling adequate	
Energy verification (rating)	

10. Handover

Legislative items in place	
Maintenance regime in place	
O&M/asset information, health and safety in place	
Minimal defects to clear	

11. Occupation

BMS 'fine tuned' over 1st year of building occupation	
The optimum, energy efficient building meeting user requirement	
Re-check energy	

| Feedback occupation and experience, knowledge for benefit of future projects | |

3 Maintenance techniques and their applications

Summary

The section outlines a series of items that can influence an organisation in establishing its maintenance policy. The management of maintenance is subdivided into 'technical' and 'control' elements, and the objectives of each are summarised.

The principal options for maintenance are discussed and the various types described together with some examples of prospective applications. Guidance is given on the establishment of a maintenance policy for an organisation and the choices of maintenance strategy open to the maintenance or facilities manager.

A flowchart is presented to help in deciding the optimum type of maintenance to apply to a particular installation and an example is given of the typical range of services that can be covered by maintenance.

The engineering plant and equipment used in buildings serve a variety of purposes. They provide the environmental conditions which make occupants comfortable (e.g. heating, ventilation, air conditioning, lighting), communication facilities (e.g. telephones, staff location systems and data transmission equipment), normal and emergency standby power supplies (electrical distribution systems, batteries and generators) and basic necessities such as water supplies. Once such services are installed in the building, they require continuing attention to ensure that they operate correctly and economically and that they are available for use when required.

As an example, most buildings are provided with heat by boiler plant which converts the potential energy in fuel to realisable heat in the building, using a combustion process. The efficiency of this conversion will depend on the condition of the plant involved. If it is properly adjusted and monitored, there will be a commensurate saving in energy use, stemming from a high level of operational efficiency. Inadequate or no attention could mean that the plant is unsafe to operate.

Such adjustment and monitoring, and other activities that ensure plant is available and can perform its required function, are in essence the maintenance requirements.

Many reasons can be put forward to justify maintenance being carried out, such as to:

— comply with the law, in particular health and safety requirements

— comply with the terms of occupation (e.g. lease)

— protect the value of the property as an investment

— maximise plant utilisation and minimise non-availability of the engineering services

— provide a service to the building occupants

— ensure a safe, healthy environment for the building occupants

— ensure energy is used efficiently

— project and help protect a corporate image

— fulfil a business need.

3.1 Management of maintenance

Management of maintenance can comprise more than the control of activities associated with each item of equipment and can be addressed broadly under the headings of 'technical' and 'control'.

The technical content includes determining what plant is to be maintained, how and when; identifying problems and diagnosing causes; monitoring effects; preparing and analysing records and technical information; initiating procedures to cope with situations before they arise; and ensuring that the chosen techniques are achieving the required results.

The control element is aimed at providing the required technical service at minimum expense, and can involve management of labour, spares and equipment to match the workload; locating where work is required; organising transport; setting priorities; and coordinating action. It can extend to setting budgets, monitoring expenditure, identifying high maintenance cost plant and collecting information to form a basis for decision making.

Effective maintenance management minimises the costs associated with the non-availability of an engineering service. It should be recognised that in addition to enabling the engineering services to be available when required, maintenance is vital to ensure that the services retain their value as assets within the building.

3.2   Options

Maintenance of engineering plant and services within buildings has traditionally been carried out in a variety of ways by a variety of people. For buildings with relatively simple engineering services, e.g. small shops and commercial offices, small schools and industrial units, the building operator may view the services installations in much the same way as those for domestic premises. Similar options exist. For example, basic routine maintenance may be done to meet statutory requirements (see Appendix 5.A2), with plant and equipment being left until it breaks down, on the assumption that adequate resources can be called on for action when such an event occurs. Typical organisations that might be used are the utility supply companies, and local contractors offering a similar service. Large organisations such as local authorities may have some form of agreement, either formal or informal, with local or national contractors to respond to such breakdown situations at agreed labour rates. Supervision of such work may be by an individual or organisation specifically appointed for this purpose by the building operator, the local manager of the property, or at the discretion of the contractor.

A second option is to make a more formal arrangement for a particular property with a maintenance contractor. Examples could be a service and maintenance agreement with the utility supply company for gas-fired equipment, or regular testing of the electrical installation by an electricity supply company. Such services will also be offered by maintenance contractors. The Heating and Ventilation Contractors Association (HVCA) operates an independent inspection and assessment scheme which verifies compliance with recognised industry standards by its members.

A third option is to employ directly a maintenance labour force which routinely inspects and maintains all the engineering services. For building operators with small to medium sized property, the cost of employing such personnel cannot usually be justified — where such staff are employed they would probably be expected to carry out additional tasks, such as portering and message services or waste disposal. They may be regarded as 'general handymen', able to turn a hand to most routine problems but calling on specialist advice when non-routine problems occur.

In larger buildings such as major office complexes, shopping centres, hospitals and hotels, where there can be a variety of engineering plant and services, some perhaps providing essential services, a more formal maintenance structure needs to be adopted. The principal options are:

— use directly employed labour

— let the work to a maintenance contractor.

Table 3.1 Comparison between contract and directly employed service provision

Contract	Direct labour
Flexible service provided	Workforce more familiar with plant and equipment
Large workforce potentially available to get work done faster	Workforce available immediately to respond to problems
Workforce has skills and experience to tackle complicated jobs	Workforce may not have specific skills
Workforce does not have to be reduced in size after major jobs	Difficult to hire and fire as work load fluctuates
Special tools and equipment provided by contractor	Additional or specialist tools need to be provided when required
Monitoring by client may be necessary	In-house supervision required
Versatile workforce; can handle many types of jobs	Breakdowns or other emergencies likely to delay other work
Productivity may be measured	May not be possible to measure productivity
Short term contracts may not inspire full commitment to the client	Potential for greater accountability
Can offer performance guarantees	
Can provide plant replacement guarantees or extended warranties	

— combining the above with sub-contracts let for specialist equipment and services such as fire alarms, chiller plant, BMS and water treatment.

In a particular case, reasons will exist for adopting any of these options.

Table 3.1 provides some comparisons between service provision by contracted-in labour and directly employed labour.

As the size of building or property estate increases, so does the justification for employing a specialist to be responsible for maintaining the engineering services. Directly employed labour and maintenance contractors may sub-let work on specialist equipment where they have insufficiently detailed expertise.

3.3   Types of maintenance

Maintenance can be divided into two broad categories: unplanned and planned. Figure 3.1 provides an overview.

In unplanned maintenance there is no organised arrangement to follow and everything is carried out as a reaction to a situation, possibly resulting in prolonged breakdowns, frustration and loss of control. Unplanned maintenance suggests that the building operator takes no responsibility for the failure of the engineering services and the inevitable consequences. It could put building operators at risk of not meeting their statutory requirements and is not recommended as a technique to be adopted. It is, therefore, not considered further.

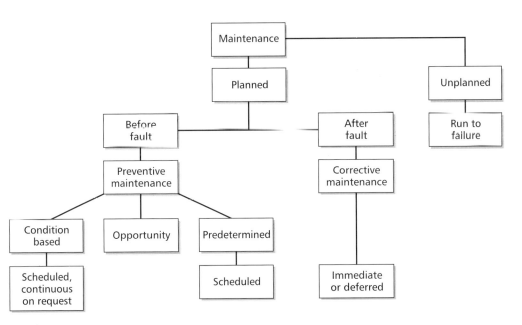

Figure 3.1 Overview of planned and unplanned maintenance

Planned maintenance is organised, controlled and follows a recognisable procedure. It can take several forms, such as:

(a) *Preventive maintenance*: carried out at predetermined intervals or corresponding to prescribed criteria and intended to reduce the probability of failure.

(b) *Corrective (or 'reactive') maintenance*: work done once a fault has occurred to restore plant to normal operation; this approach would be subject to prior agreement by the building user that this is an acceptable basis for maintenance.

(c) *Immediate maintenance*: necessitated by unforeseen breakdown or damage and needing to be put in hand immediately.

(d) *Scheduled maintenance*: preventive maintenance carried out to predetermined intervals, number of operations, hours run etc. The HVCA's *Standard maintenance specification for building services*[1] covers the majority of building services plant and equipment. This provides a useful source of reference for maintenance requirements and typical frequencies.

(e) *Opportunity maintenance*: work done as and when possible within the limits of operational demand.

(f) *Design-out maintenance*: other forms of maintenance may be inappropriate, therefore maintenance needs are 'designed-out' to achieve the required level of reliability.

(g) *Condition-based maintenance*: work initiated by trends highlighted by routine or continuous monitoring of the condition of plant, such as general performance or specific parameters (e.g. bearing vibration and motor-winding temperature).

(h) *Reliability-centred maintenance*: based on the operational requirements of specific plant in relation to known reliability information.

(i) *Business-focused (or 'risk-based') maintenance*: prioritising maintenance according to the core business activities, taking into account business risk, resilience and performance of the installed plant to ensure the function of the business is optimised.

(j) *Run to failure*: the consequences are such that plant can be safely and cost effectively run to destruction without serious loss of service and there is no risk of failing to comply with statutory requirements. This may assume there is a standby unit that will automatically operate on failure of the duty unit.

Whichever overall maintenance plan is adopted, it is likely to consist of a mixture of these methods. It needs to start with an assessment of what is effective followed by a decision as to what is desirable and a consideration of the resources available in terms of labour, materials and facilities; together, these should provide a rational basis for preparing a programme of planned maintenance.

Condition-based maintenance is initiated by monitoring the condition of plant. This is becoming more applicable to building services as the techniques gain understanding and credibility, the instruments and equipment become simpler and cheaper, and clients become more demanding in terms of plant reliability. The concept is that a parameter can be established which gives a good indication of plant condition and also reflects the likely mode of failure. By monitoring this parameter, the required timing and type of maintenance can be determined. Monitoring can be assessed by establishing trends over time to identify marked departures from the normal, or by condition checking where readings are compared with established parameters for the particular item of plant or equipment on a 'go/no go' basis.

Various techniques are available, generally requiring routine plant inspections. These include visual inspections; thermography, oil wear analysis; terrography, temperature, pressure, speed and flow monitoring; vibration analysis; bearing shock measurement, voltage, current, power, frequency monitoring; and non-destructive testing. Plant that could justify condition monitoring would typically be:

— expensive to maintain

— expensive to replace if run to failure

— failure could lead to high consequential costs

— failure could lead to an unacceptable situation (creating a safety hazard or causing an essential building function, such as a data processing, to cease to operate)

— critical to the overall building operation.

'Designing-out' may appear an ideal solution but should be considered only where other options are not available. For example, where health and safety considerations, operational requirements, reliability demands or even building location dictate that other maintenance requirements are not viable. The use of designing-out can put a major responsibility on the design engineer. In most building services applications it is unlikely to be encountered as the only option, but the client should be aware of it and ensure that this is clearly defined in the brief if considered appropriate. This requirement may have a significant cost implication, but is far more readily addressed at the design stage than during or after installation.

A technique increasingly being adopted in the process industry is known as 'reliability-centred maintenance' (RCM). It entails relating the operational requirements of specific plant to known or recorded reliability information using a structured maintenance decision making tool that focuses resources to areas of greatest effect. This can allow more cost effective use to be made of maintenance resources, particularly labour. It can be implemented by methodically listing plant items and components, and using group analyses (the group being drawn from plant and maintenance operatives, supervisors and managers) to review and improve the maintenance regime. Ongoing monitoring of the results of changes may be used to meet the aim of continuing improvement. One part of the process is identifying significant modes of failure using 'failure modes and effects critical analysis' (FMECA) to lead to the appropriate maintenance tasks. The technique has been developed for use in the area of building services and further information is available in the BSRIA BG 3/2004: *Business-focused maintenance — guidance and sample schedules*[2]. A useful overview is also provided in *Reliability-centred maintenance*[3].

3.4 Establishing a maintenance policy

The traditional manner in which a building services project progresses is shown in Figure 3.2. This figure demonstrates how the earliest concepts of a project can affect its eventual outcome as they become translated from concept to reality. For the final scheme to be successful and capable of proper and adequate operation and maintenance, due allowance needs to be made at the earliest stages, ideally in the form of a policy statement by the client when briefing the design consultant. The design stage can then take full account of this policy. If a maintenance policy is not available, perhaps because the client does not have the necessary expertise, it should be established at an early design stage by the designer recommending a series of suitable options to the client and agreeing the optimum approach with the client.

During installation, the specified maintenance policy can ensure that appropriate and safe means of access and isolation are provided, proper means of identification and test facilities are available, and information such as maintenance requirements and suitable spare parts lists are on hand. The testing and commissioning stages should ensure that the installation can be operated and maintained effectively from handover in line with the original maintenance policy (see also chapters 8 and 9).

The maintenance policy for any installation is likely to be unique, but many of the variables are likely to apply generally. The following questions are intended to help in the formulation of a policy:

(*a*)   What are the implications of failure?

(*b*)   How is this plant likely to fail?

(*c*)   What is the probability of failure?

(*d*)   Are standby facilities available?

(*e*)   What level of usage is envisaged?

(*f*)   What type of maintenance is envisaged?

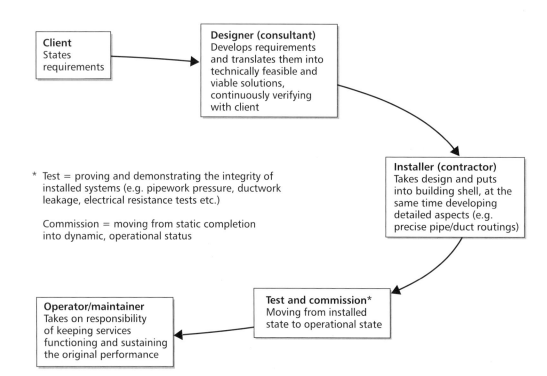

* Test = proving and demonstrating the integrity of installed systems (e.g. pipework pressure, ductwork leakage, electrical resistance tests etc.)

Commission = moving from static completion into dynamic, operational status

Client
States requirements

Designer (consultant)
Develops requirements and translates them into technically feasible and viable solutions, continuously verifying with client

Installer (contractor)
Takes design and puts into building shell, at the same time developing detailed aspects (e.g. precise pipe/duct routings)

Test and commission*
Moving from installed state to operational state

Operator/maintainer
Takes on responsibility of keeping services functioning and sustaining the original performance

Figure 3.2 Traditional manner of progress for a building services project

(g)   What level of technical expertise will be available, and how will it be organised?

(h)   Will spares be available on site?

(i)   Can equipment be purchased or rented locally?

(j)   Can a standard of maintenance be stated?

(k)   Will all necessary documentation be provided?

(l)   What financial resources will be available for maintenance?

(m)   How will compliance be demonstrated?

The answers to these questions are also likely to affect how subsequent maintenance decisions are taken, but as more detailed stages are reached beyond the initial design brief the types of decisions needing to be taken may not always relate directly to the policy statement. A structured approach at these stages can be beneficial by ensuring that a consistent and logical method is followed. Figure 3.3 shows how such a structured consideration could be applied to the design process and could also influence maintenance planning.

3.5   Choice of maintenance strategy

A building operator needs to determine the most appropriate choice of maintenance procedures when a building is eventually handed over and put into full operational use. The strategy may closely follow the original maintenance policy established by the client in conjunction with the designer but, as the project progresses to completion, other factors may need to be considered. The usage pattern of any functioning building is likely to be continually changing and the maintenance procedures will need to adapt to suit the circumstances.

For example, in the early years it may be appropriate to keep an installation close to its original condition but, as wear becomes more pronounced and the needs of the occupants change and technology improves, there is likely to be an increasing demand for extensive replacement and refurbishment. In many cases it may be left to the person responsible for carrying out maintenance to recommend a course of action, perhaps solely on the grounds of cost without fully appreciating the implications of alternatives.

Whichever approach is finally adopted, it should take account of anticipated future requirements of a building and its services, the current physical performance and functional suitability of plant, proposed changes of use (particularly where they affect plant and services), statutory and legal requirements, and any standards of maintenance specified by the building operator.

Appendix A3.1 sets out an example of how this could be approached. It shows part of a list of the services in a building and the analysis to establish the detailed maintenance requirements. To be effective, such a procedure needs to be kept up-to-date — perhaps on a five-yearly basis for a relatively new property with little

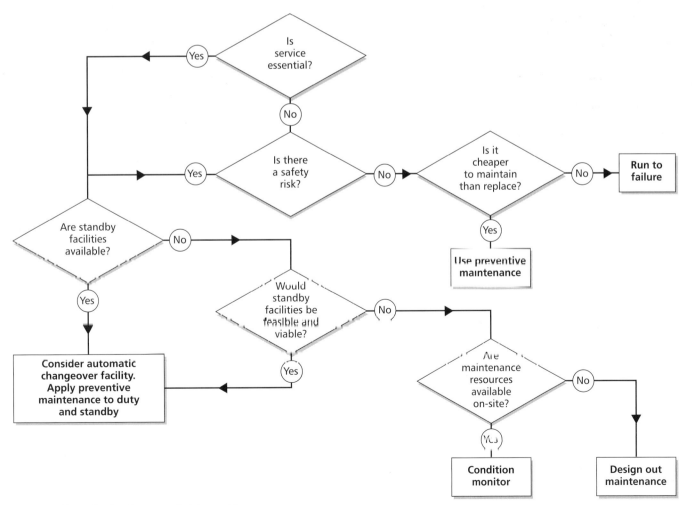

Figure 3.3 Example of maintenance decision-making

change of use but more frequently where services are approaching the end of their economic life or the building use is changing frequently.

3.6 Main principles of a planned maintenance system

The following checklist itemises the details that need to be established for a planned maintenance system:

(*a*)   items to be maintained (the asset register)

(*b*)   maintenance policy appropriate to each item

(*c*)   work to be done on each item

(*d*)   labour required

(*e*)   material resources required

(*f*)   when and how frequently the work is to be done (the maintenance programme)

(*g*)   how the maintenance system will be administered

(*h*)   how the results will be recorded, monitored and analysed.

3.7 Typical range of maintenance services

An example of the range of services carried out by a direct labour organisation or maintenance contractor is set out below; additions may be appropriate to meet particular requirements.

(*a*)   Routine inspection and maintenance of engineering plant.

(*b*)   Planned lamp replacement.

(*c*)   Five-yearly electrical inspection.

(*d*)   Portable appliance testing.

(*e*)   Monitoring of plumbing and water services operation (for legionellosis control).

(*f*)   Inspection and operation of high-voltage electric installation.

(*g*)   First line response to emergencies and pre-agreed critical alarms (response time agreed with client).

(*h*)   Ensuring compliance with statutory requirements for services installations.

(*i*)   Provision and control of on-site engineering stores.

(*j*)   Purchase of engineering plant and equipment (consumable spares and materials, client requested items, replacement of minor and major plant).

(*k*)   Installation of engineering plant and equipment (minor items including response to client requests and major capital plant).

(*l*)   Energy management by:
— ensuring efficient plant operation
— purchase and, where appropriate, storage of fuel.

(*m*)   Supervision and control of specialist contractors.

(*n*)   Inspection, compliance testing and monitoring of fire systems and equipment.

(*o*)   Trouble-shooting.

References

1   *Standard maintenance specification for building services* (electronic database) HVCA SFG20 (London: Heating and Ventilating Contractors Association)

2   *Business-focused maintenance — guidance and sample schedules* BSRIA BG3/2004 (Bracknell: BSRIA) (2004)

3   Moubray J *Reliability-centred maintenance* (2nd. edn.) (Oxford: Butterworth-Heinemann) (1997)

Bibliography

BS 3811: 1993: *Glossary of terms used in terotechnology* (London: British Standards Institution) (1993)

BS 3843: *Guide to terotechnology (economic management of assets)*; Part 1: 1992: *Introduction to terotechnology*; Part 2: 1992: *Introduction to the techniques and applications*; Part 3: 1992: *Guide to the available techniques* (London: British Standards Institution) (1992)

BREEAM: BRE Environmental Assessment Method (website) (Garston: Building Research Establishment) (http://www.breeam.org) (accessed March 2008)

Nanayakkara R and Smith M H *Operation and maintenance audits* BSRIA Technical Note TN24/97 (Bracknell: BSRIA) (Building Services Research and Information Association)

Hastings P, Pennycook K and Bunn R *Handover, O&M manuals, and project feedback. A toolkit for designers and contractors* BSRIA BG1:2007 (Bracknell: BSRIA) (2007)

Smith M H *Maintenance contracts for building engineering services* BSRIA AG 4/89.2 (Bracknell: Building Services Research and Information Association) (1992)

Smith M H and Tate A *Maintenance programme set-up* BSRIA AG1/98 (Bracknell: Building Services Research and Information Association) (1998)

Health issues in building services environment CIBSE TM40 (London: Chartered Institution of Building Services Engineers) (2006)

The Construction (Design and Management) Regulations 2007 Reprinted March 2007 Statutory Instruments 2007 No. 320 (London: The Stationery Office) (2007)

The Control of Substances Hazardous to Health (COSHH) Regulations 1999 Statutory Instrument 1999 No. 437 (London: The Stationery Office) (1999)

The Electricity at Work Regulations 1989 Statutory Instrument 1989 No. 635 (London: The Stationery Office) (1989)

Appendix 3.A1: Example maintenance policy review

Building type: Hotel   **Location:** Brighton

Engineering plant or service	Minimum statutory requirement	Implication of failure	Age (years at 2007)	Estimated remaining life (years)	Assessed current reliability	Relative energy use	Notes
Gas-fired cast iron boilers serving low-temperature hot water radiators and hot water services calorifiers. All pumps have on-line standby with manual changeover	Gas Safety Regulations annual inspection	100% loss of building function	15	15	Good if inspected six-monthly	90% of total gas consumption of building	Energy consumption below average for type of property. Good service by local contractor (24-hour call out). Boiler efficiency 80%
Lifts	Six-monthly inspection	Virtual loss of 75% building function	2	28	Good	3% of total electricity consumption of building	Statutory inspection essential; current arrangement with XYZ insurance satisfactory; no service contract required at present
Electric power installation	Five-yearly inspection	100% loss of building function; no lights or heating, no standby generator	25	5	Fair: localised breakdowns of subcircuits		Last inspection report indicated deteriorating situation. Inspect every two years using local electrical contractor; ensure 24-hour standby. Hotel management to isolate sections in emergency — training needed
Kitchen		Minimal: can use catering facilities in hotel next door (planned arrangement)	Generally >20	0	Poor	High: inefficient and badly managed	Imminent plan to amalgamate catering and do away with this kitchen. No maintenance except make safe on breakdown

4 Maintenance contracts

Summary

General guidance is given on the essential elements of a contract, differentiating between contracts 'under hand' and 'under seal' and outlining details of particular statutes that directly affect contracts.

The major components of contract documentation which provide the basis for competitive tendering and the 'rules' for the management of a contract are described, with particular reference to specialist contractors.

A comprehensive breakdown is provided of the types of maintenance contract available, the elements of each being outlined.

Guidance is given on the invitation and analysis of tenders for maintenance contracts, the initiation of a contract and the various articles of a contract that offer protection to the client. These need to be included in the documentation but may present difficulties in applying in practice. Advice on the management of a contract is outlined and a sample questionnaire for the pre-qualification of prospective tenderers is provided.

Unlike installation contracts, which are for a specific period and provide a tangible product, maintenance contracts have a specific duration but no easily measurable or deliverable product since they are essentially providing a service. There is no point at which the parties can say that the service is finished or complete, apart from at the end of the contract. The need for the service continues.

There is a variety of industry standard forms of contract that can be used for the procurement of building services operation and maintenance. In addition there are also standard forms of contract for the procurement of facilities management (FM) services. Some of these, for example, the GC/Works series of contracts are intended for the use by public sector but they are in the public domain and may be adapted for use in the private sector. Examples of standard forms are:

— GC/Works/9: *Lump sum term contract for operation, maintenance and repair of mechanical and electrical plant, equipment and installations*[1]

— CIOB *Facilities Management Contract*[2].

When providing maintenance contract documentation, special effort should be put into recognising the legal aspects of the task and engaging the support of relevant advisers where necessary. There is nothing special about the terms associated with maintenance contracts compared with other types of contract, nor the way that they are put in place. The key aspect to bear in mind is that they are service related.

It is important to recognise the different requirement of the scope of maintenance work compared with an installation project and how satisfactory performance will be measured. These factors need to be put into a context that can be included in the contractual framework.

Appendix 4.A1 provides a checklist covering information needing to be decided by the client prior to setting up a maintenance contract. BSRIA Applications Guide AG4/89.2: *Maintenance contracts for building services*[3] provides comprehensive coverage of the subject with particular attention to contractual clauses and the tendering and monitoring processes. This section extends the guidance on contract and procedural matters.

4.1 Contract details

4.1.1 Essence of a contract

The intention in this section is to warn how easily a legal agreement can be formed, and the obligations that may unintentionally arise.

A contract may be formed when three basic steps have occurred:

— there is the intention to create a legal relationship (i.e. there is no contract if the parties are conspiring to commit a crime) and that litigation will arise in the event of default

— an offer has been made by the contractor and it has been accepted without qualification by the client

— consideration has been agreed (some form of benefit or payment).

In addition, the following must be true:

— *possibility of performance*: the contracted obligations are capable of being performed

— *contractual capacity*: neither party is of a type of whom advantage might be taken

— *genuineness of consent*: neither party gave consent to the contract by fraud, deceit, duress or misrepresentation, either deliberate or otherwise; also the person giving the consent was duly authorised to do so.

Each of these steps may occur almost without the parties realising. Contracts can be established on a verbal basis, but it is always preferable to make arrangements in writing. Verbal agreements cannot be easily verified at a later date, whereas the written word is reproducible.

4.1.2   Confirmation of contracts

A contractor may make an offer in writing that may be accepted verbally. The verbal acceptance may, in reality, be in the form 'yes but...'. Unfortunately, the 'but' may not be obvious or not thought to be that important and certainly, being verbal, will not have been recorded. The contract will therefore be based upon the written evidence of the contractor's offer.

A formal acceptance frequently comprises the issue of a company's 'standard order', often with company conditions on the back. In the event of a dispute, these company conditions may be interpreted as a counter offer, invalidating the contractor's bid. If confirming an otherwise variable estimate (compared with a fixed quotation), the issue of such an order consolidates that estimate into a fixed price and cannot be revised later when it is recognised that the estimate was higher than need be.

4.1.3   'Under hand' and 'under seal'

Where contracts are in writing, they may be 'under hand' or 'under seal'. The reference to 'under hand' merely means a signed contract. 'Under seal' refers to signatures upon a document bearing a seal or stamp. With contracts 'under hand' there is a limitation of liability for a period of six years whereas with 'under seal' the period extends to 12 years. The seal ensures that the extended liability period is recognised by both parties at the time of signing. Due to the ongoing nature of a maintenance service, the question of 'under hand' or 'under seal' may not arise.

Signatures are not essential to form a contract. The carrying out of the service can be taken to prove that the agreement exists, particularly if a payment has been made to the contractor. The contract will be based upon the last exchange of understanding between the partners. This allows counter offers to replace the tender document requirements or other means of explaining the client's needs. Counter offers may consist of the contractor's response to the tender inquiry in a letter where the body of the letter contains qualifying comments and the standard terms and conditions are on the back.

It is important to be aware of the standing of these exchanges. If both parties carry out the intentions of their agreement and both are content with the outcome, it is unlikely that the terms and standing of the contract will be examined. When things go wrong and the contract is brought into play to determine the way forward, the situation changes. If legal opinion is sought, it is then that the client and professional adviser who prepared the contract realise the true quality or otherwise of the contract put in place. This is usually too late and the eventual apportionment of blame and cost may not be placed in the way intended by the person drafting the original contract.

Those producing contract documents should recognise their own limitations, particularly in understanding the law and arriving at a contract agreement. This is not to say that a lawyer is needed on every occasion; standard forms of contract are relatively safe to use provided that they are not heavily amended and the procedures are properly understood and followed. Where contract conditions are specially written, or amendments are made to existing contract terms, the client should be advised to obtain legal advice.

4.1.4   Legislation

Two Acts of Parliament directly affect maintenance contracts: the Unfair Contract Terms Act 1977[4] and the Supply of Goods and Services Act 1982[5]. The former allows the courts to apply 'tests of reasonableness' to any exclusion clauses and prevents exclusion of liability for death or personal injury resulting from negligence. The latter implies quality into contracts for supply and 'fitness for purpose'. This places maintenance contracts on a par with those governed by the Sale of Goods Act 1979[6], which requires that:

— where no specific time has been agreed before the contract was made, the work must be completed within a reasonable time

— if no specific charge was agreed before the contract was made, the price must be a reasonable one

— the work must be performed with reasonable care and skill.

If new legislation comes into force during a contract period and results in extra expenditure by the contractor, particularly if related to the execution of the works rather than a general requirement upon the contractor, it is reasonable to expect the client to pay some or all of the extra cost.

4.2   Components of contract documents

4.2.1   Content

Generally, a set of contract documentation will contain the following sections:

(a)   *contract conditions*, which deal with issues such as:

— definitions

— payment

— the service required, in principle only

— commencement and duration of the contract

— how the contract might be terminated

— insurances

(b)   *schedules to the contract*, which include job-related details such as the job specification, its scope and demarcations.

For further details, see BSRIA Applications Guide AG4/89.2[3].

The definitions section should be considered carefully, as it will create the meaning of any word and make it specific to the contract. Other interpretations will no longer apply.

It would seem reasonable for the contract to reflect the complexity of the service to be provided, and in particular that simple services have simple contracts. If neither party understands the meaning of the contract terms, the best that can happen is that they become subsidiary to getting the work done. The worst that can happen is that both parties waste their energies in arguing

The core contract conditions are usually worded in general terms and should not be altered to become specific. The specific requirements will be detailed in the schedules referenced from within the contract conditions. For example, contract conditions may refer to the payment clauses ('The payments as stated at Schedule One') or 'The scope of work as detailed at Schedule Two'.

4.2.2   Scope of work

The scope of work schedule will be tailored for each project but will have particular headings:

—   service required within the price

—   type of maintenance regime

—   hours of access for the contractor

—   response times for call-outs

—   quality of staff

—   resident or visiting maintenance technicians.

More headings are listed in BSRIA Applications Guide AG4/89.2[3].

Typically the scope of work will make it clear whether any or all the following services are to be provided and how each will be paid for:

—   operation of services

—   maintenance only

—   repair

—   component or partial plant replacement

—   total plant replacement

—   call-out services

—   record keeping and updating of as-fitted drawings

—   energy monitoring and energy management

—   environmental management

—   legislation compliance

—   spares management

—   budget planning

—   small works.

4.2.3   Specialist contractors

Specialist contractors (e.g. refrigeration plant, water treatment, controls, ductwork cleaning) normally fulfil their duties on a visiting basis and should not be asked to operate plant in the day-to-day sense. They may require attendance from other personnel (e.g. the on-site technician who knows the building) to be able to work safely or to open work areas for access.

When preparing the contract documentation, it will be necessary to determine whether the contractor is to maintain a particular item of plant or a system, or have an overall responsibility including multiple plant and systems (e.g. chillers, automatic controls, the building management system, fire alarms and lifts) and perhaps involving specialist subcontractors. The basic concepts of assembling the documents do not change, but the service that can be expected will be different because it will be provided by another party.

The schedules of work for specialist contractors will deal with information such as asset registers, any relevant drawings and the specific maintenance tasks to be carried out.

Responsibilities for health and safety, insurance inspections and legislative matters must also be made clear.

4.3   Types of contract

There are a variety of types of maintenance contract:

—   service level agreements

—   labour only

—   inspection and maintenance

—   planned preventive maintenance

—   caretaker maintenance

—   measured

—   fully comprehensive (all inclusive cost)

—   semi-comprehensive (repairs up to an agreed value included)

—   call-out only

—   specialist services.

There are also different forms of financial agreement:

—   fixed price with or without inflation or variation adjustments

—   lump sum

—   estimated price

—   cost plus

—   measured work

         competitive or negotiated

The essential point is that the parties need to recognise exactly which type of contract they are entering, what the contract details and financial arrangements include and, more particularly, do not include. In practice it might be found that even a contract perceived as fully comprehensive with fixed annual payments may have extra costs, such as replacing major capital plant should it reach the end of its economic life during the contract period.

Whichever type of contract is chosen, the purpose, objectives and methods of measuring success must continue to be understood by all involved parties throughout the duration. Contract performance measurement by negative indicators (such as the number of breakdowns or the incidence of environmental conditions being outside agreed performance parameters) can inhibit success by creating adverse working relationships. The client must also be aware of the need for an adequate type of contract to be in place for the contractor to perform. If the intention of the contract is to care for plant and systems fully and to prolong their economic life, more than breakdown maintenance will be required.

The following paragraphs expand on the types of contract available and reflect the general interpretation of the maintenance industry. The effectiveness of the contract documentation for each type of contract is totally dependent upon the quality of the wording in the scope of works, the tailoring of the work content to the specific plant installed, understanding the client's requirements, and the successful implementation of the system design, installation and commissioning.

Service level agreements

This is a contract where the duties are not laid down as a series of tasks but as performance standards. The contractor may use any method of achieving the defined services and performance standards (e.g. space temperature will be between 21 °C and 23 °C during all hours of occupancy).

Labour only

A purchaser may wish to avoid the complication of employing staff directly; under this type of contract the provision of labour including the skills and expertise required is the responsibility of the contractor. This may extend to site supervision but the purchaser is responsible for direction, supervision and control of the maintenance labour force.

Inspection and maintenance

A large number of contracts with specialist contractors are of this type. For a fixed sum, the contractor will undertake to visit a site and look at the item of plant to confirm if it is working correctly. If the plant is capable of having any maintenance carried out on it (such as topping up oil, filters checked etc.), this is also done, possibly with materials used charged as additional costs. Any work of a more specific nature or any repair will have an extra cost associated with it. Thus for, say, £1000 per year a chiller specialist may visit a site four times, check that the chiller is operating and is performing as expected. Additional costs arising out of these inspections (e.g. subsequent repair work) can easily double the basic cost.

The choice of contractors should be heavily influenced by their experience and familiarity with the specific plant. Specialist plant manufacturers may be the most suitable

supplier of this service as they will have access to spares and knowledge of the expected operational performance.

Planned preventive maintenance

Planned preventive maintenance (PPM) entails the contractor carrying out maintenance tasks to an agreed plan with the intention that its proper completion will minimise the risk of loss of service from the plant and optimise its economic life. The detailed maintenance tasks may form part of the tender documentation or be provided by the contractor within its tender return. Both tend to be unrelated to a specific manufacturer of plant or installed systems. The maintenance tasks can be made site- and usage-specific. This could bring significant value to the contract for the purchaser by defining in detail the client's requirements, but is a more costly exercise than the use of standard tasking such as that given in HVCA's *Standard maintenance specification for building services*[7].

Caretaker maintenance

It should not be assumed that an unoccupied building requires no maintenance attendance. Caretaker maintenance, sometimes referred to as 'a watching brief' when applied to installations in unoccupied buildings, is an undervalued and widely interpreted service.

In an empty building there is value in looking after the building services in such a way that they will work and can be readily recommissioned when the building is re-occupied. The building insurer may also require that selected systems, such as fire detection and protection, are active and maintained to minimise the risk. Over long periods, because water is not being drawn off, it may become a breeding ground for bacteria, or water traps in drainage systems may dry out and release foul fumes into the space. The health and safety of security staff who may be resident in the building for 24 hours per day and of visiting surveyors and purchasers may need to be considered, not just for drinking water but emergency lighting and the maintenance of passenger lifts. Some plant may be suitable for 'mothballing' where the water systems may be drained or be treated to minimise deterioration. It should not be assumed that an unoccupied building requires no maintenance.

Measured

Measured contracts for maintenance are not very common due to the difficulty and cost of measuring the work. The measure may be by completion of tasks or, more often, by hours worked and materials used. A measured type contract could be the best way of starting a maintenance regime in a badly run down building in order to direct effort and cost most effectively. Once the installation has been assessed and brought to a known level of repair, a more traditional type of contract can be applied. The cost of the direction and measurement process can equal the cost of the measured work.

Fully comprehensive

A fully comprehensive contract covers the supply of labour, materials and any other necessary resources to manage the maintenance of the building services plant over an agreed period. Should plant items fail under such an agreement, they will be repaired or replaced as deemed appropriate by the contractor, at no additional cost to the client.

A fully comprehensive contract needs an appropriate duration to ensure that the premiums taken for full plant replacement risk are likely to be called upon. To have a five-year plant replacement contract would appear to be more of an insurance than a business-based plan. A five year fully comprehensive contract placed on a 15-year-old building would be a high risk to the contractor, since at least some of the capital plant is likely to need replacing during the contract period. The true condition of plant and systems may not be determined before the price is agreed, leading to conflict regarding the basis of the contract, particularly where the actual requirements for plant replacement significantly exceed what may have been viewed as a reasonable competitive estimate.

Semi-comprehensive

This is a variant of the fully comprehensive agreement that limits the liability of the contractor. For example, cover may include replacement of component parts up to a stated unit value (e.g. £500) but exclude complete systems and major plant items (such as heating, boiler plant, air conditioning and chiller plant).

Call-out only

The contractor provides an agreed response service (e.g. to attend to the site and repair or make safe within four hours). The actual cost of attendance plus materials will be charged at an agreed rate when used. There may be a minimum attendance time charged, or a retainer cost for making this facility available.

Specialist services

Lifts, escalators, complex automatic controls, major refrigeration plant, fire alarm systems, security systems, uninterruptible power supplies and water treatment are all examples of specialist services within building services maintenance where particular expertise is required. This may be obtained through the main maintenance contractor who arranges subcontracts and incorporates their costs into the charge to the client, or the client may appoint the specialist services contractors directly.

Shared savings

With the range of services of a comprehensive agreement, it may be possible to identify opportunities for cost savings. These will directly benefit the client, but it may be advantageous to agree some form of sharing to provide an incentive to the contractor to identify cost savings to the client. Examples are:

— reducing the inspections on specific plant based on reliability gained from operational experience

— replacing capital plant at the end of its economic life with a high efficiency equivalent to give energy savings.

Private Finance Initiative (PFI)

Under a Private Finance Initiative (PFI), major projects are let as a single contract for the anticipated lifespan (e.g. 20 years) rather than considering the work in two stages (initial capital installation followed by ongoing operation, maintenance and repair). The PFI contractor will need to arrange the finance for the initial cost, put up the installation and be responsible for its maintenance and operation throughout the full contract term. The client is then committed to regular payments over the lifespan that will cover the initial capital cost and interest plus the subsequent ongoing costs.

PFI contracts allocate the risks for design, funding, installation and operation to those best able to manage them, leaving the client (or service user) to concentrate on core business activities. The concept is being applied particularly in the public sector to enable capital developments to take place. It puts more onerous responsibilities on the development contractor who has to accept the risk of the ongoing viability of the installation over the full life of the contract.

A number of issues are raised under PFI. These include:

— performance measurement (e.g. using service level agreements and key performance indicators) and facility availability

— a clearly defined brief for the installation and its requirements (the infrastructure specification), together with its stated purpose throughout its lifespan

— contract documentation and terminology to ensure full commitment and risk transfer by all parties for the duration of the contract

— how to predict plant life expectancy to make due allowance in the cost model (i.e. life cycle costs and major maintenance funds)

— protecting the value of the assets during the contract period (the assets may devolve back to the client at the end of this period).

4.4 Tender and award of maintenance contracts

Maintenance contracts can be placed in many ways varying from selecting one contractor and negotiating a contract with them to a complete formal selection, tendering and award procedure. The choice will be influenced by available time and the needs of the client. The tender process should reflect the duties placed upon the successful contractor.

A full formal procedure might include:

— pre-qualification of contractors to form a tender list

— the tender period

— site visit by the tenderers

— response to tenderers' queries

— receipt of sealed tender returns by a qualifying time and date

— tender opening procedure

— written tender analysis

— post-tender return interviews

— recommendations

— award

— contract document and signing

— start of contract meeting and site familiarisation

— acceptance and reporting period for sites incorporating full plant replacement contracts.

4.4.1 Pre-qualification

Pre-qualification is a process intended to ensure that tenderers are capable, suitable and competent for the work and to confirm that they will provide a tender price. Many different factors may be appropriate to allow a choice to be made, including the location of the contractor's office in relation to the site, the size of the company and the workforce (particularly those local to the site), basic hourly rates and management policies such as training, health and safety. Larger contractors may be unhappy about being on the same list as a small contractor for reasons of differing overheads or capabilities. The pre-qualification process should be designed to answer such criticisms.

Appendix 4.A1 shows a sample questionnaire for use in the pre-qualification process. The minimum selection criteria are:

(a) capability to supply the type of service required

(b) degree of previous experience in the specialisation required

(c) ability to provide the skills for the type and complexity of the activity required

(d) ability to provide the resources necessary to carry out the work wherever required

(e) economic aspects

(f) financial standing and/or availability of external financial support

(g) need for guarantees for performance over the time of the contract

(h) check of information provided by the supplier for accuracy

(i) competence of personnel (e.g. skills certifications, refrigerant handling, approved gas operatives, welding).

Tender lists need be no longer than five contractors. With only three contractors, the spread of prices may not help with tender evaluation. With more than five, it becomes uneconomic for the contractor to invest time in studying the particular needs. The likelihood of losing the bid is greater and thus the costs incurred will not be repaid. That cost will be put into the company overheads and must be recouped on future jobs won. Excessively long tender lists will be bad in two senses: the overall price of contracts will go up for no more return and the contractor's interest in pricing the tender accurately will be reduced.

4.4.2 Tender period

The tender period will influence the contractor's ability to price the tender. Too short a period and the information that it may need to seek from subcontractors may not be obtainable. Too long a period and the contractor will postpone dealing with the inquiry. Three or four weeks would appear appropriate for the average tender. Particularly large or complex tenders will need longer.

4.4.3 Site visits

A visit to the site by the contractor may be deemed essential and might be most appropriate at the middle of the tender period. Most maintenance contractors have sales and estimating departments who prepare their tenders. Many will involve the contract manager who would run the project in the bid preparation. A conducted site visit allows both the tenderer and the engineer to meet each other and helps to ensure a common understanding of the intended scope of the contract. The engineer can receive feedback on the specification and gain some insight into the contractor's thinking and interpretation. This can often allow clarifications to be circulated to all tenderers in good time during the tender period, promoting the chances of successful operation of the contract once awarded.

As a guide, a minimum of 1.5 hours is needed for a site visit and should encompass those aspects of the site that will exert the most influence on the contractor's price. Viewing the plant is obvious, but if access to occupied spaces or storage are potential problems, the site visit is a good opportunity to allow these issues to be aired. Individual visits for five contractors might take a full working day; a collective visit reduces the time and allows more opportunity to explore the details of the site.

Individual site visits for each contractor are costly for the engineer or client and may not achieve the intention of keeping the tender list private. Where subcontractors have been named in the tender documents, the tendering contractors will need to contact them for information. This may also result in the names of the tendering contractors being divulged.

4.4.4 Responses to contractors' queries

Responses to contractors' queries during the tender stage should be copied to the other tenderers to ensure equality of interpretation. (However, if a tenderer asks a specific question that would affect only his/her own bid, the sharing of this information may not be helpful or relevant.) Such questions will indicate how clear the wording is in the tender documentation. Responses need to be timely as they may affect the ability of the contractor to return a price and thus leave the engineer in a difficult position at tender evaluation stage.

4.4.5 Receipt of tenders and opening procedure

Some procurement groups require tenders to be returned in unmarked envelopes to avoid identifying the source and subsequent confidentiality issues. Franking machines which state the sender's name and courier labels tend to work against this. The tenders returned within the specified time limit should be opened at a formal session in the presence of a witness and the salient details recorded and signed by those present.

4.4.6 Tender analysis, interviews, recommendations, award

Tender prices should be analysed against an agreed set of criteria that will normally be determined when the tender documents are being prepared. This can include total tender price, labour costs (normal and premium rates), mark-up rates for materials and subcontractors, travel costs, ability to resource the work and understanding of the client's requirements.

Post tender, it can help to gain confidence in the potential contractors and resolve concerns by selecting a shortlist and then conducting interviews. The interviews should be conducted by the client and the professional adviser (if one is being used) and be based on a prepared framework and address such issues as:

— quality and skills of labour force

— programme of work

— responding to client's additional requirements

— client reporting procedure

— out-of-hours response

— training and health and safety policies

— track record.

Following the interviews and any further assessment of tenders which may be shown to be appropriate, the engineer and other professional advisers (such as the quantity surveyor) should be in a position to recommend the most favourable contractor to the client. Once decided, notification should be provided in writing. The unsuccessful tenders should also be advised and ideally given an opportunity of feedback.

4.4.7 Contract initiation

Once the successful contractor is selected and agreed by all parties, the contract start date needs to be confirmed. This allows the full contract documents based on the tender documentation, and any subsequent matters clarified during the tender process, to be produced.

The contractor should sign and date two copies for submission to the client, who also signs and dates them, retains one and issues the other to the contractor. It may be possible to arrange this at a formal session with both parties present. Such a meeting can also provide an opportunity to start the contract formally and to resolve outstanding issues and matters of concern, such as:

— security vetting of contractor's staff

— method of gaining access to building

— password procedures

— invoicing procedures

— contractor reporting process

— timetable for future meetings

— review of client requirements

— contractor review period to accept plant condition or report need for replacement or remedial works

— storage and workshop facilities.

4.5 Practical difficulties

Writing a specification that describes what is needed can be the start of a long journey. Where the person drafting the specification is well versed in what the marketplace can provide and can compile a specification that asks for exactly what the contractor normally and routinely does, this should result in a competitive and realistic price for the work. The service provided should be properly and satisfactorily delivered. However, this is not always achieved.

4.5.1 Enforcing the contract

Getting someone to agree to enter into a contract is one thing; regulating the implementation of the contract and, where necessary, enforcing this is another matter. When a contractor fails to do something that is written into the specification, it is important to know what the contract allows. The more detailed the requirements at tender, the easier it is to discuss the difference between expectation and delivery. The contractor may have been asked to keep records of maintenance. If the record forms or examples of the forms had been included as part of the tender documentation, it would be easier to discuss departures from the specified requirements with the contractor and to make a decision to either accept the departure or take some action. (See also chapter 14, *Maintenance audits*)

4.5.2 Manufacturer and installing contractor warranties

It is very difficult to obtain the benefit of these. It may seem simplistic but eventually it all comes down to money. For a new building, the owners assume and expect that for perhaps one year after handover any defect in the installation will be put right at no cost to them. This may be stated in the construction contract. Chillers or boilers installed early in a construction project may be five years old at project completion, and the manufacturer's warranty no longer valid.

For an extra premium the building operator might extend the warranty period, but has the manufacturer been given the opportunity to care for the product while it has been sitting dormant on site? If an extra premium has been paid to extend a warranty, who was it paid to and how far down the chain did the payment pass? Who is carrying the risk and what is the procedure for the presumed warranty holder to mobilise the warranty?

These are essential issues to be clear on when bringing warranties into a maintenance contract. The warranty may also state that appropriate maintenance must have been carried out for it to remain valid.

The construction warranty probably does not say how quickly the defect is to be put right. A maintenance contract may require a two-hour response to a breakdown, which is unlikely to be written into the warranty of a manufacturer or installing contractor.

The real cause of a failure or loss of service will be hard to determine and non-technical people will have to fall back on the contract to determine who will pay. An insurance policy similar to that used for domestic appliances might prove to be a less confrontational and more satisfactory approach.

4.5.3 Performance bonds

Performance bonds are another form of insurance against non-performance, but they are not common in maintenance contracts. A client may require a contractor to provide a guarantee to pay a specified sum of money to the client if a measurable or detectable event fails to happen. The contractor will go to a bank or insurance company and pay a premium to the bond provider on the understanding that the bond provider will pay the agreed sum to the client in the event of the contractor's default.

The most important aspect of a performance bond is that all the parties are clear on the event that will trigger payment of the bond. If the trigger event is not clear, the bond may become worthless.

4.5.4 Collateral warranties

Most services are procured contractually between two parties. The providing party may use subcontractors or even sub-subcontractors. If a subcontractor defaults, the client body may have recourse only to the company it has contracted to. If the contractor ceases trading for any reason, there may be no contractual route to the subcontractors. Collateral warranties are warranties given to clients directly by subcontractors or by contractors to remote parties working on behalf of the client.

An insistence on collateral warranties can extend contract negotiations unacceptably. It can almost make a nonsense of the tender process if the details of the maintenance service being offered have been revised during negotiation. A sensible review of risk and benefit and alternative means of covering the risk may be worth greater consideration.

4.5.5 Parent company guarantees

Over a period of time, maintenance companies may change their names or ownership, or cease trading. Some advisers consider that a guarantee by the company's parent or owner to continue to provide the service in the event of the contracted company's demise gives some degree of protection.

In terms of the continuance of service, even if the contracting company has ceased trading the technicians with the site-specific knowledge and technical skills may still exist and be able to continue the service. Payments are usually in arrears for services so there may not be any financial loss unless the contract was on a fully comprehensive, full plant replacement basis when the benefit of replacement without cost and any associated premiums will be lost.

4.5.6 Disputes and their resolution

A contract is an agreement between two parties. If one party thinks that the other is not performing its part of the agreement, they have a dispute. Ideally they discuss it and find a way in which they can continue with the agreement, modify it by mutual consent to take account of the new factor or agree to terminate their arrangements. If they cannot achieve this by mutual agreement they need a third party, whose decision they are both prepared to accept, to consider the issues and report formally, recommending a solution.

At one time, the only third party was a judge whose opinion was obtained by going to court, i.e. litigation. This was seen to be an expensive way to settle a dispute and the concept of a qualified arbitrator was conceived. Events show that this route may be no less expensive and now the concept of adjudication has been introduced by the Housing Grants, Construction and Regeneration Act[8].

An alternative process being considered to resolve disputes is mediation, using an independent expert or mediation specialist where appropriate. Another possible recourse is to use a recognised trade association, when it would help if the contractor with whom there is a dispute is a member.

The inclusion in a contract of a specified means of settling a dispute means that this method must be used. However, the absence of a reference to this in contract does not preclude appropriate means being used.

4.5.7 Insurances

Insurances are always mentioned in the contract conditions. There are several types of insurance and the engineer should consider their relevance.

The absence of insurance or the inability to obtain it has other implications. Insurance against particular events is meant to provide recompense to the client or a third party: obtaining that recompense directly from a contractor will be more protracted than an insurance claim. However, requesting too high a level of insurance can be self-defeating. The insurance companies are prepared to underwrite a contractor's risk if they know the risk record for the particular circumstances. Hence, professional indemnity insurance may be expensive for a contractor whereas accidental damage may not, for similar sums of risk.

There are many different types of insurance. It is important to understand the types of insurance requested and offered in response. Also the recipient of the pay-out needs to be identified and how the level of insurance is set. If there are multiple insurances for the same event, and various companies could share the pay-out, there may be no worth in the final settlement to the client.

Typical insurances referred to in contracts are:

— employer's liability (a legal requirement)

— public liability

— damage to persons and property

— professional indemnity

— consequential loss including loss of profit

— fire.

There is also the question of plant insurance for unexpected events such as catastrophic boiler failure (note this does not provide cover for gradual degradation).

If the contractor is not insured, it does not mean that the contractor cannot be asked to pay for damage caused; it merely means that the contractor may not have the resources to pay.

'Employer's liability' refers to the liability the contractor has to its employees. (a legal requirement)

'Public liability' provides insurance cover for an incident affecting a member of the public due to the work being undertaken by the contractor.

Damage to people and property is relatively straightforward. Most building owners are already insured through their own insurance for damage caused by contractors while on their premises. Many contractors can offer £2 million or even £5 million of damage cover, but if a client insists on more extensive cover, it may be easier to obtain this directly rather than seeking it from the contractor. It can be difficult and expensive for contractors to obtain more than £5 million of damage cover, and sums of, say, £20 million may be unobtainable. It should also be remembered that the client pays for the insurance in the end because it is an element of the contractor's price.

(HVCA requires its members to have £2m public liability insurance in place. This figure is likely to be time-related, i.e. there may be a defined point after the end of a contract when liability covered by insurance ceases to be available.)

'Professional indemnity' refers to claims against the contractor in the event of faulty advice or design. In the past, contractors have not been asked for this form of insurance, but as they change their market position from contracting to design/build or providing more than maintenance services (e.g. energy management, small works design and project management, plant inspections), clients will expect such insurance. Depending on the levels of competence of their staff, maintenance contractors may have difficulty obtaining this type of insurance at acceptable rates.

Some consideration should be given to defining who the beneficiary of any insurance should be. The common assumption is that the beneficiary to the insurance will apply the funds to the reparation of the insured loss, but this does not necessarily follow. Insurance in joint names is often referred to, and proper advice should be sought and understood to ensure that the intention is achievable in practice.

Ongoing proof of insurance is essential. For professional indemnity insurance it will be necessary for the insurance to be in place at the time of the claim, which may be several years after the original appointment has concluded.

4.5.8 Damages

Liquidated and ascertained damages refer to the ability of the employer in the contract to recoup losses from the contractor (insured or not). Liquidated damages are where the employer has set a fixed sum to represent the loss it might suffer. In the event of a claim, it will not have to prove the loss but merely claim the agreed sum. Ascertained damages are where the loss must be proven. Such a concept is normally associated with failure to complete a construction contract. The application of liquidated and ascertained damages to maintenance contracts is far more difficult and requires clear criteria for a claim.

4.5.9 Withholding payment

A contract is a two-way agreement. Each party is promising to provide something to the other, and both have obligations. Withholding payment is not an automatic right of the purchaser of services and may even be a direct breach of the contract. Payment is becoming an important issue. 'Pay when paid' became illegal in 1998 and other attempts at delaying payment unfairly may also become subject to legal constraints. Payment may have to take place and reclaiming of money dealt with by taking legal action.

4.5.10 Letter of intent

Even a properly written letter of intent can have little value; it merely suggests that 'I may enter into a contract'. Whatever the value of such a letter, the intention of issuing it is to encourage a contractor to take the risk of preparing itself for that contract and perhaps to incur costs in the process. The issuer of the letter of intent may include a statement that it will pay any costs reasonably incurred by the contractor in making ready. This seems fair. Too often, the letter of intent is intended to obtain preparation but without liability for such costs. Any contractor prepared to incur costs under these arrangements is at risk and may well prefer to delay until something more formally binding is available.

4.5.11 Defects liability period

A properly completed construction project is expected to arrive at practical completion with a fully working system and a list of minor defects that can be corrected without disruption to the owner's enjoyment of the new facility. There is then a further 12 months (the defects liability period) in which the installation contractor must put these minor defects right and any others that may occur within the period. After that, the latent defects period is entered. Many people have only a tenuous grasp of this area.

During the defects liability period and beyond, the owner/occupier has a duty to maintain the installation. This starts from the day of handover, and includes the duty to operate the systems in accordance with the operation and maintenance instruction manual issued under the contract at handover, and in a way that will not harm the systems. If a client intends to use independent contractors to maintain an installation, the process of specification and tendering should have begun approximately six months before handover and to have been concluded before handover. This would enable contractors to be available for system demonstrations by the engineer and installation contractors.

Failure to provide adequate evidence of proper maintenance during the defects liability period will seriously undermine any attempt to mobilise construction warranties. The design engineer can become drawn in at this stage particularly when terms such as 'maintenance free' are used in life cycle costing reports associated with design selection decisions.

4.5.12 Consumable items and replacements

The definition of what is a consumable item and what is a replacement is important, particularly where the contract states the former is included within the contract while the latter is chargeable. The maintenance industry has a fairly clear understanding of the terms but they can be open to interpretation. BS EN 13306: *Maintenance terminology*[9] defines a consumable item as 'maintenance material that is not item specific and not repairable'. Where the tenant/landlord relationship comes into the discussion, it becomes more important to define what is meant, and not to rely on common sense.

4.5.13 Permits-to-work

Permits-to-work can be a misunderstood and mis-applied concept. Many contracts refer to 'permit-to-work' systems but fail to recognise whether the contractor is in a position to issue such permits.

In the field of high voltage electrical work, permits-to-work have a very specific meaning and relate to a codified process designed to save accidents and lives. Other reference to permits-to-work needs to consider the purpose of having such a system and address who is 'competent' to issue the permit. Competent in this instance should mean a person who has received sufficient instruction or training to have the judgement to fulfil the purpose of restricting and controlling access. The term has to apply to an individual and not a company.

The purpose of the permit may be to:

— prevent unexpected loss of service through unauthorised entry into a plant room or service route

— prevent injury to people entering plant areas

— identify the perpetrators of damage to plant or the dumping of rubbish

— control use of tools applying flames or heat.

Entry to plant rooms will need to be managed by a person who is present at all times that access to the plant rooms is possible. A maintenance technician who visits a site once per month is not able to do this. If damage or rubbish is the concern, any persons authorised to enter the room should be accompanied or the room revisited in their company before they leave site.

Plant rooms can be dangerous places. They should be kept locked and only people instructed in safe conduct in plant rooms should enter them unless accompanied by someone who is trained. Use as a storeroom should be prohibited.

4.6   Contract management

A key to the success of a contract is understanding that it will not happen unless it is managed. This will require some form of monitoring to ensure that the details of the specification are being followed. Chapter 14 describes this further and sets out typical elements to be included in a monitoring programme, plus guidance on how it should be carried out.

Quality assurance should also be adopted to ensure that documented procedures are in place and being followed. This will introduce the necessary controls, attitude and discipline to provide a consistent service to meet the client's expectations and requirements. The quality system being followed will need to incorporate flexibility to meet individual needs and to accommodate change during the contract period.

Recording of performance feedback, both technical and financial, can provide a valuable management tool. Technical feedback should aim to identify not only that maintenance is being correctly carried out, but also where it results in over- or under-maintenance, thus indicating that frequencies or specifications need to be modified. It is important to create an open environment for discussion with the contractor to allow the maintainer to put forward constructive comment.

Technical feedback should provide the impetus to make changes to the original strategy in the light of experience. Sufficient flexibility should exist for this, together with a formal procedure to record changes and their reasons.

Financial feedback will be primarily concerned with meeting budget expenditure plans. It should not be a simplistic comparison of overall expenditure against budget: there should be a detailed understanding of how individual areas have committed expenditure and, thus, where improvements and savings could be made in the future.

Should the maintenance strategy not achieve the desired results, some means of enforcement may need to be adopted. Suggested options are improved supervision, better workforce motivation or some form of incentive. An example of this is defining objectives, monitoring results against targets and offering financial rewards if agreed targets are reached or exceeded. Financial incentives alone are recognised as not being a motivating force; attempts at motivation are more likely to be successful if regular opportunities are provided to discuss performance with supervisors and managers, to give encouragement, direction and support, and to generate enthusiasm about the work.

It can be beneficial to assess the perceived position of the contractor within a market matrix in terms of the attractiveness of the client's account and the client's expenditure (see Figure 4.1). If the client makes this assessment and determines that it is in Box 1 (Develop potential) in terms of the attractiveness of the account to the contractor and expenditure, it may find the contractor focusing on ways of generating income other than providing the expected service, possibly causing poor performance. In Box 2 (Core business), the client can expect to be important to the contractor and receive the attention and performance specified. In Box 3 (Nuisance), the contract may be viewed as a routine acquisition with little profit margin and the service could reflect this. In Box 4 (Exploit opportunity) the contractor sees an opportunity for high income with a client that it may not wish to retain. From such an assessment, the client can be in a position to develop the relationship to where they wish to be positioned, for example in Box 2.

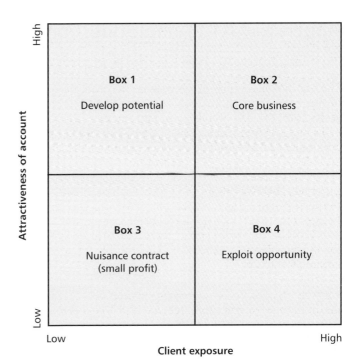

Figure 4.1 A simple contractor market matrix

References

1   *Lump sum term contract for operation, maintenance and repair of mechanical and electrical plant, equipment and installations* GC/Works/9 (London: Her Majesty's Stationery Office) (1999)

2   *Facilities management contract* (Ascot: Chartered Institute of Building) (2001)

3   Smith M *Maintenance contracts for building services* BSRIA AG4/89.2 (Bracknell: Building Services Research and Information Association) (1992)

4   Unfair Contract Terms Act 1977 (London: Her Majesty's Stationery Office) (1977)

5   Supply of Goods and Services Act 1982 (London: Her Majesty's Stationery Office) (1982)

6   Sale of Goods Act 1979 (London: Her Majesty's Stationery Office) (1979)

7   *Standard maintenance specification for building services* (electronic database) HVCA SFG20 (London: Heating and Ventilating Contractors Association)

8   Housing Grants, Construction and Regeneration Act 1966 (London: Her Majesty's Stationery Office) (1966)

9   BS EN 13306: 2001: *Maintenance terminology* (London: British Standards Institution) (2001)

Bibliography

Estates and Property Management Guidance Index (London: Property Adviser to the Civil Estate) (2000) (http://www.ogc.gov.uk/documents/PACE_-_Estates_and_Property_Management_Guidance_Index.pdf) (accessed March 2008)

Rooley R 'Maintenance and refurbishment' *Building Services and Environmental Engineer* **21**(4) 11–18 (1997)

Building maintenance: strategy, planning and procurement: Guidance Note RICS 3076 (London: Royal Institution of Chartered Surveyors) (2000)

Appendix 4.A1: Sample questionnaire for use at pre-qualification stage

1   Name and address of maintenance contractor

....

....

....

2   General Information

2.1   Personnel

Total number of staff providing the maintenance service   ....

Total number of technical staff providing the maintenance service   ....

2.2   Company activity

What proportion of the total turnover of the organisation is that provided by the maintenance service?
(e.g. total company turnover £3 million, maintenance service turnover £1 million, proportion as % = 33%)

State proportion by value over past three years

	Year	20.....	20.....	20.....
Proportion of turnover		......%	......%	......%

State value of maintenance service provided over past three years

	Year	20.....	20.....	20.....
	Value	£......	£......	£......

2.3   List current principal clients

....

....

.   ...

2.4   Envisaged development of maintenance activities

....

....

....

2.5   Provide an organisation chart showing functions, staff numbers and interrelationships

3   Means of maintenance

3.1   What IT systems do you use?

....

....

3.2   Personnel

What are your normal working hours?

....

Do you divide work groups into teams? If so, how is this arranged?

....

....

3.3   What safety training is provided?

....

....

3.4   List the training and technical qualifications of staff providing the maintenance service

....

....

.   ...

.   ...

3.5   What is the method of travelling for mobile staff?

....

3.6 How are telephone calls and other messaging systems handled and recorded?

....

....

3.7 Describe how standby duties and emergency call outs are provided

....

....

4 Associated operations

4.1 Describe the size, location and facility for materials storage

....

....

4.2 Describe the type of stock you normally hold and how non-stocked items are obtained (including during emergency call-outs)

....

....

....

5 Administrative and commercial issues

5.1 List the extent of insurances in place

....

....

5.2 Do you participate in or are you a member of professional, trade or commercial institutions or organisations in the field of maintenance?

....

....

6 Methods and procedures

6.1 List your maintenance methods or procedures (e.g. planned maintenance programme, issuing process for follow-on work)

....

....

6.2 Do you follow a quality assurance procedure?

....

6.3 Do you have a methodology for reviewing and improving procedures?

....

7 Safety

7.1 Do you have safety procedures in place? If so, describe their operation

....

....

....

7.2 Provide copies of the annual safety report for the past three years listing safety statistics, frequency of occurrence and gravity of incidents

5 Maintenance strategy and inspection frequencies

Summary

Strategic considerations for maintenance are presented under two subheadings: design stage and operational stage.

A broad spectrum of factors affecting maintenance decisions is set out in the form of a checklist under each heading.

Maintenance monitoring and control techniques are outlined briefly with references to sources of comprehensive guidance. An introduction to operating oversized plant is also provided.

Buildings and their associated engineering services play a significant role in the achievement of the corporate objectives of an organisation by providing the internal comfort conditions for the building occupants. Many organisations are also addressing the impact of their property estate on the environment within their annual statement on corporate social responsibility (CSR). Building services installations are largely responsible for the working environment of an establishment, and their operation and maintenance therefore form a crucial part of the total facilities management process.

The formulation of a maintenance strategy should start at the initial design stage of a building or a facility, with a critical appraisal of the maintenance implications of different design options carried out at the conceptual stage. One method of achieving this is by the appointment of a maintenance advisor at the earliest stage of concept design, a process being adopted by clients who need to ensure that completion dates, budget costs and operational capabilities are accomplished satisfactorily. The operation and maintenance strategy for the building and its engineering services should receive serious consideration by both building owners and occupiers. For owners, a building constructed to optimise maintenance and to match user requirements should be easier to rent or to sell. For occupiers, the effects of maintenance on core business

objectives should be considered before buying, leasing or constructing a building.

At boardroom level, maintenance strategy should be directed to improving the organisation's profitability, both in the short and long terms. Inadequate or inappropriate maintenance will inevitably result in breakdowns. In the long term it could cause assets to depreciate more rapidly and, as a result, affect the company's prosperity. Over-maintaining will drain resources unnecessarily and could introduce problems such as maintenance-induced failures. Senior management responsible for the facility must establish the correct level of operation and maintenance and ensure adequate funds are available to carry out this work.

At the operational level, maintenance strategy is about improving production economies and the effectiveness of the maintenance organisation. This may require a culture change from using traditional approaches such as time-based activities to maintenance that is linked to the essential plant operating conditions to a focus on the business requirements and potential implications of failure of plant and systems. Planned preventive maintenance systems that require maintenance tasks to be performed at fixed frequencies irrespective of the plant function and condition could result in work that is not necessary or even maintenance-induced failures.

Technologies such as condition-based maintenance[1] and diagnosis by expert systems can enable the building services industry to determine the maintenance requirements of plant and equipment to suit the operational needs of the business. This can enable the maintenance activities to be carried out only when required to satisfy a business operational need. It is also important to note that any maintenance regime should not adopt a single approach to maintenance, i.e. reactive, preventive or predictive. It will be a combination of all such methods and their correct mix is essential for the optimisation of the maintenance regime (see chapter 3).

Quality management systems can be used by organisations to ensure maintenance is consistent and matches the business needs.

5.1 Maintenance strategy

The maintenance strategy for building services needs to be addressed at two stages of the life of plant and installations:

(a)   the design stage

(b)   the operational stage.

5.1.1 Design stage

The starting point for the maintenance strategy is the design (see chapter 2). Designers must evaluate the maintenance requirements of different design options. They should also consider the extent to which maintenance can be 'designed out' and how support systems can be built into the installation to facilitate efficient and cost-effective operation and maintenance.

Some key issues that need consideration are:

(a)   Positioning and sizing of plant rooms and access to plant:

—   human, vehicular and materials traffic

—   access for operation, maintenance and refurbishment

—   storage.

(b)   Plant reliability, availability and the provision of redundant systems:

—   user requirements for plant availability

—   reliability of the systems, plant and components

—   likely down-time (repair time as well as the time required to carry out diagnosis and to obtain spares and, where necessary, specialist labour).

(c)   Requirement for specialist knowledge for maintenance and its availability:

—   specialist versus non-specialist plant

—   local availability of specialists and cost

—   training requirements.

(d)   Requirement for specialist labour for maintenance and its availability:

—   specialist versus non-specialist plant

—   local availability of specialist labour and cost

—   local availability of specialist tools and cost

—   training requirements.

(e)   Spares requirement and availability:

—   local availability of spare parts

—   delivery periods

—   cost of spares

—   the likelihood of spares availability throughout the life of the plant

—   identification and availability of critical components.

(f)   After-sales support from the suppliers of plant and systems:

—   technical support

—   proximity of the company, agents or representatives

—   financial standing of the supplier.

(g)   Standardisation of plant and components:

—   to reduce down-time

—   to minimise stock level of spares.

(h)   Built-in systems for monitoring and feedback of plant status:

—   building management systems

—   condition monitoring equipment.

(i)   Designing out maintenance:

—   components requiring no maintenance

—   reduce failure consequence by distributing risk (e.g. duplicate services; ready access for alternative power sources).

—   increased mean time between failure.

(j)   Ease of maintenance:

—   accessibility

—   simplicity

—   established versus new technology.

(k)   Health and safety considerations.

It is not normally possible to reduce the factors described above to a common denominator such as a monetary equivalent. The decision as to the best design solution to fit maintenance and other organisational needs is often a subjective judgement based on a comparison between qualitative and quantitative aspects.

5.1.2 Building operation stage

The extent to which a particular type of plant needs to be maintained can be different from one installation to another. Apart from statutory requirements, (e.g. the frequency and nature of competent person examinations), maintenance tasks and frequencies need to be selected to suit the needs of the particular item of plant. For example a heavily loaded electrical installation may need to be inspected, tested and maintained more frequently than a similar installation which is lightly loaded. The determination of the level of maintenance should be based on a risk assessment process (see chapter 11). Industry standard maintenance schedules and manufacturers instructions for maintenance usually specify generic maintenance requirements based on most likely operational conditions and these should be reviewed to suit local requirements. BSRIA publications BG3/2004[2] and BG7/2004[3] on business-focused maintenance provide guidance on how this can be done.

The performance of building services is important to the operation of an organisation. Senior management has the responsibility for setting the policy for wider issues of operation and maintenance of building services that will affect the organisation's corporate objectives. This involves deciding:

— *the level of risk the organisation is willing to tolerate*: e.g. financial, business loss, health and safety, employee satisfaction

— *method of resourcing maintenance*: e.g. in-house, outsourced, mixed

— *budgets*: e.g. level of finance available for maintenance, financial targets

— *benchmarks*: cost targets, performance targets.

At this stage, maintenance strategy should be to establish the level of operation and maintenance that needs to be carried out to match the expectations of the organisation. Key criteria that need consideration are:

— compliance with the requirements of legislation and authoritative bodies

— meeting the health and safety needs of the building users and those who operate and maintain the plant

— ensuring the function, reliability and availability of plant and equipment that are critical to company objectives

— optimising the utilisation of resources

— satisfying other key objectives of the organisation

— safeguarding assets.

Once the level of operation and maintenance required to satisfy the company objectives is understood, it is the responsibility of the operational management to:

— carry out risk assessments (see chapter 11)

— establish the health and safety policy (e.g. level of action to achieve the company objectives for health and safety, allocation of responsibilities and establishing action plans)

— establish the operation and maintenance policy (e.g. level of planned versus corrective maintenance, run to failure and condition monitoring)

— develop information systems for operation and maintenance (e.g. method of record keeping such as computer-based, manual, location of archiving; nature of records to be kept such as asset registers and planned maintenance log books; and responsibilities for maintaining records)

— procure and manage operation and maintenance activities (e.g. in-house; out-sourcing such as term contracts, lump-sum contracts or facilities management contracts; mix between in-house and external resources)

— set performance targets to meet the bench marks determined by senior management (e.g. cost, plant availability, response times, quality of records, quality of workmanship)

— set budgets (allocating finance to each function)

— monitor performance

— provide feedback to senior management

— organise improvements or changes to suit evolving business needs.

5.2 Clients' requirements: a policy

5.2.1 The client's role

The most important aspect of the role of the client in maintenance is to define requirements clearly and to express these as the management policy. There may be conflicting interests involved when, for example, the occupier is not the client who has responsibility for running and maintaining the building and its services. The occupier may have expectations at variance with the objectives of the client or even the owner of the property.

If quality assurance is to be practiced, it is essential to define the maintenance requirements. Without a rigid specification, the client's needs cannot be clearly understood and there is no measure against which quality can be judged. The detailed maintenance procedures that are required will, in part, be governed by legislation, health and safety regulations, codes of practice and advisory literature. Also relevant are mandatory requirements relating to a particular building, such as tenancy agreements or other conditions relating to occupancy that may cover the frequency of maintenance work or inspection, or the responsibilities of the occupant in the event of plant failure.

The client's role also extends to ensuring adequate financial resources and facilities are available for maintenance. This may be in terms of directly employed labour, materials and tools, or, alternatively, using contractors to provide the maintenance service. In budgeting for annual costs, unforeseen extras and breakdowns must be allowed for (e.g. plant replacement and specialist subcontractors such as lift engineers and control engineers). When contractors are used, a framework of mutual trust needs to be established, under which not only does the contractor demonstrate competence to undertake the specified work, but receives assurance that there will be prompt reimbursement once the obligations are fulfiled.

Whether direct labour or contractors are used, the client must be prepared to monitor the work to ensure that it is satisfactory and that value for money is being obtained.

5.2.2 Maintenance policy

Having clarified the owner's objectives with regard to a building, the client should develop the maintenance policy. This may conveniently be expressed as a written statement issued by, or on the authority of, the client and acceptable to the owner of the building or a nominee.

Once issued, the maintenance policy will normally remain fixed until such time as the ownership or use of the building is changed or there is a significant alteration to the installed engineering services. The maintenance policy can be considered as the client's plan for operation and maintenance to provide the necessary environment for the occupants within the constraints of the owner's objectives and of legal requirements. At the same time the policy provides the framework within which the maintenance manager can operate.

5.3 Control of maintenance

See also chapter 4, *Maintenance contracts*, and chapter 14 *Maintenance audits*.

Controlling operation and maintenance is an ongoing activity. It is the process of continually monitoring the maintenance system and its performance against pre-set goals, and reporting the performance to those responsible for management of these functions. Where performance fails to achieve set targets, changes to the maintenance regime should be made to correct any deviations. Alternatively, where failure is consistent, the targets themselves may be unrealistic or unattainable and may need to be reviewed and changed.

A quality management system for the maintenance function will define roles and responsibilities and establish procedures and reporting formats, thereby helping to ensure consistent and effective control.

Controlling maintenance usually requires two levels of audit:

(a)   a system audit to check the detailed formal procedures that constitute the maintenance regime (e.g. procedures for planned maintenance, procedures for record keeping and managerial procedures) to ensure that they satisfy legal requirements and company objectives

(b)   a performance audit to monitor the performance of the maintenance regime against set bench marks (e.g. cost targets, response times, plant down-time and quality of records).

5.4 Operating oversized plant

Many existing systems contain oversized plant, which can result in excessive energy consumption, instabilities at low loads, an undermining of the economic life of the plant,

premature equipment failure etc. This was noted in BSRIA AG1/2000: *Enhancing the performance of oversized plant*[4]. It is estimated that oversizing is typically responsible for approximately 10–15% of energy consumption for heating, ventilation and air conditioning. Plant oversizing is rarely a deliberate decision, but more often the cumulative result of a number of factors including:

—   in-built allowances in design data and calculation procedures

—   margins added during the design process

—   specified client requirements being in excess of operational needs

—   changes that occur after the design stages, e.g. to fabric and glazing specifications

—   difficulties in matching system requirements to available equipment: proprietary equipment ranges often come in standard sizes with large increments between product capacities.

The cumulative impact of these is that most systems contain some degree of oversizing; indeed it is estimated that fans and pumps are usually oversized by at least 10–15% while boiler and chiller plants can be oversized by anything up to a factor of two.

In view of this it is very much in the interests of the occupier not to allow the operation of oversized plant to continue. To meet this aim, the occupier should look to the facilities manager, first, to identify what plant is oversized and, secondly, to advise on what to do to improve matters.

Pointers that could indicate oversizing include:

(a)   design conditions easily maintained even in extreme weather

(b)   relatively short warm-up/cool-down times

(c)   plant modules that never operate, or plant (e.g. boilers and water chillers) that never runs continuously, even in extreme weather

(d)   drive motor running currents well below the full-load current

(e)   distribution system temperature differentials that never reach the declared design parameters

(f)   control valves serving heating/cooling coils never fully open (under steady state conditions) and tending to 'hunt'

(g) CO_2 levels in accommodation always below 600 ppm (indicative of excess ventilation).

Performance monitoring over a reasonable period and extending over all weather conditions, including the appropriate seasonal extremes, is necessary to confirm oversizing. The monitoring also needs to include some attempt to indicate the degree of oversizing. To assist in finalising the assessment, consideration should be given to using a commissioning specialist to check performances under varying conditions and to help tie down the causes and effects.

Where oversizing has been identified, action needs to be taken to reduce energy consumption and improve plant efficiency. Prospective actions can vary considerably in cost (and, hence, payback prospects) and may include:

(a)   isolate, drain down and 'mothball' plant modules surplus to requirements

(b)   reduce the driven speed of belt-driven equipment to match measured requirements

(c)   reduce fluid volume flow rates in distribution systems to match measured requirements

(d)   use reduced size components in control valves or dampers to give better control (but avoid abrupt pipe/duct contractions)

(e)   isolate terminal units, emitters and air distribution outlets (or inlets)

(f)   reduce fresh air volume flow rates to match requirements more closely

(g)   check the control regime generally and ensure that plant operating times are trimmed to an absolute minimum.

When taking corrective actions on plant operation it is unreasonable to expect adjustments to be right the first time. There should be a readiness to try several increments of adjustment, progressively homing in on the optimum setting.

5.5   Plant maintenance frequencies

The purpose of regular maintenance of plant, equipment and services is to sustain their operating efficiency and to prolong their economic life.

Servicing will incur labour costs and require the provision of materials such as consumables (e.g. lubricants) or replacement components. The life-cycle cost for serviced plant will therefore comprise its initial capital cost, any replacement costs and its service costs over its complete life. There will be an optimum situation where these cost components combine to offer a minimum life-cycle cost for the plant.

Service frequencies applied in practice may be derived from a variety of sources including:

(a)   statutory requirements (for instance, as required by health and safety or other legislation)

(b)   manufacturers' recommendations

(c)   'standard' frequencies.

5.5.1   Statutory inspection frequencies

The inspection frequencies for a plant and systems where condition and fitness for purpose are critical in terms of the health and safety of users (e.g. lift installations, lifting equipment, pressure vessels, electrical installations) are controlled by statutory legislation such as that relating to health and safety (see Appendix 5.A1). In the majority of

cases the frequency is based on a risk assessment of the particular plant and system related to condition and use and undertaken by a competent person. Failure to have undertaken appropriate inspections and have the relevant records available could expose the building operator to action by the Health and Safety Executive.

5.5.2   Manufacturer recommendations

Manufacturers of plant and equipment usually publish maintenance guidance or instructions for issue with their products. This documentation comprises details of the service or maintenance attention required together with a recommended frequency of attention.

In general, manufacturers' maintenance recommendations are standard lists compiled with no knowledge of the particular application of the product. For this reason, these instructions tend to err on the safe side and the maintenance frequencies quoted are often generous. In applying manufacturers' recommendations, it is prudent to review maintenance frequencies continually to achieve an optimum or more cost-effective regime.

It should be noted, however, that where it is apparent that a manufacturer's maintenance instructions have not been followed, this may be claimed to invalidate equipment warranties or guarantees. In the event of a premature failure of a product, therefore, evidence of compliance with the manufacturer's instructions may be an important consideration.

5.5.3   'Standard' maintenance frequencies

Maintenance frequencies are, for convenience, generally based on calendar increments (e.g. daily, weekly, fortnightly, monthly, quarterly, six-monthly, annually and multiples of years). In some instances, the selection of a frequency for a particular maintenance function is fairly arbitrary while, for other applications, extensive statistical data may be available. The important consideration is that a frequency must be appropriate to the specific application and take account of all relevant conditions of the usage.

With plant where the operational duty is predominantly seasonal (e.g. heating boilers), major servicing requirements should be scheduled to ensure no interference with availability of the plant when it is most required.

The most effective approach to what might be termed 'standard' maintenance frequencies are those published by the Heating and Ventilating Contractors' Association (HVCA) in its comprehensive Standard maintenance specification for building services[5]. These standards have been produced by the HVCA with wide collaboration from the building services industry and are subject to regular review. The maintenance frequencies may, therefore, be considered to reflect a broad spectrum of opinion and should be appropriate for a wide range of applications.

5.6   Inviting maintenance tenders

Maintenance costs relate to the maintenance service being provided and its frequency; because of labour cost implications, the labour cost probably exerts the most significant long-term influence. To ensure equitability of tendering it is essential to state the required maintenance service frequencies in the tender documentation as well as details of the maintenance to be carried-out.

For tendering purposes, arbitrary service frequencies may be stated, with more appropriate service intervals being arrived at by negotiation with the successful tenderer based on its quoted schedule of rates. Alternatively, both the servicing and the frequencies may be stipulated as being in accordance with the HVCA's *Standard maintenance specification for building services*[5].

5.7   Adjustment of maintenance frequencies

Optimising the frequency of individual maintenance visits is likely to be impractical due to the amount of information required to be collated and the logistics of organising the labour resource. However, maintenance frequencies should be kept under review.

For example, a possible indication of a need for more frequent maintenance (or a different mode of maintenance) could be the frequent failure of a particular component or mechanism. Conversely, where there is no loss of performance efficiency of a particular mechanism, there may be scope for an increase in the intervals between maintenance.

Generally, marginal increases in maintenance frequencies can be made with reasonable confidence and, with a large-scale operation, can result in worthwhile savings on labour. For there to be confidence in significant extensions of maintenance intervals there would need to be supporting considerations. These may take the form of condition monitoring or wide-ranging, long-term records of maintenance experience with similar plant and equipment. It may also be advisable to discuss any proposed extensions of maintenance intervals with the equipment manufacturer.

References

1   Seaman A *Condition based maintenance — an evaluation guide for building services* BSRIA AG5/2001 (Bracknell: BSRIA) (2001)

2   Harris J and Hastings P *Business-focused maintenance — guidance and sample schedules* BSRIA BG3/2004 (Bracknell: BSRIA) (2004)

3   Harris J and Hastings P *Business-focused maintenance toolkit* BSRIA BG7/2004 (Bracknell: BSRIA) (2004)

4   *Enhancing the performance of oversized plant* BSRIA AG1/2000 (Bracknell: BSRIA) (2000)

5   *Standard maintenance specification for building services* (electronic database) SFG20 (London: Heating and Ventilating Contractors Association) (2002)

Bibliography

Brittain J R *Oversized air handling plant* BSRIA GN11/97 (Bracknell: Building Services Research and Information Association) (1997)

Brittain J R *Oversized heating plant* BSRIA GN12/97 (Bracknell: Building Services Research and Information Association) (1997)

Brittain J R *Oversized cooling and pumping plant* BSRIA GN13/97 (Bracknell: Building Services Research and Information Association) (1997)

Appendix 5.A1: Statutory documentation for buildings

5.A1.1   All buildings

(1)   Fire risk assessment, including records of fire training, drills, and instructions (Fire Precautions Act 1971).

(2)   Records of fire detection, smoke detection and alarm tests (Fire Precautions Act 1971).

(3)   Checks on fire protection systems with supporting records (to cover extinguishers, hose reels and sprinkler systems).

(4)   Risk assessments in relation to the Management of Health and Safety at Work Regulations 1992 and associated regulations.

(5)   *Legionella* risk assessment and records of *legionella* risk management implementation (Health and Safety at Work Act 1974 and Control of Substances Hazardous to Health Regulations 1988), to cover stored water, showers and evaporative coolers, plus general water hygiene.

(6)   Control of substances hazardous to health (COSHH) risk assessments and records (Control of Substances Hazardous to Health Regulations 1988).

(7)   Operation and maintenance manuals including sections dealing with equipment isolation and emergency procedures (Health and Safety at Work Act 1974).

(8)   Installation record drawings (Health and Safety at Work Act 1974).

(9)   Emergency lighting system test records (exits and walkways) (Fire Precautions Act 1971).

(10)   Electrical earthing and insulation test records (Electricity at Work Regulations 1989).

(11)   Portable appliance testing records (Electricity at Work Regulations 1989).

(12)   Documentation for waste disposal (Environmental Protection Act 1990).

(13)   Gas safety inspection record (Gas Safety (Installation and Use) Regulations 1998).

5.A1.2   Buildings where applicable

(1)   Records of sprinkler system tests (Fire Precautions Act 1971).

(2)   Lift inspection reports (Factories Act 1961, Offices, Shops and Railway Premises (Lift and Hoist) Regulations 1968, Lifting Plant and Equipment (Records of Test and Examination) Regulations 1992).

(3)   Lifting equipment test reports and certificates (Factories Act 1961, Lifting Plant and Equipment (Records of Test and Examination) Regulations 1992).

(4)   Pressure systems reports and certificates (Pressure Systems and Transportable Gas Containers Regulations 1989).

(5)   Smoke extract system test records (Fire Precautions Act 1971).

(6)   Records of maintenance and servicing of equipment containing refrigerants (European Union F-gas Regulation No. 842/2006).

(7)   Asbestos register (Asbestos Regulations).

(8)   Environmental impact assessment (Environmental Protection Act).

(9)   Sustainability assessment.

(10)   Records to demonstrate compliance with PUWER (Provision and Use of Work Equipment Regulations 1998) and LOLAR (Lifting Operations and Lifting Equipment Regulations 1998); see also Appendix 5.A2.

Appendix 5.A2: Statutory regulations affecting plant service requirements

The Provision and Use of Work Equipment Regulations 1998[1] (PUWER) relates to the provision of work equipment and its safe use. The regulations require consideration to be given to:

— the nature and degree of risk associated with the equipment and its use

— the means available to reduce those risks.

The Lifting Operations and Lifting Equipment Regulations 1998[2] (LOLER) applies in addition to the requirements of PUWER, for lifting equipment and lifting operations. These regulations require:

— the planning, supervision and execution of lifting operations to ensure safety

— the safe use of lifting equipment

— the periodic thorough examination of lifting equipment by a competent person.

These regulations place strict requirements on all employers to consider the hazards connected with the use of work and lifting equipment and reduce the associated risks.

PUWER requires that, where the risk assessment carried out under the requirements of The Management of Health and Safety at Work Regulations 1999[3] has identified a significant risk to the operator or other workers from the installation or the use of the work equipment, a suitable inspection should be carried out. Inspections should be undertaken by persons who have the necessary knowledge and experience to do so.

Where the work equipment is of a type where the safe operation is critically dependent on its condition in use and deterioration would lead to a significant risk to the operator or other person, the frequency of the inspections should be based on how quickly the work equipment is likely to deteriorate and therefore give rise to significant risk.

The scope of equipment requiring inspection, the type of person considered most appropriate for undertaking inspections and the recommended maximum periodicities are detailed in Table 5.A2.1. Note that the tables are non-exclusive. They indicate where the inherent risks from the installation or use of the work equipment would normally be such to warrant inspection by an independent competent person (C), where inspection by an appropriately trained and qualified person would normally be adequate (T) and where normally only the result of a risk assessment would be able to determine which of the two inspection routes is appropriate (T/C).

The indicated inspection periods are for guidance only. The risks imposed by work equipment and its performance must be evaluated by the client or by an organisation competent to do so.

LOLER Regulation 9 requires the thorough examination of lifting equipment at specified situations. Unlike previous lifting legislation where the scope of lifting equipment requiring thorough examination was clearly

Table 5.A2.1 Guidance list of work equipment requiring inspection

Item	Competent or trained person	Recommended maximum periodicity (months)
Doors (sliding)	T	12
Doors (automatic/revolving)	T	12
Escalators (PM45)	C	6
Fire doors and fire curtains	C	12
Food processing equipment	T	12
Guards and safety equipment	C	6
Guillotine (moveable/fixed guard)	C	6
Ladders/steps/stairs	T	12
Masts, radio and TV	C	12
Racking/warehouse stillage	T/C	12
Safety harness (if not under LOLER)	C	12
Gymnast equipment (if not under LOLER)	C	12
Stage equipment (also LOLER)	C	12
Waste compactors	C	12
Waste disposal units	T	12

'C' indicates inspection by competent person; 'T' indicates inspection by person trained and qualified to make such inspections of equipment concerned is sufficient under normal circumstances

defined, LOLER does not define what equipment needs to be thoroughly examined. LOLER gives the owner of lifting equipment the option of adhering to a new set of prescribed periodicities for thorough examination or to have in place or to follow a scheme of examination produced by a competent person.

The types of lifting equipment requiring thorough examination by a competent person and the recommended periodicities for those examinations are detailed in Table 5.A2.2.

References

1   The Provision and Use of Work Equipment Regulations 1998 Statutory Instrument 1998 No. 2306 (London: The Stationery Office) (1998)

2   The Lifting Operations and Lifting Equipment Regulations 1998 Statutory Instrument 1998 No. 2307 (London: The Stationery Office) (1998)

3   The Management of Health and Safety at Work Regulations 1999 Statutory Instrument 1999 No. 3242 (London: The Stationery Office) (1999)

Bibliography

Simple guide to The Provision and Use of Work Equipment Regulations 1998 HSE INDG290 (London: HSE Books) (1999)

Simple guide to The Lifting Operations and Lifting Equipment Regulations 1998 HSE INDG291 (London: HSE Books) (1999)

Table 5.A2.2 Guidance list of lifting equipment requiring examination

Item	Examination periodicity (months)
Lift/hoist:	
— passenger	6
— goods only	12
— passenger/goods	6
Lifts:	
— service	12
— domestic	6
— scissor	6
— stair	6
— teagle	12
— patient	6
Winches/capstans	12
Blocks, ropes, hoist, pulleys etc.	12
Bosun's chair	6
Harness with lanyard	6
Safety belts	6
Supports for lifting gantry equipment	12
Eyebolts	6
Cradle	6
Fork lift truck attachments	6
Lifting beams/frames	6
Shackles	6
Slings	6
Suspended access equipment	6
Window cleaning rig	6
Fork lift truck	6
Stage equipment hoist	6
Gymnasium equipment	12
Roller shutter doors	12

6 Energy efficiency and maintenance

Summary

Techniques by which the maintenance team might improve energy efficiency are outlined, starting with good housekeeping. In addition to input from the maintenance team, this requires support from building occupants and commitment from management.

The importance of maintenance staff 'knowing' their building and being aware of hot (and cold) spots is noted; the importance of the automatic controls system is stressed.

With ventilation and air conditioning, simple things such as regularly changing or cleaning filters can help to reduce fan power; with refrigerating systems trained personnel can ensure that the systems operate to optimum efficiency.

Hints for improving the effectiveness of artificial lighting are provided, routine boiler efficiency checks for heating and hot water services systems are recommended and it is suggested that the merits of variable volume pumping be considered for some water distribution systems.

Finally, it is pointed out that the maintenance engineer or contractor should prepare supporting financial justification for any energy efficiency improvement proposals.

All organisations use energy in some way in their operational regime and improving energy efficiency can offer a ready means of making cost reductions. For any drive towards improved energy efficiency to succeed, however, there must be unreserved commitment from the building user's top management. Buildings consume nearly half the energy used in the UK, see Figures 6.1 to 6.5, and all building professionals have a responsibility to reduce this through good practice, much of which is set out in CIBSE Guide F: *Energy efficiency in buildings*[1].

Total 6695 PJ

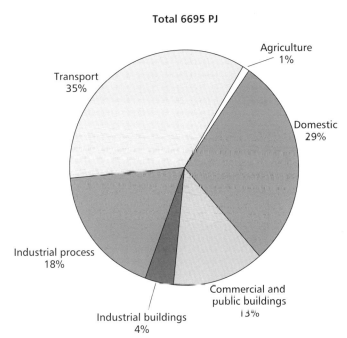

Figure 6.1 Total UK delivered energy consumption by sector in 2000

Total 3122 PJ

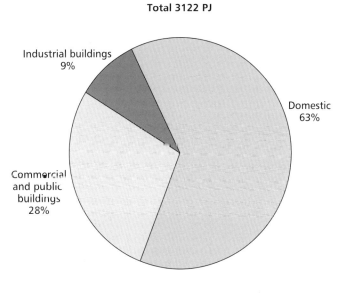

Figure 6.2 Total UK delivered energy consumption by buildings in 2000

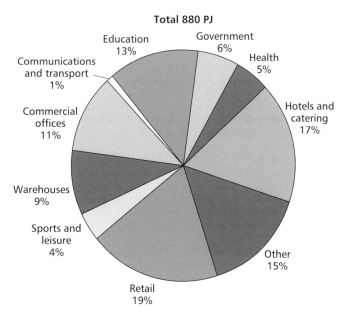

Figure 6.3 UK delivered energy consumption by end use in 2000

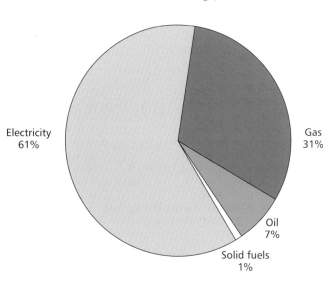

Figure 6.4 UK CO_2 emissions from energy use in non-domestic buildings by fuel in 2000[1]

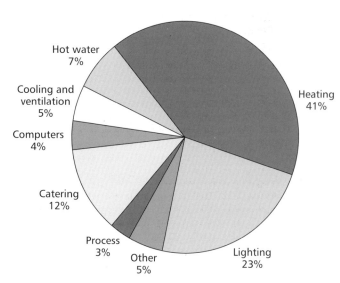

Figure 6.5 UK CO_2 emissions from energy use in non-domestic buildings by end use in 2000

Any organisation seeking to improve its operational energy efficiency would probably initially look for in-house leadership from its facilities manager. The facilities manager, in turn, is likely to consult the maintenance specialist to tap his/her overall knowledge of the building services.

To meet such a request for advice and guidance, maintenance engineers need to move beyond keeping the plant in good working order, although this is important in itself. As a minimum, they should be able to comment on the scope for varying the operational modes of systems to match the actual usage of the building more closely.

The energy used by a building is broadly determined by the building fabric, the building services and the management of the building. The influence of management on energy consumption is commonly underestimated[1]. Although improvements may be made to the fabric and services, the management of the building often has the greatest impact on day-to-day energy consumption. It is common to find well designed buildings operating badly due to poor management. Conversely, poorly designed buildings can be optimised to a great extent through good management practice[1].

Even where all technical measures have been considered and implemented, there is often considerable scope for improving energy efficiency by adopting changes in the management, operation and maintenance of the building. The key to energy efficient management of existing buildings is to:

—   gain a sound understanding of how the building is meant to work, at both strategic and detailed levels

—   set out a clear energy management policy alongside a clear maintenance policy for the building and its engineering services, and implement these policies rigorously

—   put into place organisational structures to ensure that responsibilities are clear, regular reporting/ feedback is taking place and the necessary resources are made available

—   encourage occupants to use the building correctly and motivate them to reduce energy consumption

—   set energy targets and continually monitor performance in order to keep consumption under control.

6.1   Gaining an overview

To establish how the building is intended to be used and how this relates to the overall heating, lighting, ventilation and control strategies, the following need to be clearly established through auditing by suitably qualified and experienced specialists:

—   occupancy levels, including cleaners, late working etc.

—   any different uses of particular areas within the building

— gross and treated floor areas broken down into use and tenancies

— landlord/tenant agreements (who is responsible for what)

— key items of plant, what they supply and which areas they serve

— the means of heating and cooling, areas served, means of control

— means of ventilation and its control

— types of lighting, areas served, methods of control, availability and use of daylight

— how the building is managed, maintained and the operation monitored.

Tangible benefits from energy efficiency range from the individual to the national level and include:

— improved design and operation of buildings

— better working environments

— life cycle cost savings

— environmental (reduced CO_2 emissions) — a key performance measurement in most environmental management systems

— added market value of buildings.

6.2 Legislation and codes of practice

The Building Regulations for England and Wales[2] and their equivalents for Scotland[3] and Northern Ireland[4] impose requirements aimed at improving energy efficiency in both domestic and non-domestic buildings. Building Regulations Approved Document L2[5] (and their equivalents for Scotland and Northern Ireland) offer various means for meeting these requirements. In summary the intent is to provide:

— energy efficient and properly commissioned fixed building services with effective controls

— operators with sufficient information about the building and its engineering services to operate and maintain them using no more fuel and power than is reasonable in the circumstances.

The requirements include:

— limiting the heat loss and gains through the fabric of new and refurbished buildings

— providing space heating and hot water systems which are energy efficient

— providing lighting systems with appropriate lamps and sufficient controls so that energy can be used efficiently

— limiting exposure to solar overheating

— minimising use of mechanical ventilation and air conditioning

— providing sufficient information so that the building can be operated and maintained in such a manner as to use no more energy than is reasonable in the circumstances.

Approved Document L2[5] reflects the requirements of the European Directive on Energy Performance of Buildings[6] (EPBD) which requires:

— a common methodology for calculating energy performance

— minimum standards of energy performance of new and some existing buildings

— certification schemes when buildings are sold or rented out with display of energy performance certificates in public service buildings

— specific inspection and assessment of boilers and air conditioning systems.

6.3 Investing in energy efficiency

Cost savings usually drive energy efficiency. Savings in operating costs will flow directly into the building user's profits. Well managed organisations tend to re-invest some of the savings in further energy efficiency measures.

Such measures should generally be considered in their order of economic payback, complexity and ease of application. Measures will fall into three broad types:

— no/low cost, requiring no investment appraisal (e.g. general occupant awareness of closing windows and doors, switching off lights and electrical appliances when not required, provision of a building user's handbook to ensure the occupants how to operate the engineering services as efficiently as possible, instituting an energy monitoring and targeting scheme (e.g. CIBSE TM22: *Energy assessment and reporting method*[7])

— medium cost, requiring only a simple payback calculation (e.g. replacement of 20+ year old boilers could provide significant savings on energy consumption and repay the installation cost within 2 years)

— high capital cost measures, requiring a detailed design and full investigation appraisal.

6.4 The energy efficient brief

An existing or a new building should have an energy efficient brief which needs to be no more complex than is appropriate for the type and size of the building. It should incorporate:

— the client's intentions, requirements and investment criteria

— energy targets (e.g. for each fuel and individual end users)

— environmental targets (e.g. BREEAM[8], CIBSE Guide F benchmark data[1], Energy Consumption Guide ECG019[9])

— life cycle costs (see chapter 13 for plant life expectancy data)

— specific operational requirements for energy efficient equipment.

For new build and major refurbishments, Good Practice Guide GPG287: *The design team's guide to environmentally smart buildings*[10] is particularly helpful in considering the available options.

Information on internal and external design conditions is available from CIBSE Guide A: *Environmental design*[11].

6.5 Renewables

Renewable energy occurs naturally and repeatedly in the environment, e.g. from the sun, wind, rain, oceans and from plants. It also includes energy from waste and clean technologies such as fuel cells. There is a wide range of renewable energy sources and technologies, varying in technical and commercial viability. These include:

— wind power

— hydroelectric power

— wave and tidal power

— photovoltaics

— active solar heating

— passive solar design

— waste heat generation

— landfill gas

— geothermal energy

— agricultural and forestry wastes

— energy crops

— ground source heat pumps.

Renewable energy produces few if any harmful emissions. Exploiting renewables also reduces the rate at which other energy sources are consumed. Renewables therefore promise to play an increasingly significant role. At the end of 2004, 3.1% of electricity supply was generated from renewable sources; under the Renewables Obligation[12–14] this is intended to rise to 15.4% by 2015–2016. For further information, see CIBSE TM38: *Renewable energy sources for buildings*[15].

6.6 Fuel selection

Fuel selection is a strategic decision usually taken early in the design process. During the life of a building there may be opportunities to review the original decisions which are often dominated by practical issues such as the availability of fuels to the site, access for delivery, space and cost of storage. Typical fuel specifications and combustion details are shown in chapter 5 of CIBSE Guide C[16] and chapter 1 of CIBSE Guide B[17].

6.6.1 Fuel prices

The price of fuels remains a very important factor affecting choice and life cycle cost. Current energy prices and trends are available through web sites such as http://www.ukpower.co.uk.

6.6.2 Environmental emissions of fuels

The use of energy affects the environment both at the point of use and indirectly through the 'upstream' activities associated with production, conversion and delivery, having detrimental impacts locally on air quality and acid deposition and causing global climate change, primarily through carbon dioxide emissions, see Table 6.1.

Table 6.1 CO_2 emission per unit of utility

Utility	CO_2 emission / $kgCO_2$
Electricity	0.43 per kW·h
Natural gas	0.19 per kW·h 5.50 per therm
Gas fuel oil and diesel	2.68 per litre
Petrol	2.31 per litre
Liquid petroleum gas (LPG)	1.51 per litre
Coal	2419 per tonne

Source: based on data from the National Energy Foundation (http://www.nef.org.uk) and DEFRA (http://www.defra.gov.uk).

6.6.3 Factors affecting fuel choice

Where a mains supply of natural gas is available, it is likely to be the preferred option given its advantages of clean combustion and low price. Reliability of supply may become an issue as traditional resources close to the UK cease to be available. Other options are oil, LPG and solid fuel. Electricity is generally a premium fuel but relatively expensive. It is the most versatile form in which energy is delivered and may serve almost any energy end-use. Further information on fuel selection is provided in chapter 5 of CIBSE Guide F[1].

The impact of the following documents should be taken into consideration in the storage and usage of liquid fuels as they demand that only certain lower sulphur fuels may be burnt after certain dates:

— The Sulphur Content of Liquid Fuels (England and Wales) Regulations 2000 Statutory Instruments 2000 No. 1460[18]

— The Sulphur Content of Liquid Fuels Regulations (Northern Ireland) 2002 Statutory Rule 2002 No. 28[19]

— The Sulphur Content of Liquid Fuels (Scotland) Regulations 2000 Scottish Statutory Instrument 2000 No. 169[20].

6.7 Combined heat and power

Combined heat and power (CHP) can offer a highly economic method of providing heat and power that is less environmentally harmful than conventional methods. Where applicable, CHP is the single most effective means of reducing building-related CO_2 emissions and running costs. CHP has proved highly cost-effective in a wide range of buildings (see section 5.3.1 of CIBSE Guide F[1]) with over 1000 installations providing more than 300 MW of electrical power. Small scale CHP is being used in hospitals, hotels, leisure centres, universities, residential buildings and defence establishments. Large scale CHP installations are being successfully used at major hospitals, airports and universities.

Key features of CHP are:

— provision of on-site electricity generation with heat recovery

— typically over 80% efficient

— generally applicable to locations with year-round heat demand

— generally economic if run for more than 4500 hours per year

— an independent feasibility study is essential, based on reliable and realistic demand profiles

— avoidance of Climate Change Levy for gas consumed by the prime mover and possibly some of the boiler plant provides a major financial incentive for CHP

— CHP should always be the lead 'boiler'

— economics of CHP improve if standby generation or boiler replacement is being considered

— sizing CHP somewhat above base heat load usually provides the best economics

— oversizing can lead to excessive heat dumping which undermines the economics.

Further information is provided in CIBSE Guide F[1] and can be found on the DEFRA CHPQA website (http://www.chpqa.com).

6.8 Metering

Metering is a key part of the feedback mechanisms that are essential to monitor the status and operation of a building and allow the building manager to determine whether energy consumption is greater than expected. A good maxim is 'if you cannot measure it, you cannot manage it.'

Good metering is fundamental to the monitoring and targeting process that is, in turn, an essential part of energy management.

Improved sub-metering and benchmarking of end-uses will help building operators to understand and manage their buildings better, resulting in energy savings. Sub-metering is particularly important where there are large process loads such as a computer suite or a kitchen, which may mask the true performance of a building. It will also allow fair billing for energy use where a building is subdivided for occupation by more than one organisation or where one occupant has a variety of cost centres. For example, a meter that identifies pumps being left on 24 hours a day, seven days a week, may save 60% of the energy passing through it.

Building Regulations Approved Document L2[5] includes recommendations for sub-metering in non-domestic buildings. Owners/occupiers should be given sufficient instruction, including an overall metering strategy that shows how to attribute energy consumption to end uses and how the meter readings can be used to compare operating performance with published benchmarks. CIBSE Guide F[1] provides further detailed guidance.

Reasonable provision of meters would be to install incoming meters in every building greater than 500 m² gross floor area. Reasonable provision of sub-metering would be to provide additional meters so that the following consumptions can be directly measured or estimated:

— electricity, gas, oil and LPG to each separate tenanted area greater than 500 m²

— energy consumed by plant items with input power greater than that shown in Table 6.2[5]

— heating or cooling supplied to separately tenanted space

— any process load to be discounted from the building's energy consumption when comparing measured consumption against published benchmarks.

Table 6.3 (reproduced from CIBSE in Guide F[1]) identifies the key considerations when selecting meters. For further information on metering, see CIBSE TM39: *Building energy metering*[21].

Table 6.2 Size of plant for which separate metering would be reasonable[5]

Plant item	Rated input power / kW
Boiler installations comprising one or more boilers or CHP plant feeding a common distribution circuit	50
Chiller installations comprising one or more chiller units feeding a common distribution circuit	20
Electric humidifiers	10
Motor control centres providing power to fans and pumps	10
Final electrical distribution boards	5

6.9 Lighting

Building Regulations Approved Document L2[5] states that lighting systems should be reasonably efficient and make effective use of daylight where appropriate. It suggests that the initial efficacy averaged over whole building should be not less than 40 lumens per circuit.

Requirements include:

— minimum efficacies of lamps

Table 6.3 Key considerations when selecting meters (reproduced from CIBSE Guide F[1])

Service	Type of meter	Approximate installed cost	Typical accuracy	Key issues (see CIBSE Guide F)
Electricity	Single phase Three phase	£100–200 £500 upwards	±1%	Single or three phase? Will current transformers be needed?
Gas	Diaphragm Turbine	£300–700 £700–1300	±2%	Pressure drop? Will pressure and temperature compensation be needed? (May cost an extra £1000.)
Oil	—	£350–2800	±1%	Strainer needed to avoid blockages?
Water	—	£250–700	±1%	
Heat	Electromagnetic Turbine	£450–1200 £400–900	±(3 to 5)%	Electromagnetic meters are more accurate. Dirty systems can be a problem

Source: General Information Leaflet GIL065[22]

— minimum efficiencies of lamp/luminaire/control gear combinations

— maximum power consumption of high efficiency control gear.

Table 6.4 (reproduced from CIBSE Guide F[1]) suggests benchmarks for installed overall lighting for offices.

Starting with the simplest and most economic options, every effort should be made to ensure the best use of daylight. This may require action to minimise solar gain and to ensure glare does not cause a nuisance to occupants. Automatic dimming control of luminaires near to windows can be used as part of the daylight regime. Provision for lighting switching should be arranged to match the usage of the accommodation. For cellular layouts this would entail individual switching while in open plan areas switching arrangements should ideally coincide with departmental 'boundaries'. Where the switching match is poor, wiring circuit provisions should be investigated to see if there is scope for improvement.

Maintenance routines can improve lighting efficiency by using a regular programme of cleaning for lighting diffusers and by replacing luminaires as they become less efficient with age.

There may also be advantages in replacing older type tubular fluorescent lamps with modern, improved efficiency units with an equivalent lighting output.

6.10   Heating and hot water

Periodic boiler efficiency tests, checks on boiler cycling, ensuring that system air venting is good, distribution temperature checks to highlight insulation deficiencies and monitoring of control set-points all have a contribution to make to energy efficiency.

The calibration of the set-points for frost and condensation protection should be checked routinely to ensure that actuation temperatures are kept as low as practicable. As most buildings have a high thermal capacity and take a long time to cool, the actuation setting for condensation protection systems should be experimentally reduced so that the true need is established.

Temperatures of hot water systems need to be kept at appropriate levels to minimise legionellosis risk but there is usually some scope for timing the operating hours.

Variable speed pumping should be considered wherever the heating load profile shows this to be worthwhile.

Typical and good practice performance indicators for space heating in offices are shown in CIBSE Guide F[1], Table 10.10. The energy use indicator is also described.

Table 6.4 Overall lighting benchmarks for offices (reproduced from CIBSE Guide F[1])

Parameter	Benchmark for stated office type							
	Naturally ventilated cellular office (Type 1)		Naturally ventilated open plan office (Type 2)		Air conditioned standard office (Type 3)		Air conditioned prestige office (Type 4)	
	Good practice	Typical	Good practice	Typical	Good practice	Typical	Good practice	Typical
Installed capacity* ($W \cdot m^{-2}$)	12	15	12	18	12	20	12	20
Running hours (h/year)	2500	2500	3000	3000	3200	3200	3500	3500
Utilisation (%)	45	60	60	70	70	85	70	85
Energy use indicator (EUI) (($kW \cdot h) \cdot m^{-2}$/year)	14	23	22	38	27	54	29	60

* Per m^2 treated floor area; factors for converting treated floor area to nett and gross are given in CIBSE Guide F, Table 20.2

Source: Energy Consumption Guide ECG019[9]

6.11 Electrical power

Large and small electrical power loads form a significant part of the total energy use in buildings. Office equipment can typically account for more than 20% of the energy used in an office (lighting can be up to 25%). In larger offices, significant energy is consumed by the power systems supplying the IT equipment. Careful design and selection can result in large energy savings. Transformers found on larger sites (usually taking supplies at 3.3 kV or 11 kV) will typically produce losses of about 1%, which, although small, can again be significant and selection of the most efficient is important. Uninterruptible power supplies (UPS) provide 'clean' power to critical IT equipment. They have fixed losses which become a larger proportion of output as the load falls, thus reducing their efficiency. Computer room air conditioning is often wasteful, using as much energy as the computer equipment although current best practice installations use some 65% of the computer power. In air conditioned offices, it can take 50% more energy to remove heat generated by the installed equipment than that used to run the equipment itself. Oversized plant will reduce operating efficiency. Catering equipment (e.g. hot water boilers, kettles, refrigerators and vending machines) can contribute significantly to heat gains.

Much electrical power is used by electric motors and their rating should be appropriate to the required duty. The use of variable speed drives should be considered wherever feasible and cost effective. To put this into perspective, a fan or pump drive motor operating at half speed reduces power consumption by more than 85%. Further information on motor control and variable speed controls can be found in CIBSE Guide H[23] and CIBSE Guide F[1].

6.12 Controls

Control systems can be complex. As well as trying to ensure that a control system is performing its function effectively, facilities managers need to ask whether they fully understand the system and determine if it is manageable. Controls need to be managed and maintained efficiently and economically. Where this is not possible, the need for a change is indicated. Perhaps the control system should be simplified or, possibly, the facilities manager and maintenance team be given better training.

Calibration of control sensors is a critical factor in ensuring that a control system functions properly. In some instances, recalibration of controls is a demanding requirement consuming a significant proportion of the system maintenance costs. The replacement of sensors with better quality components can reduce, or even eliminate, the problem of set-point drift as well as improving energy efficiency.

Simple disciplines can exert a strong, positive influence on energy efficiency. Routine maintenance checks are important on time switches and optimiser controls to ensure that the settings are as intended and appropriate to the operational regime.

Where occupants are provided with control interfaces, it is important that they appreciate the mode of operation that will give the best results. This information should be given in a user's handbook.

For centralised system controls, access should be restricted to authorised personnel with the appropriate training and expertise. Even these operatives should be instructed to modify control settings only in accordance with proposals that have been properly discussed and agreed. Unauthorised tampering with controls must be avoided.

Further information is available in CIBSE Knowledge Series KS4: *Understanding controls*[24] and CIBSE Guide H: *Building control systems*[23].

6.13 Refrigeration systems

It is important that the operation and maintenance of refrigeration systems be carried out only by trained personnel with the appropriate expertise. The Refrigerant Handling Certification Scheme operated by the Air Conditioning and Refrigeration Industry Board (www.acrib.org.uk) provides some scope for evaluating competence in this respect. Skill and expertise are essential for effective monitoring of the factors that influence the efficient operation of a refrigeration system, including refrigerant charge levels, compressor cycling, and pressures and temperatures throughout the refrigeration system circuits. The EU 'F-gas Regulation'[25] requires documented records to be in place relating to the maintenance and servicing of equipment containing refrigerants.

Water treatment needs to be applied and maintained to keep heat exchange surfaces clean and to maximise efficiency. This applies particularly to units with evaporative cooling where water treatment is crucial to the control of algae and microbial and bacterial activity, including legionellosis.

Refrigerating efficiency can be improved significantly by allowing the condensing pressure to vary on a seasonal basis. Where this facility is not included in the installation, advice should be sought from the manufacturer.

6.14 Energy policy

Adopting an appropriate and realistic energy policy delivers increased and sustainable performance and provides a clear sense of direction. Any new policy should review current practices and provide a good starting point to an energy campaign. The process of preparing the policy will educate the decision makers and help secure financial approval for investment. For most organisations, the policy document will comprise a few pages. It should be reviewed annually, and part of this review process should be to ensure the continuing commitment of senior management to energy management within the organisation.

An energy policy will:

— establish clear management commitment to energy efficiency

— improve the overall approach to energy management

— help to keep the main objectives in full view

— maximise the use of resources, both in time and money

— provide goals against which to monitor

— provide a clear direction for the energy team

— give senior management a way forward.

The energy policy should ideally be developed in conjunction with the maintenance policy. It should also be integrated with any environmental policy where this exists.

Energy and purchasing managers should periodically review the arrangements for purchasing energy. There is a wide range of energy supply contracts available, with significant cost savings possible through judicious competitive tendering. Whilst this does not directly affect energy consumption, it can alter the energy supply tariff structures and this can influence energy management procedures. A responsible energy strategy can often be combined with energy procurement services to give a valid environmental aspect to what otherwise might be a purely cost-saving exercise.

6.15   Checking energy consumption

Energy consumption can be estimated using installed loads, estimated hours run and simple diversity factors, as shown in CIBSE TM22[7]. Benchmark energy data for a representative range of buildings are provided in Appendix 6.A1. These data are reproduced from CIBSE Guide F[1], which includes more extensive benchmark data.

References

1   *Energy efficiency in buildings* CIBSE Guide F (London: Chartered Institution of Building Services Engineers) (2004)

2   The Building Regulations 2000 Statutory Instruments 2000 No. 2531, as amended by The Building (Amendment) Regulations 2001 Statutory Instruments 2001 No. 3335 and The Building and Approved Inspectors (Amendment) Regulations 2006 Statutory Instruments 2006 No. 652 (London: The Stationery Office) (dates as indicated)

3   The Building (Scotland) Regulations 2004 Scottish Statutory Instruments 2004 No. 406 (London: The Stationery Office) (2004)

4   Building Regulations (Northern Ireland) 2000 Statutory Rules of Northern Ireland 2000 No. 389 (London: The Stationery Office) (2000)

5   *Conservation of fuel and power* Building Regulations 2000 Approved Document L (4 parts) (London: NBS/RIBA Publications) (2006)

6   Directive 2002/91/EC of the European Parliament and of the Council of 16 December 2002 on the energy performance of buildings ('The Energy Performance of Buildings Directive') *Official J. of the European Communities* L1/65 (4.1.2003) (Brussels: Commission for the European Communities) (2003)

7   *Energy assessment and reporting method* CIBSE TM22 (London: Chartered Institution of Building Services Engineers) (2006)

8   *BREEAM: BRE Environmental Assessment Method* (website) (Garston: Building Research Establishment) (http://www.breeam.org) (accessed March 2008)

9   *Energy use in offices* Energy Consumption Guide ECG019 (The Carbon Trust) (2003) (available from http://www.carbontrust.co.uk) (accessed March 2008)

10   *The design team's guide to environmentally smart buildings* Good Practice Guide GPG287 (The Carbon Trust) (1996) (available from http://www.carbontrust.co.uk) (accessed March 2008)

11   *Environmental design* CIBSE Guide A (London: Chartered Institution of Building Services Engineers) (2006)

12   The Renewables Obligation Order 2006 Statutory Instruments 2006 No. 1004 (London: The Stationery Office) (2006)

13   The Renewables Obligation (Scotland) Order 2007 Scottish Statutory Instruments 2007 No. 267 (London: The Stationery Office) (2007)

14   The Renewables Obligation Order (Northern Ireland) 2007 Statutory Rules of Northern Ireland 2007 No. 104 (London: The Stationery Office) (2007)

15   *Renewable energy sources for buildings* CIBSE TM38 (London: Chartered Institution of Building Services Engineers) (2006)

16   *Reference data* CIBSE Guide C (London: Chartered Institution of Building Services Engineers) (2007)

17   *Heating, ventilating, air conditioning and refrigeration* CIBSE Guide B (London: Chartered Institution of Building Services Engineers) (2001–2)

18   The Sulphur Content of Liquid Fuels (England and Wales) Regulations 2000 Statutory Instruments 2000 No. 1460 (London: The Stationery Office) (2000)

19   The Sulphur Content of Liquid Fuels Regulations (Northern Ireland) 2002 Statutory Rule 2002 No. 28 (London: The Stationery Office) (2002)

20   The Sulphur Content of Liquid Fuels (Scotland) Regulations 2000 Scottish Statutory Instrument 2000 No. 169 (London: The Stationery Office) (2000)

21   *Building energy metering* CIBSE TM39 (London: Chartered Institution of Building Services Engineers) (2006)

22   *Metering energy use in non-domestic buildings* General Information Leaflet GIL065 (The Carbon Trust) (2002) (available from http://www.carbontrust.co.uk) (accessed March 2008)

23   *Building control systems* CIBSE Guide H (London: Chartered Institution of Building Services Engineers) (2000)

21   *Understanding controls* CIBSE Knowledge Series KS04 (London: Chartered Institution of Building Services Engineers) (2005)

22   Regulation (EC) No 842/2006 of the European Parliament and of the Council of 17 May 2006 on certain fluorinated greenhouse gases *Official J. of the European Union* L 161/1 (14.6.2006) (Brussels: Commission for the European Communities) (2006) ('The F-gas Regulation')

Bibliography

Organising energy management — a corporate approach Good Practice Guide GPG 119 (Action Energy) (1997) (available from http://www.carbontrust.co.uk) (accessed March 2008)

BCO Guide to Environmental Management (London: British Council for Offices) (2006)

Appendix 6.A1: Energy benchmark data

Table 6.A1.1 Energy benchmark data (from Table 20.1 of CIBSE Guide F: *Energy efficiency in buildings*[1])

Building type	Annual energy consumption good practice benchmark for existing buildings / $kW \cdot h \cdot m^{-2}$	
	Fossil fuels	Electricity
Theatre	420	180
Cinema	515	135
School:		
— primary	113	22
— secondary	108	25
Teaching hospital	339	86
Hotel (luxury)	300	90
Industrial building, post-1995 (5000 m^2)	92	
Office:		
— standard, air conditioned	97	128
— naturally ventilated, open plan	79	54
Library	113	32
Museum and art gallery	96	57
Prison (kW·h per prisoner)	18861	3736
Residential nursing home	247	44
Bank/building society	63	71
Clothes shop	65	234
Department store	194	237
Distribution warehouse	103	53
Supermarket	200	915
Sports and recreation centre	264	96
Swimming pool	573	152

7 Controls for building services

Summary

In discussing the purpose of controls, reference is made to the importance of providing building occupants with the ability to regulate their own environment and ensuring that they understand how the control system operates. A user's handbook is recommended.

Regarding the maintenance of controls, the possible need for periodic recommissioning is highlighted and the maintenance benefits of better quality sensors and control equipment is outlined.

The advantages of monitoring contract performance are noted and examples given of contract options particular to controls maintenance.

Typical routine maintenance checks for controls are outlined, with particular reference to building management systems.

Finally, the scope for exploiting the continual development of controls technology to effect viable upgrading of control systems is discussed.

Controls and control systems are an essential part of buildings and the management of the internal environment. Some jargon and terminology used in control engineering may seem incomprehensible to the non-expert. CIBSE Knowledge Series KS04: *Understanding controls*[1] provides a useful source of reference to the understanding of the terminology, functions, limitations of controls and how clients and building users can explain their requirements. Detailed information is provided in CIBSE Guide H: *Building control systems*[2]. Experience suggests that many buildings do not work as well as intended or do not satisfactorily meet the occupants' requirements due to problems with the controls.

Control irregularities are also a significant cause of excessive energy consumption. These may be the result of an inappropriate controls concept, poor design of the control system, poor equipment selection (e.g. low quality sensors, oversized control valves or dampers), incorrect commissioning or inadequate maintenance. Any one of these shortcomings is capable of producing serious adverse effects.

While maintenance may not be responsible for a particular fault in a control system, it can identify and rectify problems originating from earlier work, including improvements to the control system design. This places maintenance of controls in a significant position to exert a favourable influence on the performance and operational efficiency of the building services installation.

7.1   Purpose of controls

The fundamental purpose of building engineering services controls, whether automatic or manual, is to regulate the performance of systems to meet operational and environmental requirements, in accordance with the design intent. In most instances the designer takes account of energy efficiency in selecting control sequences and set-point parameters.

Controls are needed to ensure safe operation and to achieve the required output from the building services systems, and as such they act to achieve and then maintain a specific condition, for example temperature or lighting level. The controls of the building services play a key role in meeting the requirements of Building Regulations Part L[3] which require that buildings be operated in an energy efficient manner. They operate by measuring and adjusting specific variables such as temperature, flow rate, pressure and electrical resistance. These then alter the system output to enable the conditions required by the occupant to be satisfied, see Figures 7.1 and 7.2. The three main functions of building control systems are simply:

—   to switch equipment on and off

—   to adjust the output of equipment to maintain the required operating conditions

—   to provide monitoring and metering functions.

The terms 'controls' and 'control systems' are often used interchangeably but, although for most practical purposes,

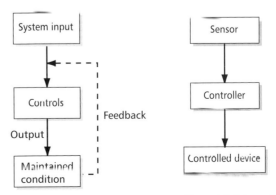

Figure 7.1 The principle of controls

Figure 7.2 Schematic of a basic control system

they mean the same, strictly speaking there are some minor differences. 'Controls' is a more generic term, used for a collection of individual control elements, from sensors, valves and timers to control panels. A control system performs the control function, comprising in its simplest format a sensor, a controller and the controlled device, see Figure 7.2. The sensor detects or measures a variable such as temperature and transmits its value to the controller, which acts on the information. Generally, any control system is only as good as its sensors, and the quality and accuracy of the information they provide. Ideally, the simplest control system should be selected that meets the needs of the building operator, has sufficient capability and efficiently delivers the required quality of system operation.

Figure 7.3 shows the relative capability and complexity of key control systems[4].

Surveys of building users have shown that occupants accept building services installations more readily where they are able to intervene in the control system to some degree and to exercise their own preferences. In its simplest form, this may entail opening a window to increase ventilation or adjusting a thermostatic radiator valve to influence space temperature. Similarly, it can be beneficial to offer occupants a measure of influence on automatic control set-points.

The original design intent should be made clear to building users and occupants. For simple building service installations, such as low temperature hot water (LTHW) heating systems, this may be self evident. Other installations, such as air conditioning systems, may be quite complex with various operating modes and sophisticated control sequences. The 'good practice' approach is for the system designer to provide a full design description covering all building services systems and their control concepts. This should describe the way the systems are intended to operate and may be supported by schematic diagrams to clarify particular operational details. Control sequences to regulate the operation of the system and to specify design set-point parameters may be included within the design description or presented as a separate document.

The design description should be aimed primarily at the building user and compiled in everyday language. For the sake of clarity and comprehension, it is important to avoid jargon, to define engineering terms and to ensure that the complete document is relevant to the particular installation.

Care should be taken to describe fully the scope the building occupier has to adjust the operation of the systems to suit the specific requirements. In this respect, it may be helpful to schedule all system control set-points and to indicate reasonable ranges of adjustment to facilitate resetting by authorised personnel where this is shown to be appropriate. Such a schedule should also include comments on the likely effect of set-point adjustments on operational energy efficiency as well as occupant comfort.

Ideally, the designer should provide a user's handbook to guide the building occupants on how to gain maximum benefit from the environmental systems; again this is part of the requirements of Building Regulations Part L[3] to provide information to allow the building to be run in an energy efficient manner. The handbook should be easy to understand with, where possible, illustrations to aid comprehension. Guidance on producing building log books and a Microsoft® Word template for producing log books are contained in CIBSE TM31: *Building log book toolkit*[5]. Where a user's handbook is not provided as part of the installation contract, the building occupier should consider separately commissioning the designer to produce one. Much relevant information for preparation of such a handbook is likely to be provided in the building's operation and maintenance (O&M) manual, see chapter 10.

7.2   Maintenance requirements

An industry standard approach is provided by the HVCA's *Standard maintenance specification for building services*[6].

Mechanical maintenance of manual controls and automatic control actuators is necessary to ensure that these operate smoothly over their complete range. It is also important to check the set-points and calibration of all control sensors to ensure satisfactory operation of the control system. In addition, the performance of the system should be monitored. The result of this approach is, in effect, a continuous fine-tuning of the control system. For this to be fully effective, a written record of all changes and adjustments must be kept and the building log book[5] annotated accordingly.

This requires a high standard of expertise and commitment from the controls maintenance specialist who should be able to demonstrate that ongoing training is being provided to ensure the competence of the operatives.

7.2.1   Periodic recommissioning

With some systems, monitoring may show a progressive deterioration of performance to a degree where recommissioning eventually becomes necessary. Where this can be shown to be due to ineffective maintenance, it would be reasonable to countercharge the maintenance contractor

Manually operated controls

Simple automatic controls

Direct digital controls (DDC)

Building management systems (BMS)

Integrated control systems

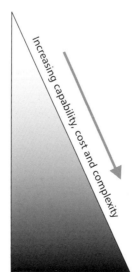

Figure 7.3 Relative capability and complexity of key control systems (based on diagram from BSRIA AG15/2002[4])

for a proportion of the recommissioning costs, provided that the terms of the contract made provision for this.

It is recommended that consideration be given to re-commissioning the controls installation when a major change of use or refurbishment takes place or when a new energy management policy is implemented.

7.2.2 Control component influences

Design provisions can aid the maintenance task. For example, the provision of high quality sensors can reduce the tendency for set-point 'drift' and, thus, the need for regular recalibration or even replacement. Intelligent controls can be arranged for self-monitoring; this can be a valuable asset in maintenance, provided that not too much faith is placed in this facility. The truly significant factor is system performance and the maintenance engineer must always challenge and cross-check self-monitoring features. For example, the particular location of a monitoring sensor in a fluid distribution pipework or ductwork system can influence the reading and result in a misleading indication.

7.2.3 Contract options

The form and terms of the contract agreement for the maintenance of the control system and the selection of the service provider can influence performance. Examples of maintenance service provision include the following:

(a) *Manufacturer-based contracts*: the contractor has an implicit incentive to ensure effective maintenance to support the reputation of that manufacturer's products. They would normally have input to the design of the control system.

(b) *Contract maintenance*: this arrangement can range from simple inspection and checking to the responsibility for full repair of the control system for a specified contract period, which may also entail performance targets.

Performance-related incentives may be included in the terms of the contract; these may be based on:

— energy consumption performance targets

— for process applications, including computer room environmental systems, the consistent achievement of control parameters with penalties for deviation

— penalty clauses for control system failure or for other proven shortcomings

— incentives to rearrange maintenance schedules to minimise unnecessary service duties (e.g. 'shared' savings arrangements).

controls that are most critical to the effective performance of the design.

The range and frequency of routine checks of controls will depend on the actual installation but useful indications of the necessary approach are provided in publications such as the HVCA's *Standard maintenance specification for building services*[6]. Due account must also be taken of manufacturers' instructions but these may tend towards 'over maintenance'.

Typical controls checks include:

— the effective functioning of all safety devices (of primary importance)

— sensor set-point calibration, typically on a rolling programme basis, perhaps with more frequent checks on selected critical devices (see section 7.2)

— actuator functionality through the full operational range, with more frequent checks on devices critical to the normal functioning of the organisation.

Details of routine checks should be recorded in the system log book in sufficient depth to permit the identification of recurring problems, trends or faults. Where such records indicate a suspect component, this should be taken up with the manufacturer with a view to replacement by an improved design.

It should be good practice within maintenance of the control system to check on the energy consumption of the installation. Energy targets should be set by the designer and, where measured performance falls outside these, some form of reporting and further investigation should be carried out. The energy targets and subsequent performance data should be included in the building log book[5], as required for new buildings by Building Regulations Approved Document L2A (2006)[7]. Example energy benchmarks are included in chapter 6, Appendix 6.A1.

As occupant satisfaction is one of the main aims of a control system, it would be reasonable for the client to consider the operation of a system of user reports compiled by the building occupants. Where appropriate, the user reports would be passed to the controls maintenance service providers for them to consider and recommend appropriate courses of action.

Clients should consider routine review meetings with the controls maintenance service provider. The object of the meetings would be to monitor maintenance performance and to seek continuing improvement. Where independent maintenance contract performance monitoring is employed, the monitoring consultant should be present at review meetings.

7.3 Routine maintenance checks

Ideally, the necessary routine checks of the control system should be identified at the design stage and it would be prudent to seek guidance from the controls specialist. The installation designer should identify and highlight those

7.4 Building management systems

A building management system (BMS) is a control system which performs the overall control and monitoring functions for some or all the building's plant and systems, see Figure 7.4, it is a networked system with one or more

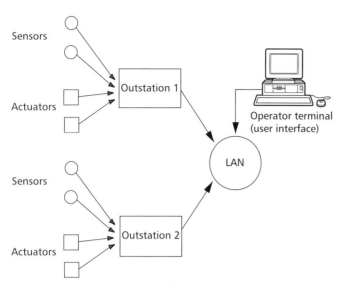

Figure 7.4 Schematic of a building management system

operator stations providing the user interface. For most applications the sensors and actuators are linked into outstations which gather data, act to provide the form of control and transmit information to the operator terminal.

The building services system designer will have devised the controls concept which the building management system (BMS) is intended to fulfil. However, the designer may have only a limited understanding of how the actual BMS functions. A full understanding of the BMS is generally confined to the BMS manufacturer and it is not uncommon for a thorough understanding to be further limited to the specialists responsible for constructing the system software. Industry standard algorithms[8] for particular functions are available which can be adapted to suit a particular application. The extent to which the BMS manufacturer's maintenance team understands the system operation depends to a large degree on the quality of the back-up documentation provided by the installer.

The effectiveness of a BMS depends directly and fundamentally on the software which it comprises. It is not unusual for BMS manufacturers to be cautious in disclosing details of their systems and software, the reasons stated for this generally concern commercial sensitivity.

The commissioning of a BMS is often undertaken by the manufacturer. The degree of monitoring of this process, which can be applied by the designer, the commissioning specialist or manager, or the witnessing authority, will depend on their terms of appointment.

Maintenance of a BMS is also generally undertaken by the manufacturer or systems house. Maintenance is typically separated out into functional checking of the operation of the control system hardware (e.g. valve and damper actuator operation, sensor accuracy) and software tuning (e.g. control loop tuning). BSRIA A4/2003[9] provides guidance on BMS maintenance. Software system access is controlled by password and may be arranged to permit varying levels of access for different personnel. Typically, ascending order of access would be arranged for the system operator, the controls specialist maintenance engineer and the controls specialist design team. As noted above, there is no guarantee that the BMS manufacturer's maintenance technicians will have a thorough under-

standing of the software. They can, however, reasonably be expected to be fully familiar with the hardware components used in the BMS installation.

As with all control systems, the effective functioning of any element will depend fundamentally on the correct location, positioning and calibration of each control sensor. Incorrect positioning or calibration will result in spurious readings which, arguably, may be less subject to challenge with a BMS than with conventional controls. This tendency results from the 'centralised' nature of the BMS which discourages maintenance checks and inspections at remote locations and relies on the 'monitoring' capability of the installation itself.

Ideally, the BMS maintenance engineer should retain a measure of scepticism regarding the capability of the system. To foster this approach, BMS maintenance routine schedules should include checks on control elements on a rolling programme basis. These should comprise checks of sensor location and calibration, ensuring that these are measuring true conditions and are not adversely influenced by fluid turbulence or incomplete mixing of fluid streams. Actuator operation should be checked over the complete control range movement. Most important of all, however, is the need to check the 'end result' of each control element, i.e. that the control is meeting its design intent efficiently and effectively.

The outcome of all these checks should be recorded in the BMS log book, the entries being kept under continuing review by the maintenance engineer for indicative trends. Any indications such as deterioration in reliability of any components should be reported promptly to the client, together with supporting evidence, and acted upon as appropriate.

Energy consumption checks and recording or graphical plotting of control variables may be a suitable means of assessing the effectiveness of control performance.

7.5   Upgrading control systems

Developing technology tends to provide continuing opportunities for improvement of control systems, for example by enhanced capabilities of the system components, enhanced software or by improvements in the original concept. The cost effectiveness of any prospective improvement, however, should be assessed carefully by comparing the cost of the replacement or upgraded controls against the benefits likely to be achieved by more efficient operation.

To provide incentive for change, it may be necessary to make allowances based on the economic life expectancy of the existing control components (see chapter 13). Individual components may benefit from upgrade. In particular, the installation of better quality sensors may be beneficial, especially where these provide a controlling function rather than just monitoring. Some sensors are prone to 'drift' and may require frequent re-calibration. An independent consultant, where appointed, would be the logical arbiter to confirm any recommendation in respect of the viability of a replacement proposal, based on the consultant's knowledge of the control system and its performance.

Another motivation for controls replacement could arise if the existing system proved to be too sophisticated, to an extent where it was not understood by the users and was too complex for the maintenance contractor to manage effectively. Such a situation would require a frank review, involving all the parties with an interest in the issue, taking account of all relevant factors and deciding on an appropriate course of action. Cost control of this action would be an important consideration. Again, an independent maintenance consultant, where appointed, would play an important part.

It is not uncommon for new technology to fall short of its initially predicted capabilities and performance. For this reason, the user should be cautious of revolutionary or 'panacea' proposals from the controls manufacturer or maintenance contractor. Even apparently successful track records in other applications may have limited relevance to the user's system. A prospective approach in this sort of instance would be for the user to be offered the enhancement on a payment-by-results basis. Clearly, it would be necessary to exercise care in drawing up the basis of a truly equitable means of assessing performance and any improvement.

The speed of development in the BMS field lends some credibility to the claim that a system is obsolescent the day after it is installed. Due to the cost of development, it is necessary for manufacturers to recoup these costs. This can lead to a tendency towards 'stepped' development rather than continuous improvement to provide a market for and an income from the existing BMS version. Where this policy is operated, the improvement between successive versions can be very marked. There may be some scope for users with an existing BMS to negotiate an arrangement with the proprietary supplier to provide version updates at reduced costs.

7.6 Need for training

Controls manufacturers and systems houses have an obligation to provide training in the installation, commissioning and maintenance of their own products for their own workforce. Some manufacturers also provide training for individuals other than their own personnel.

The low level of skills in some organisations in the building engineering services sector of the construction industry has led to trade organisations introducing operative certification to provide some reassurance to customers (e.g. the welder's certificate operated by the Heating and Ventilating Contractors Association* and the refrigerant handling certificate operated by the Air Conditioning and Refrigeration Industry Board†). The Building Controls Industry Association‡ has developed a training scheme for controls personnel, leading to a certificate of competance. It would be prudent for prospective customers to enquire at tender stage about the competence of the operatives to be dedicated to their work.

---

* Heating and Ventilating Contractors Association, ESCA House, 34 Palace Gate, London W2 4JG (http://www.hvca.org.uk)

† Air Conditioning and Refrigeration Industry Board, Kelvin House, 76 Mill Lane, Carshalton, Surrey SM52JR (http://www.acrib.org.uk)

‡ Building Controls Industry Association, 2 Waltham Court, Milley Lane, Hare Hatch, Reading, Berkshire, RG10 9TH (http://www.feta.co.uk/bcia)

In addition to manual and craft skills it is important for a controls maintenance technician to have a good technical understanding of controls principles. Ideally, this knowledge should extend to an appreciation of controls concepts. Where the maintenance technician does not have this knowledge base, arrangements should be in place to provide ready access to technical back-up and the technicians encouraged to make proper use of this. Without this knowledge, the maintenance technician will be unable to effect improvements to the control system and, indeed, would be unlikely to identify deterioration in control system performance.

From the viewpoint of the controls maintenance contractor, the skills of its workforce are probably its major asset. In view of this, it is not unreasonable to expect the contractor to develop and promote these skills. The contractor should also recognise individual operative skills. In addition to continuing formal training, it is likely to be cost effective to provide staged opportunities for cross-fertilisation of skills and techniques between operatives. Innovations and suggestion schemes or other forms of incentives may offer appropriate means of deriving corporate benefit from this source.

It is implicit in the terms of any maintenance contract that the workforce will be skilled, experienced, properly trained and fully competent. It is, however, incumbent on the customers to monitor the service they receive and to ensure that the contract standards continue to be achieved. Where customers are unable to effect this monitoring from their own resources, it may be advantageous to retain the services of an independent auditor to carry out assessments of contractual performance on their behalf.

References

1 *Understanding controls* CIBSE Knowledge Series KS04 (London: Chartered Institution of Building Services Engineers) (2005)

2 *Building control systems* CIBSE Guide H (London: Chartered Institution of Building Services Engineers) (2000)

3 The Building Regulations 2000 Statutory Instruments 2000 No. 2531, as amended by The Building (Amendment) Regulations 2001 Statutory Instruments 2001 No. 3335 and The Building and Approved Inspectors (Amendment) Regulations 2006 Statutory Instruments 2006 No. 652 (London: The Stationery Office) (dates as indicated)

4 De Saulles T *Illustrated guide to mechanical building services* BSRIA AG15/2002 (Bracknell: BSRIA) (2002)

5 *Building log book toolkit* CIBSE TM31 (London: Chartered Institution of Building Services Engineers) (2006)

6 *Standard maintenance specification for building services* (electronic database) HVCA SFG20 (London: Heating and Ventilating Contractors Association) (2007)

7 *Conservation of fuel and power in new buildings other than dwellings* Building Regulations 2000 Approved Document L2A (London: NBS/RIBA Publications) (2006)

8 Martin A and Banyard C *Library of system control strategies* BSRIA AG7/97 (Bracknell: BSRIA) (1997)

9 Martin A *BMS Maintenance Guide* BSRIA AG4/2003 (Bracknell: BSRIA) (2003)

Bibliography

Energy efficiency in buildings CIBSE Guide F (London: Chartered Institution of Building Services Engineers) (2004)

BS EN ISO 16474-2: 2004: *Building automation and control systems hardware* (London: British Standards Institution) (2004)

Building Performance Group *Building services component life manual* (Oxford: Blackwell Science) (2000)

The Construction (Design and Management) Regulations 1994 Statutory Instrument 1994 No. 3140 (London: The Stationery Office) (1994)

8 Commissioning and testing

Summary

Reference is made to the scope of work of a commissioning specialist and the areas of involvement of a commissioning manager are described.

The need for comprehensive documentary support is stated and the various record requirements are outlined. The need to update records is noted.

The process of fine tuning the performance of an installation is outlined and details given of troubleshooting investigations and operational situations where repeat commissioning may be appropriate.

A designer's checklist for commissioning is provided and guidance on the decommissioning and mothballing of an installation given.

The commissioning and testing functions are defined and explained fully in the series of CIBSE Commissioning Codes[1–7].

— *Commissioning* is the advancement of an installation from static completion to working order according to specified requirements.

— *Testing* is the measurement and recording of system parameters to assess specification compliance.

Commissioning of buildings and their engineering services is very important to their safe and energy efficient operation. This key stage in the construction process enables the installed systems to be operated according to the design intent. When coupled with good maintenance practice, commissioning (and periodic re-commissioning) helps provide the building occupants with a safe, good quality, comfortable internal environment using heat and electrical energy (whether generated on site or obtained from public networks) efficiently and cost effectively. Compliance with CIBSE Commissioning Codes should also help to achieve compliance with the requirements of Part L of the Building Regulations[8] for commissioning of building services systems. Building Regulations Approved Document L2[9] requires heating, mechanical ventilation, cooling/refrigeration, lighting, controls and water systems to be commissioned in accordance with the design intent and emphasises the need for commissioning to be certified by suitably qualified persons.

The main factors influenced by the commissioning of the building services are:

— plant operation within the specified design parameters, including internal and external conditions

— maintenance of internal design parameters within defined tolerances at all load conditions

— minimising energy consumption

— future maintenance requirements.

Good commissioning of building services requires specialist skills and knowledge. It also requires an early input in the life of a project, when key decisions relating to the construction process are taken.

8.1 Commissioning management

The main objective of commissioning management is to manage the overall pre-commissioning and commissioning activities, including programming and co-ordination of energising the installation, to achieve the project completion date. All major projects should be assessed to see if there is justification for appointing a commissioning manager. A detailed consideration of commissioning management is provided in CIBSE Commissioning Code M: *Commissioning management*[5].

A number of buildings are built to 'shell and core' status and a set of commissioning parameters need to be set out by the designers and agreed prior to contract commencement. It is to be expected that the final performance of the building will change as fit-out is completed and the building comes fully on line. These changes in system performance must be recorded by the commissioning specialist, and the building log book[10] and other record documentation updated to suit.

A similar exercise should be carried out when a tenant carries out 'category B' fit-out in a building that has been finished to 'category A' fit-out standard.

8.2 Summary of commissioning requirements

Building services plant and systems should be inherently commissionable. This is most likely to be achieved if the requirement is in the brief from the outset, and specialist commissioning advice is sought early in the design process. The following summarises the key requirements for successfully commissioned building services:

— The contractor and client should allow sufficient time for the complete commissioning process and ensure integration into the overall programme.

— Cost of fuel for testing and commissioning should be allowed for.

— A commissioning management team should be formed early in the design and construction process to advise on buildability and commissionability.

— Maximum use should be made of off-site pre-commissioning activities.

— Manufacturers of equipment should be involved in the commissioning process.

— Thorough commissioning procedures should be adopted.

— Documentary evidence that the requirements of the Building Regulations have been met must be provided.

— User feedback should be obtained to confirm the performance of the installed systems and the attainment of required internal environmental conditions.

8.3 Commissioning manager and commissioning specialist responsibilities

The responsibilities of the commissioning specialist can be extensive and various depending on how early the person is appointed and the extent of the brief. If appointed early enough, the commissioning specialist's input at the design stage can make a significant contribution to ensuring the success and timely completion of a project.

If the brief extends to a commissioning management role, the commissioning manager's responsibility is to interface all the activities of the work package so as to produce complete operational systems on time. The commissioning manager should be appointed to the project/management team as early as possible so that the interfacing can happen in a proactive manner.

It would normally be expected that the commissioning manager would be appointed to the project management team with a separate contract to the 'hands-on' commissioning specialists to enable him/her to report objectively to the management team.

The hands-on commissioning specialists are often mono-disciplined specialists and employed by the relevant sub-contractors as part of their contract of supply.

The function of the commissioning manager is as a facilitator and catalyst bringing together diverse specialist operations by cooperation, consensus and coordination and dealing with any or all the following:

(a)   Electrical services:

—   high voltage and low voltage

—   uninterruptible power supply generators

—   security and fire systems

—   audio and information technology systems.

(b)   Mechanical services:

—   air and water systems

—   all mechanical plant.

(c)   Control systems:

—   lighting control systems

—   field controls and panels

—   building management systems

—   software.

(d)   Specialist equipment (normally commissioned by the equipment/system supplier):

—   lifts and escalators

—   sprinkler systems

—   car park barriers etc.

—   large refrigerating and boiler plant.

Terms of appointment vary, but the scope of works for a commissioning manager, which could apply to all the above for a complete project or to one specific element, could be:

—   design review

—   drawing review (including buildability, commissionability and maintainability)

—   planning/programming for commissioning

—   witnessing of works testing

—   monitoring services installation against the specification and programme

—   coordination of commissioning and maintenance documentation

— witnessing of site testing

— witnessing of the flushing and cleaning of pipework distribution systems

— witnessing of commissioning

— coordination of record documentation

— organisation of client training.

It must be emphasised that all installations, irrespective of size, need to be properly commissioned and the following general principles will apply. The appointed organisation must also have an understanding of the implications of The Construction (Design and Management) Regulations 2007[11] (CDM Regulations) and a policy and strategy for working to meet the regulations.

Commissioning specialist responsibilities may include some or all the following activities, depending on whether the appointment is for commissioning or for a wider commissioning management role.

(a) Design stage:

— review commissionability of design

— review maintainability of design

— review commissioning and testing content of specification.

(b) Post-design stage:

— produce project-specific commissioning and testing method statements

— prepare an integrated commissioning and testing programme.

(c) On-site duties:

— monitor and review installation in line with specified requirements

— coordinate, oversee and witness progressively the testing and commissioning

— monitor commissioning and testing programme and report progress

— collate test data

— oversee/coordinate production of operating and maintenance manuals and record drawings

— coordinate client training

— coordinate demonstrations of the safety systems to the local authorities, fire officer, district surveyor and building insurer.

Where the above duties are excluded from the terms of reference of the commissioning engineer, the appropriate responsibilities must be delegated to other suitably qualified members of the building services team.

Where the employer uses the skills of a commissioning manager in the first instance as his/her mechanical and electrical (M&E) design manager, the commissioning manager will be working alongside the designers of the systems.

8.4 Documentation

Comprehensive documentation to support commissioning and testing activities is of paramount importance. Such records will show that statutory requirements have been met both mechanically and electrically allowing the building to be certified as safe for occupation.

Of much greater importance in the longer term, the commissioning documentation should provide a record that the commissioned systems operate in accordance with the design intent. These records will also be invaluable in ensuring that the performance of the system is kept up to standard. Additionally, they provide an essential basis for the logical adjustment of system performance or for the recommissioning of systems following modifications or adaptations of the accommodation or its services.

Part L2 of the Building Regulations[8] puts an onus on the building owner to maintain the building in the optimum condition for energy consumption. It is also a requirement that a building log book be provided and kept up to date. The final commissioning results for energy utilisation will need to be entered into the log book prior to handover. Part L2 requires a certificate of satisfactory commissioning completion to be signed by a competent and accredited person before the building control authority will issue a certificate of completion. See CIBSE TM31[10] for information relating to the development of building log books.

It is essential that the completed documentation is kept safe and made readily available to everyone involved with the operation and maintenance of the building and its services. This documentation will form a permanent record and reference manual to which interested parties can refer when checking the ongoing performance of the building services. It is essential that any changes, modifications or investigations carried out are undertaken in a controlled and logical manner and that a thorough audit trail of these events is kept with the original commissioning and testing records.

The production of operation and maintenance (O&M) manuals, health and safety files and building log books in an electronic web-based format is proving to be both time- and cost-effective as it reduces the need for production and/or duplication of hard copies and provides simple cross referencing by hyperlinks. It also makes updating and archiving a simple one-step process.

At practical completion, the following tabulated commissioning information should be available:

— main plant performance results

— air and water (flow regulation) results

— specialist plant commissioning/test results

— pipework and ductwork pressure test certificates

— fire alarm test certificate

— security/CCTV test certificates

— sprinkler/dry riser test and insurance certificates

— check-sheets recording systems interface

— check-sheets recording the commissioning of building management/controls systems

—   electrical completion and inspection certificate

—   emergency lighting test certificate

—   lightning protection test certificate

—   test sheets recording the progressive testing of the electrical installation in accordance with BS 7671[12] (the 'IEE Wiring Regulations')

—   chlorination certificate

—   district surveyors' approvals

—   statutory authorities' approvals

—   as-fitted record drawings (indicating location of test points)

—   operation and maintenance manuals

—   flushing and cleaning, water treatment regimes.

8.5   Designer's checklist

The following checklist is applicable to all sizes of installations:

(a)   Has the appointment of a commissioning specialist been considered?

(b)   Can the systems be commissioned in accordance with the specification and the CIBSE Commissioning Codes[1–7]?

(c)   Can the installed building services be adequately and safely maintained after handover?

(d)   Have validation checks at manufacturers' works been allowed for on the major plant items?

(e)   Have the patented systems been checked or tested rather than just assumed to be working.

(f)   Has sufficient detailed design information been provided, especially in respect of control regimes, including set-points, system flow rates and plant capacities?

(g)   Is the specification definitive in its content of the commissioning responsibilities and acceptance criteria and tolerances?

(h)   Is the specification adequately detailed in respect of the protection of plant and equipment during transportation, installation, commissioning and testing?

(i)   Has a feedback procedure been implemented to recognise and address design problems that emerge during commissioning and testing in order to prevent repetition on future projects?

8.6   System characteristics

In the course of their work on a system, commissioning specialists learn a considerable amount about its operating characteristics. Commissioning specialists should be encouraged to include anecdotal notes on record documentation to highlight system characteristics and peculiarities which become apparent. Similarly, maintenance engineers should be encouraged to add written notes of their experiences in operating and servicing the system. In this way, documentation will be compiled on:

—   accessibility

—   modifications and/or upgrades to plant, equipment or systems

—   system report

—   system description

—   experiences and observations made during periodic maintenance.

Such details often provide a valuable start point in a troubleshooting exercise.

8.7   Fine tuning

As defined earlier, the function of commissioning is to set a system into the required mode of operation, as envisaged by the designer. Fine tuning is the function of adjusting the operation of a commissioned system to match the actual need of the building occupier more closely. In certain instances this may include some form of remedial action to mitigate any adverse operational effects of overdesign (see section 5.4).

The design of a building services system is normally based on the interpretation of the client's requirements and a series of criteria assessments made by the designer. Inevitably, the specified parameters against which a system is commissioned do not generally coincide precisely with the actual operational requirements of the building occupier. The design provision may either exceed or underestimate the eventual requirements.

In the early stages of building occupation, these imbalances may lead to adjustments to flow rates in the air and water distribution systems to accommodate the occupier's requirements. The need for amendment to the flow rates should be assessed, the revised flow rates decided, appropriate adjustments made to the system and the actual modified flow rate measured and recorded. Additionally, the commissioning record documentation should be amended as necessary and, as with any installation modification, checks made to measure and record any effect on the remaining fluid distribution in the adjusted system.

Depending on the precise requirements of the occupants, the commissioning carried out to the original design may need to be readdressed if the final requirements differ from those envisaged in the initial design. This could justify a separate commissioning process to fine tune a system to match the occupants' specific needs.

If a building is designed as a speculative building and not bespoke for a particular client, there would be significant benefits in including a retuning commissioning process as part of the original installation contract or as a separate instruction issued subsequently. These benefits would include:

—   in-built flexibility to meet a range of tenant needs

—   reduction in post-contract problems evolving from inadequate control of environmental conditions

— reduced risk of the building user tampering with preset damper, grille, valve and control positions and settings affecting the system characteristics

— potential for cost savings due to accumulated site and systems knowledge.

8.8 Repeat testing and commissioning

There are a number of situations where repeat commissioning and testing/commissioning checks should be considered during the life of a building. These include the following:

— changes of use within a building: these may result in physical modifications to a system and/or amendments to the design information which necessitates the proportional adjustment of air and/or water volume flow rates and the effect that this may have on central plant relative to fan/pump power consumption

— a period of non-occupation and/or prolonged system shutdown (i.e. in excess of three months) depending on the complexity of the system and assuming that caretaker maintenance has been carried out during the shut down

— complaints from the building users regarding environmental conditions which, in turn, could result in a troubleshooting survey being required; this may indicate the need for aspects of the services installation to be recommissioned

— a periodic validation: regular testing and recording of particular specified aspects of the performance of an installation

— following a periodic ductwork cleaning operation; for details refer to the HVCA's *Guide to good practice: internal cleanliness of ventilation systems*[13].

Each of the above situations requires different recommissioning techniques and logical approaches as detailed in the following sections.

Repeat commissioning or other means of system performance checks may indicate that plant and equipment are oversized for their required duty. Guidance on improving the operational performance of oversized plant is given in section 5.4 and BSRIA AG1/2000: *Enhancing the performance of oversized plant*[14].

8.8.1 Modifications to building services

Where there has been a change of use of a specific area within a building, it is important to consider the implications of local changes for the performance of the overall system. Where modifications are made to part of an air or water distribution system, the system characteristics may be affected and, consequently, the volume flow rates and power consumption of the fan/pump. Consideration should be given to modifying the fan or pump to better match the new performance requirement.

It is not possible to increase the flow rate to a particular area without reducing the flow by the same amount elsewhere in the system. Where an increased total flow rate is required, the fan or pump must be uprated or changed. Equally, where a reduced flow rate is required, the fan or pump must be downrated or changed. Any implications regarding electrical loads relative to the fans and pumps should be reviewed at the same time.

Local changes within variable air volume (VAV) systems may be less disruptive because the VAV terminals throughout the system will automatically self-compensate to a degree provided that they are not 'starved' of air or suffer significant reduction in static pressure.

When additions or changes are made to water distribution systems, it is important that the new pipework is thoroughly flushed and cleaned before being connected to the main system. Corrosion inhibition should also be considered as any new pipework or components would be more vulnerable to corrosion than the existing system.

The designer responsible for changes to an existing system would benefit from discussing the proposals with a commissioning specialist. Such discussion would take account of the existing commissioning records and would facilitate any recommissioning which may be necessary.

8.8.2 Non-occupation or system shutdown

If a building has been unoccupied but properly commissioned and caretaker maintenance provided, allowing water systems to be circulated and air plant to be 'spun over' at regular intervals, the services should continue to operate efficiently and air and water volume flow rates should remain in balance. This can be checked by comparing random air and water flow rates or fan/pump power consumption with the original commissioning data.

It is important that any prospective tenant or building user carries out a health and safety risk assessment for the recommissioned premises before the mechanical and electrical services are inspected and recommissioned. The inspection should ensure that the services are in good safe working condition prior to being run up and demonstrate that they are operating and performing correctly and efficiently.

This can be achieved by confirming that the documentation is in place, visually inspecting the installation and undertaking random tests to ensure that the services have remained as originally commissioned. Water samples should be taken at various locations in hydraulic systems and sent for analysis to check water quality including the iron/mineral content as an indication of the suitability of corrosion inhibitor treatment levels. With all open water systems, biological analysis should be undertaken to check for health hazards, e.g. legionellosis. This would, as a minimum, include condenser cooling water, and hot and cold water services systems.

A full report, written in layman's terms, should be issued to the prospective tenant summarising the findings of the survey and recommendations for recommissioning.

8.8.3   Troubleshooting

In the event of complaints or suspicion of incorrect operation of the services within a building, the cause should be investigated. It is important not to be too hasty in drawing conclusions. A logical, systematic approach is essential to ensure any recommended remedial works are directed at the true source of the problem and do not make the situation worse. Before the investigation starts, the following should be undertaken:

— check that the original commissioning and testing records are available

— check that the services have been maintained correctly

— listen to the occupants

— talk to the building user and consider the complaint

— check the status of systems and undertake preliminary tests

— consider how the services are designed to operate (an overview) and what particular problems may have led to the situation being experienced

— review control functions and set-points and check their correct operation.

Only when the above course of action has been followed and preliminary tests carried out can a suitable solution and a corrective action approach be decided. Assume nothing; only preliminary testing will provide definitive evidence of flow rates, temperatures etc.

It is not possible to recommend a common approach to troubleshooting. What is most important is that the engineer leading the investigation is able to maintain an overview of the systems and understands how the systems were intended to operate and to interact to achieve the required environmental conditions within the building.

Any alterations or modifications made as a result of these investigations must be fully documented and the commissioning records and operation and maintenance manuals revised accordingly.

8.8.4   Periodic validation

The requirement for periodic system validation will depend on a number of factors from the building use to commercial considerations. Within the pharmaceutical industry, regular validation checks as part of good maintenance are now mandatory under the requirements of the US Food and Drug Administration.

With the growing concern and increasing statutory requirements for providing a healthy working and process environment, regular checks should be undertaken to ensure that buildings and services systems remain within the operational state required by the occupier. To achieve this, a schedule of routine tests of building services should be set up as part of the planned preventive maintenance regime. Where appropriate, fine tuning should be undertaken and an audit trail kept of any changes made.

As the operational history of an installation is built up, changes in the system performance will become readily apparent and an optimum frequency of validation tests will evolve.

Article 7 of the European Directive on the Energy Performance of Buildings[15], implemented in England and Wales by the Energy Performance of Buildings (Certificates and Inspections) (England and Wales) Regulations 2007[16], requires periodic inspection and certification of building services to ensure that the energy performance of buildings has not degraded with a consequential rise in CO_2 emissions.

8.9   Controls and building management systems

The commissioning specialist and the controls commissioning engineer need to liaise at the earliest possible stage in a project to agree an integrated programme and ensure that the necessary interface between the two disciplines is agreed as early as possible. Both will need each other to bring a system forward to a point where it can be advanced or completed. Furthermore, both will need exclusive time on a system with no interference from others.

Close liaison is imperative for the protection of the system components. More important, however, is the need for the engineers to cooperate fully with one another when safety systems are being brought to operational status.

It is now possible with the use of web-based technology to link electronically the building management system with the O&M manuals, the health and safety file and the building log book in order to keep all of these entities updated in real time. The same system may be used to produce reactive maintenance requirements to better control overall building maintenance and thus performance.

See also section 7.4 for guidance on maintenance of building management systems.

8.10   Decommissioning and mothballing

Decommissioning and mothballing are two distinctly different processes, and the precise requirements of the client in respect of the building need to be established before detailing a plan of action. Each building will need to be assessed individually.

8.10.1   Decommissioning

This is the systematic process of isolating, draining down water systems, and purging all mechanical and electrical plant and equipment, including specialist plant and equipment and services (lifts, escalators, medical gases, fume cupboards etc.). This should be carried out through a planned sequence of events supported by method statements and permit-to-work procedures, as appropriate.

The decommissioning may be carried out as part of the process to demolish the building or to carry out a large-scale refurbishment. Alternatively, its purpose may be to render the building eligible to be zero-rated by the local authority. This may be achieved by following the above process, plus disconnecting certain plant to a point such that the building is rendered 'incapable of beneficial occupation' and would require an unreasonable amount of expenditure to make it suitable for re-occupation.

However, there are other considerations and implications that need to be taken in to account including:

— interrelationship of the building services with neighbouring premises

— integrity of the fire, security and safety systems

— provision of temporary lighting and emergency lighting on staircases and hazardous walkways

— possible retention of an in-service lift (which may be prudent in high-rise buildings)

— possible need to maintain in running order essential plant and equipment, e.g. sump pumps, sewage ejectors, sprinkler pumps, dry riser or ventilation plant.

8.10.2 Mothballing

This is the preparation of the building services to provide only essential environmental requirements in an unoccupied or unlet building. This would include frost protection, fire, security and safety features to maintain the safety and integrity of the building, and minimising the input required to restore all services to full running order. A caretaker maintenance regime will need to be set up to turn moving parts and run specific items of plant periodically.

Mothballing enables the client to:

— benefit from the local authority unoccupied property rate (50% of normal office rates)

— minimise running costs

— save energy

— maintain the building in a state of readiness to meet a change in circumstances promptly.

References

1   *Air distribution systems* CIBSE Commissioning Code A (London: Chartered Institution of Building Services Engineers) (1996/2004)

2   *Boiler plant* CIBSE Commissioning Code B (London: Chartered Institution of Building Services Engineers) (2002)

3   *Automatic controls* CIBSE Commissioning Code C (London: Chartered Institution of Building Services Engineers) (2001)

4   *Lighting* CIBSE Commissioning Code L (London: Chartered Institution of Building Services Engineers) (2003)

5   *Commissioning management* CIBSE Commissioning Code M (London: Chartered Institution of Building Services Engineers) (2003)

6   *Refrigerating systems* CIBSE Commissioning Code R (London: Chartered Institution of Building Services Engineers) (2002)

7   *Water distribution systems* CIBSE Commissioning Code W (London: Chartered Institution of Building Services Engineers) (2003)

8   The Building Regulations 2000 Statutory Instruments 2000 No. 2531, as amended by The Building (Amendment) Regulations 2001 Statutory Instruments 2001 No. 3335 and The Building and Approved Inspectors (Amendment) Regulations 2006 Statutory Instruments 2006 No. 652 (London: The Stationery Office) (dates as indicated)

9   *Conservation of fuel and power in buildings other than dwellings* Building Regulations 2000 Approved Document L2 (London: The Stationery Office) (2002)

10   *Building log book toolkit* CIBSE TM31 (London: Chartered Institution of Building Services Engineers) (2006)

11   The Construction (Design and Management) Regulations 2007 Reprinted March 2007 Statutory Instruments 2007 No. 320 (London: The Stationery Office) (2007)

12   BS 7671: 2001: *Requirements for electrical installations. IEE Wiring Regulations. Sixteenth edition* (London: British Standards Institution) (2001)

13   *Guide to good practice: internal cleanliness of ventilation systems* HVCA Technical Report TR/19 (London: Heating and Ventilating Contractors Association) (2005)

14   *Enhancing the performance of oversized plant* BSRIA AG1/2000 (Bracknell: BSRIA) (2000)

15   Directive 2002/91/EC of the European Parliament and of the Council of 16 December 2002 on the energy performance of buildings ('The Energy Performance of Buildings Directive') *Official J. of the European Communities* L1/65 (4.1.2003) (Brussels: Commission for the European Communities) (2003)

16   The Energy Performance of Buildings (Certificates and Inspections) (England and Wales) Regulations 2007 Statutory Instruments 2007 No. 991 (London: The Stationery Office) (2007)

Bibliography

Parsloe C J *Commissioning water systems. Application principles* BSRIA AG2/89.3 (Bracknell: Building Services Research and Information Association) (2002)

Parsloe C J *Commissioning air systems. Application procedures for buildings* BSRIA AG3/89.3 *The commissioning of air systems in buildings* AG3/88.3 (Bracknell: Building Services Research and Information Association) (2001)

Parsloe C J and Spencer A W *Commissioning of pipework systems — design considerations* BSRIA AG20/95 (Bracknell: Building Services Research and Information Association) (1996)

Parsloe C J *Pre commission cleaning of pipework systems* BSRIA AG1/2001.1 (Bracknell: Building Services Research and Information Association) (2004)

Teekaram A *Variable flow water systems. Design, installation and commissioning guidance* BSRIA AG16/2002 (Bracknell: Building Services Research and Information Association) (2002)

Wild J *Commissioning HVAC systems: Guidance on the division of responsibilities* BSRIA TM 1/88.1 (Bracknell: Building Services Research and Information Association) (2002)

Gill P 'The art of constructive vandalism (decommissioning)' *Building Services* 15(11) 33–35 (1983)`

Standard specification for the commissioning of mechanical engineering Services installations for buildings CSA TM1 (Horsham: Commissioning Specialists Association)

9 Handover procedures

Summary

The various activities which become relevant as handover approaches are listed, the need to make preparations for this is noted and a typical checklist provided. The importance of commissioning is discussed and the necessary arrangements for inspecting the works, including inspections required by statute, are outlined.

Provisions for user demonstrations and training are recommended and arrangements for the handover of tools, spares and keys for the services installations are referred to.

The typical contents of a handover information pack are detailed and guidance is given on defects liability and equipment warranties.

The option of phased handover and the advantages to the client of beneficial occupation are briefly described.

Handover follows on from project completion which is the point in the construction process when the architect or project manager determines that the building is, to all intents and purposes, complete and ready for the client. Once completion has been certified, the contractor gives up occupation of the site to the client who takes over responsibility for security, insurance, operation and maintenance. The other contractual actions normally triggered by completion are:

— commencement of the defects liability period

— release of a proportion of the construction contract retention fund

— commencement of the architect's final review

— opening of any reference to arbitration, mediation or other method of dispute resolution

— cessation of the contractor's liability for liquidated damages

— cessation of the contractor's liability for subsequent frost damage.

In practical terms, the handover of building services systems is a gradual process, involving numerous inspections, user demonstrations and witnessing of commissioning and tests. The main parties involved will, typically, be the mechanical and electrical contractors, the designer and the client's maintenance personnel or nominated maintenance contractor. Good communication is especially important during the final stages of construction; ideally the maintenance personnel or contractor should be involved early in the handover process. Where a commissioning manager is appointed, one role of his/her appointment may be to ensure all the stages of handover are carried out and appropriately sequenced.

It is becoming common practice for the installation contractor to be made responsible for the maintenance of the installed services during the first year of operation (i.e. the defects liability period).

9.1 Preparation

General preparations for the handover proceedings are coordinated and supervised continuously by the architect/project manager in close liaison with the other members of the design team. While the events surrounding handover occur at the end of the construction process, a coordinated programme of activities should be drawn up well in advance to help ensure minimal complications. A programme of pre-handover activities should be agreed, including allocating responsibility for all inspections and the issuing of certificates. These activities can then be monitored and controlled.

The pre-handover checklist below may assist in creating such a programme of activities. The relevance, timing and responsibility for carrying out the activities will be determined by the nature of the project and associated contracts.

9.1.1 Pre-handover checklist

9.1.1.1 Two–three months before completion

Approximately two to three months before the scheduled completion date it should be ensured that:

— the client is informed of any likelihood of change to the scheduled completion date

— contractual obligations regarding witnessing of commissioning and testing, failure defect and deficiency inspections and outstanding items of work (snagging) are clarified

— the client is made fully aware of its post-handover obligations including the need to arrange insurances and contracts for maintenance

— arrangements are made to recruit operation and maintenance personnel as required

— relevant authoritative bodies have been approached to determine any necessary inspections/approvals; this may include Building Control (i.e. the local planning authority), the Health and Safety Executive and the fire authority

— the client is consulted regarding the format and required procedures for the handover meeting

— pre-commissioning cleaning of the heating, ventilating and air conditioning systems is carried out

— utilities suppliers selected, tariffs for the utility supplies negotiated and a contract with a meter operator arranged

— the planning supervisor has issued general details of the structure's equipment, maintenance facilities and procedures, construction methods and materials for inclusion in the health and safety file

— O&M manuals being assembled and programme in place to review and accept

— inspection of works commences in accordance with inspection policy and programme.

9.1.1.2   One month before completion

Approximately one month before the scheduled completion date it should be ensured that:

— if required, an engineer is appointed to assist the client during the initial period of occupation

— licences are obtained for the storage of hazardous chemicals

— draft operation and maintenance manual and record drawings are submitted and checked

— ongoing inspections are carried out in accordance with inspection policy

— a schedule of any outstanding work is agreed

— any additional works that are required are arranged

— all necessary statutory examinations have taken place (e.g. fire systems, means of escape, pressure systems, emergency lighting, lifts)

— all utility supplies are inspected, approved and signed off

— user and occupant demonstrations and training sessions have taken place, details recorded of those in attendance and certificates of competence awarded, as appropriate

— occupant demonstration and training sessions have been completed

— air pressure leakage testing has been satisfactorily completed.

9.1.1.3   One week before completion

Approximately one week before completion it should be ensured that:

— all commissioning work has been completed and witnessed

— the commissioning report(s) and associated information have been issued

— all the required test certificates have been issued

— final inspections have been completed as required

— water treatment appropriate to the installed services has been carried out

— all warranty documentation has been issued

— the completed/semi-completed operation and maintenance manuals and record drawings have been issued and approved

— all the required tools, spares, consumables etc. have been assembled, and an inventory provided

— waste/surplus materials been removed from the site

— the health and safety file has been checked and issued

— re-lamping, filter changing and cleaning have taken place as required by the specification

— the listed outstanding defects have been rectified to acceptable standards

— all meter readings and fuel stocks have been recorded.

9.2   Commissioning

(Further information on commissioning and testing is provided in chapter 8.)

At the pre-contract stage, the design team should identify the services which must be commissioned and divide responsibility for carrying out the work between the contractor and the manufacturers or suppliers. Statutory and insurance approvals must also be identified and responsibility assigned for obtaining them. Adequate provision must be included in the contract for carrying out commissioning, including requirements for witnessing test results, and the production of commissioning information and reports to the specified format. It is a requirement of the 2006 Building Regulations Part L[1] that all controlled services (i.e. heating, lighting, domestic hot water and air conditioning) that fall within the scope of the Regulations will be commissioned. This can be demonstrated by following the CIBSE Commissioning Code M[2].

It may be appropriate to appoint a commissioning manager to oversee the commissioning process, possibly

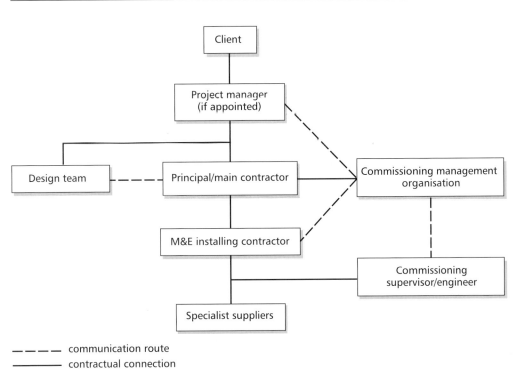

Figure 9.1 Possible contractual relationships and communications routes

from an early stage in the project when the role can include assessing whether commissioning of individual plant items and complete systems can be both practically achieved and within the planned programme. CIBSE Commissioning Code M[2] provides further information.

At the start of commissioning, the designer should ensure that a full programme of work is available. While the services may be fully installed and ready for commissioning, consideration should be given as to how any incomplete building work might affect testing, e.g. missing doors may influence air distribution system balancing. It should also be noted that to comply with the 2006 Building Regulations Part L[1], all buildings, including dwellings, are required to be subjected to air pressure leakage testing and a satisfactory certificate of performance provided.

Any failure of a system to achieve the specified design duty appropriate to the time of year that commissioning is taking place should be reported promptly by the commissioning specialist. Wherever possible, apparent or contributory reasons should be indicated in the report. It is the designer's prerogative to consider how the implications of such a failure might affect the operation of the building. This will depend on the degree of any performance shortfall and the designer's analysis of the reasons behind it. Action to remedy the situation need not delay completion unless the fault is serious.

Commissioning tests should be witnessed by the commissioning manager (where appointed), the designer and main contractor, in accordance with the contract. The final acceptance of the system will depend on how the actual commissioned performances compare with the specified duties and related tolerances. (Witnessing may be by an independent technical assessor.)

All commissioning information and related documentation must be kept safely. This includes any pre-commissioning reports and checklists. Ideally, the information should form a distinct section in the operation and maintenance manual and a provision to this effect can be included in the manual specification. Commissioning information is often helpful in resolving system performance problems and any disputes that may occur during the defects liability period.

9.3 Inspections

From a building services perspective, completion requires that, except for very minor items, all systems are installed and commissioned in accordance with the works contract. Any outstanding items must not pose a health and safety risk or interfere with the operation of the engineering system to which they relate. Furthermore, they should cause no more than very minor disruption to the activities of the building operator. The client can help to ensure that this requirement is satisfied by indicating to the architect/project manager any items of particular importance to its business which must not be outstanding at completion.

Typically, the design team will have a contractual duty to undertake a final inspection of the works for deficiencies and defects before completion. This will be preceded by a comprehensive inspection by the installing contractors and subcontractors. To help ensure that inspections can be conducted effectively, an inspection policy should be drawn up between all parties detailing the standards that must be achieved, the sequence of inspections and any specific access requirements.

9.3.1 Defect status sheet

The use of a defect status sheet will help keep track of outstanding items and enable rectification to be prioritised as appropriate but particularly where there are health and safety implications. The defects status sheet can take the form of a simple table with columns for:

— inspected item

— location

— date of inspection

— description of defect

— responsibility for rectification

— date of defect clearance

— date of re-inspection.

9.3.2   Statutory inspections

There is a legal obligation for lifting equipment and pressure systems to undergo a statutory examination before they are put into service. These examinations must be carried out by a competent person who will typically be a surveyor from a specialist insurance or maintenance organisation. Further examinations of the lifts and lifting equipment are required at regular intervals.

The frequency of pressure system examinations will be specified in a written scheme of examination drawn up by a pressure systems examiner based on the conditions of use. Pressure vessels such as boilers and air receivers will undergo an initial examination at their place of manufacture and will be dispatched with the appropriate certification. This does not, however, preclude a further site examination by a competent person.

Other plant and systems requiring inspection and certification before being put into service can include (but is not limited to) the electrical installation, emergency lighting, fire protection systems, smoke extraction, means of escape and portable appliances.

9.4   User training

If it is the client's intention to outsource all or part of the maintenance, arrangements for training should be made well in advance of handover to ensure attendance of the maintenance contractor. Where the client intends to use in-house resources for operation or maintenance, the appropriate personnel must be nominated, their responsibilities clarified and arrangements made to ensure their attendance.

Training sessions with a significant technical content should be divided into two parts. The first part should be in a classroom environment where a systems overview can be provided and the format of the operation and maintenance manual explained. The second part should be a tour of the building to allow specific elements of the engineering systems to be identified and their operation demonstrated. Wherever possible, opportunities for hands-on experience should be provided for the trainees. When planning training sessions, thought should be given to the number of contact hours required in the classroom and on-site for each system. Consideration should also be given to practical requirements such as classroom size, visual presentation equipment, and training documentation and schematics.

It may also be advisable to make provision for the training sessions to be recorded. This would provide a visual account of operating procedures which can enhance the information provided by the operation and maintenance manual and assist in the training of future operators or the arrangement of refresher courses.

The client will need to ensure that, where applicable, designated personnel within the organisation attend the training session(s) and a record is kept of the attendees, including details of any certificates of competence issued. Where relevant, a record should be kept of individuals' appointed responsibilities for specific systems, e.g. authorised personnel for high voltage and water systems, and competent persons for pressure systems and lifting equipment etc.

9.5   Occupant training

For all types and sizes of buildings, occupant training on environmental controls is desirable. For highly serviced buildings with BMS control, very little training may be required. However, where passive or low energy systems are used, there is likely to be a need for more extensive training as the occupants will play an active role in controlling the internal environment. This will require the provision of adequate time to properly convey the design intent and to help ensure that there is general 'buy-in' to the overall approach. This is particularly important for occupants more used to the stability of an air conditioned environment, requiring minimal control. Training should combine one or more presentations covering:

— an overview of the project and design intent

— importance of good occupant control

— methods of control during each season.

Involvement in this activity of the architect or other key members of the design team can be beneficial. The second part of the training should comprise a walking tour of the building, during which the use of shading systems, windows and lighting etc. are fully explained. If known, particular emphasis should be put on training occupants who will be located in perimeter positions.

9.6   Tools, spares and keys

Provisions may have been included in the contract for the supply of spares and specialist tools. Checks must be made to ensure that these have been provided by the contractor and that all items are accounted for.

Specialist tools and spares should be suitably packaged to prevent corrosion or damage and be easily identifiable. Examples of specialist tools include bearing extractors, alignment jigs and calibration equipment.

A complete description of all the spares should be provided including, where appropriate:

— drawing number

— item and part number

— details of size and type

— manufacturer's name and reference number for all items supplied by a specialist manufacturer.

Where required, clean air filters must be fitted and a check made to see that this has been carried out and that the appropriate number of spare filters is provided.

If re-lamping is specified as a contractual requirement, checks should be made to ensure that it has been carried out satisfactorily, and that the replaced lamps have been disposed of safely and to the client's environmental requirements. If re-lamping is not required, an estimation of the hours of beneficial usage may be needed so that a cash settlement can be agreed between the contractor and client. Alternatively, the contractor may be required to provide a specific number of spare lamps. (All such requirements must be detailed in the contract specification.)

The contractor should produce a key and lock schedule before handover and ensure that it is up to date when it is passed to the client. The schedule should be comprehensive, include a unique code for key identification and details of their availability on site.

9.7 Handover information

Requirements for handover information will need to be agreed well in advance of the expected date of completion and will need to take account of individual responsibilities for producing information and dates for the completion of specific items including drafts that require approval. The building services contractor is usually responsible for coordinating the handover information for building services. Building Regulations Approved Document L2[3] stipulates that a building log book be prepared, and states that preparing it in accordance with CIBSE TM31[4] will satisfy this requirement.

The majority of the information passed to the client at handover will form part of the health and safety file as required by the Construction (Design and Management) Regulations 2007[5] (CDM Regulations) (see chapter 16 for further guidance).

BSRIA BG1/2007: *Handover, O&M manuals, and project feedback*[6] contains comprehensive guidance on the broad range of documentation and drawings that should be provided at handover. This includes a checklist of the certificates and documentation that building owners and operators must have in their possession before they can legally operate the building, which is provided also in Appendix 9.1. It also provides detailed guidance on specifying and procuring operation and maintenance manuals, including a model specification and details of contractual arrangements; see chapter 10.

9.8 Equipment warranties

Equipment warranties normally run from the date of delivery or from the date when the equipment is first operated. The latter is particularly useful in situations where the time span between purchasing the equipment and handover is likely to be significantly protracted. Where cover is required beyond the standard period, an extended warranty can usually be arranged through payment of an additional premium to the supplier and ensuring that appropriate storage protection is provided and operational requirements are satisfied. The precise terms of a warranty can often be tailored to suit the particular needs of the client.

To ensure that a warranty remains valid, it is essential that the equipment is maintained in accordance with the supplier's instructions or other specified requirements. Before completion, this will be the responsibility of the installation contractor; following completion, responsibility passes to the client unless specific contractual arrangements have been made for the contractor to continue maintaining the plant. A comprehensive record of all maintenance work should be kept. Where equipment failures occur, lengthy disputes may ensue between the supplier, contractor and engineering consultant regarding the cause of the failure, i.e. whether it resulted from a fault within the equipment, the way it was operated or by features of the system which it serves. To resolve such disputes as quickly as possible, it can be beneficial for all parties to meet on site to review the failure and, if possible, reach some form of agreement regarding the cause.

9.9 Sectional completion and beneficial occupation

Sectional completion (also referred to as phased handover) is the term given to distinct phases of the works being completed sequentially where provision is made for this in the contract. The purpose of including such a provision is to allow the client to occupy a particular area (or areas) prior to practical completion so that specific equipment and services relating to the client's business can be installed without delay. Where the contract provides for sectional completion, consent from the contractor is not required before the client takes up occupation of each phase. As each phase of the works is completed, a certificate of section completion is issued. Only one certificate of practical completion is issued for the complete contract.

Beneficial occupation (also referred to as partial possession) is the term given to early occupation of the works by the client where the contract does not include a specific provision for this. The consent of the contractor is required since, contractually, the contractor has exclusive possession of the site until practical completion is reached. The contractor is likely to require financial compensation for the inconvenience that beneficial occupation will cause. It is also likely that a certificate of partial possession will be issued for the occupied area. This has the same contractual significance as practical completion, triggering the commencement of the defects liability period, the client's responsibility for operation and maintenance, and the release of part of the retention fund.

9.10 Defects liability

While many of the defects that occur after handover can be corrected towards the end of the defects liability period some may require immediate attention. An arrangement between the client and contractor for dealing with such defects should be established in advance of handover so that they can be rectified with minimal delay.

It is important that the client keeps a detailed record of any work carried out by the contractor(s) during the defects liability period in case of any subsequent disputes. This record should include details of:

— nature of the defect(s)

— any consequent or subsequent damage to other plant and systems resulting from the defect(s)

— correspondence between client and contractor

— action taken by contractor

— dates of all events, actions and correspondence

— details of maintenance work carried out.

It should be noted that failure on the client's part to ensure that the building services are operated and maintained in an effective manner during the defects liability period may reduce the responsibility of the contractor to make good latent defects.

When the end of the defects liability period is reached — typically one year after completion — the final account details can be agreed, including the adjustment of prime costs, provisional sums and variations. When all listed outstanding defects have been made good, the remainder of the retention fund is released and the final certificate issued. At this point, the right of both parties to pursue new claims comes to an end with the exception of further claims relating to defects. Liability for defects normally runs for a period of six years from the date of completion (see section 4.5.11).

An organisation procuring a building for business use has good protection afforded against defective building performance by the contract. However, owners/occupiers who are not responsible for building procurement will not have any form of contractual relationship with the architect or consulting engineer and will consequently need to protect themselves against financial loss resulting from defects which may appear in the structure or building services after completion. An example of this would be tenants with full repairing liabilities and organisations that purchase buildings from property developers.

For building services systems, this protection is likely to take the form of a collateral warranty which will be a contract between the consulting engineer, who is the warrantor, and the recipient, who is the warrantee. The warranty can either be in the form of a 'simple contract' which allows the injured party to sue up to six years after the breach of contract or a 'contract under seal' for which the period is extended to 12 years (see section 4.1.3). Consulting engineers should never enter into a collateral warranty contract without first carefully checking the terms of their professional indemnity insurance and ensuring that these are compatible.

An alternative to collateral warranties is latent defects insurance which does not require the recipient to prove negligence or breach of contract, enabling cover to be provided on a 'no fault basis'. Sources of further reading on the subject of warranties and insurance are included in the bibliography.

References

1   The Building Regulations 2000 Statutory Instruments 2000 No. 2531, as amended by The Building (Amendment) Regulations 2001 Statutory Instruments 2001 No. 3335 and The Building and Approved Inspectors (Amendment) Regulations 2006 Statutory Instruments 2006 No. 652 (London: The Stationery Office) (dates as indicated)

2   *Commissioning management* CIBSE Commissioning Code M (London: Chartered Institution of Building Services Engineers) (2003)

3   *Conservation of fuel and power in buildings other than dwellings* Building Regulations 2000 Approved Document L2 (London: The Stationery Office) (2002)

4   *Building log books* CIBSE TM31 (London: Chartered Institution of Building Services Engineers) (2006)

5   The Construction (Design and Management) Regulations 2007 Statutory Instrument 1994 No. 3140 (London: The Stationery Office) (1994)

6   Hastings P, Pennycook K and Bunn R *Handover, O&M manuals, and project feedback* BSRIA BG1/2007 (Bracknell: BSRIA) (2007)

Bibliography

Air distribution systems CIBSE Commissioning Code A (London: Chartered Institution of Building Services Engineers) (1996)

Boiler plant CIBSE Commissioning Code B (London: Chartered Institution of Building Services Engineers) (2002)

Automatic controls CIBSE Commissioning Code C (London: Chartered Institution of Building Services Engineers) (2001)

Refrigerating systems CIBSE Commissioning Code R (London: Chartered Institution of Building Services Engineers) (2002)

Water distribution systems CIBSE Commissioning Code W (London: Chartered Institution of Building Services Engineers) (2003)

Lighting CIBSE Commissioning Code L (London: Chartered Institution of Building Services Engineers) (2003)

Commissioning management: How to achieve a fully functioning building BSRIA AG5/2002 (Bracknell: BSRIA) (2002)

Preparation of operating and maintenance documentation for building systems ASHRAE Guideline 4 (Atlanta GA: American Society of Heating, Refrigeration and Air Conditioning Engineers) (1993)

Code of practice for project management for construction and development 3rd edn. (Ascot: Chartered Institute of Building) (2002)

Architect's Handbook of Practice Management 7th edn. (London: RIBA Publishing) (2001)

Cornes D L *Design liability in the construction industry* (Oxford: Blackwell Science) (1994)

Appendix 9.A1: Documentation to be held by building owner/occupier at handover

— Pressure vessel/system records and test certificates
— Pressure vessel/system records written scheme of examination
— COSHH records
— Maintenance records for all systems controlling a work environment
— *Legionella* risk assessment records
— Records of written scheme to minimise *legionella* risk
— Notification to local authority of cooling towers
— Chemical and bacteriological test results for drinking water cisterns greater than 900 litres
— Chlorination certificates for drinking water
— Source protection policy and licence to use boreholes
— Noise assessment records
— Risk assessments for plant and systems
— Operating and maintenance manuals
— Emergency procedures
— Sprinkler test log
— Emergency lighting test and examination log
— Smoke extract test log
— Fire hose reels and portable fire extinguishers test and inspection log
— Fire detection and alarm system test log
— Escape route pressurisation test log
— Fire training log book
— Examination certificates for lifts and lifting equipment and pressure systems/vessels
— Record drawings of installed plant and systems
— Fixed wiring electrical test certificate
— Record of insulation and earthing tests
— Portable appliance test records
— Water authority discharge of waste certificate
— Inventory of refrigerants
— Record of waste disposal
— Asbestos awareness report

10 Operating and maintenance information

Summary

The constituent parts suggested in BSRIA Application Guide AG1/87 are presented as a suitable basis for operation and maintenance manuals. The need for manufacturers to provide clear, explicit and relevant instructions is noted.

Mention is made of the scope for using an electronic format for manuals and the ease of extending this into a computer-based maintenance management system.

The relevance of the manual as a day-to-day working document is noted and the need for it to be readily available for use is stressed.

The engineering plant and services installed in buildings, for example those required to provide close control of environmental conditions, are of increasing technical complexity. If the requirements of the building user are to be satisfied, detailed, comprehensive and well presented information must be available to those responsible for operation and maintenance covering the exact plant installed, the design operating parameters and maintenance instructions. The preparation and presentation of a well-prepared operation and maintenance (O&M) manual should be an essential part of any building services contract. The Health and Safety File, which is the record of health and safety information identified during the construction process and needing to be available to the client or end user, is a requirement under the Construction (Design and Management) Regulations[1].

A properly prepared manual can be expected to produce cost benefits to offset the initial outlay on its preparation such as:

— providing the basis for correct and efficient plant operation

— providing an information base for effective maintenance

— providing a comprehensive reference source

— providing a reference for the standards used during design and installation

— ensuring the most economic use of energy

— helping to create and develop safety awareness

— providing a basis for staff training

— providing a basis for maintenance tendering

— providing a reference point for emergency procedures.

10.1 The importance of O&M manuals

The Construction (Design and Management) Regulations 2007[1] (CDM Regulations) and, in particular, the requirement for the health and safety file confirm the need for high-quality operation and maintenance manuals and record drawings. Further recognition of the importance of this information being made available is the requirement in the 2006 Building Regulations Approved Document L2B[2] that the owner of a building 'should be provided with sufficient information about the fixed building services and their maintenance requirements so that the building can be operated in such a manner as to use no more fuel and power than is reasonable in the circumstances'. The Approved Document goes on to state that 'a way of showing compliance would be to produce the necessary information following the guidance in CIBSE TM31: *Building log books toolkit*.'[3] The building log book 'could draw on or refer to information available as part of other documentation such as the Operation and Maintenance Manuals and the Health and Safety file required under the CDM Regulations'.

10.2 Health and safety file

The health and safety file is a record of information for the client or the end user, which focuses on health and safety. The information it contains will alert those who are responsible for the installation of the key health and safety risks that will need to be dealt with during subsequent maintenance, repair and construction work. The amount of detail needed in the health and safety file and the time and effort required to prepare it should be in proportion to the scale and complexity of the installation.

The CDM co-ordinator is responsible for ensuring that the health and safety file is prepared. Putting together the health and safety file is a task that should ideally be a continual process throughout the design and installation stages. When the client's requirements for the health and safety file are identified, including how the information is to be stored and recorded, the CDM co-ordinator should ensure that all those contributing to the health and safety file (e.g. designers, manufacturers, installation contractors) are aware of:

— what information is to be collected

— how the information is to be collected and stored.

The CDM co-ordinator may find it useful to detail in the pre-tender stage health and safety plan requirements how and when the information for the health and safety file is to be prepared and passed on. Throughout the installation stage, those who carry out design work (including contractors) will need to ensure, as far as reasonably practicable, that information about any feature which involves significant risks to health and safety during the lifetime of the installation are passed to either the CDM co-ordinator or to the principal contractor. Contractors have a special duty under the CDM Regulations to pass information for the health and safety file to the principal contractor, who in turn has to pass it to the CDM co-ordinator. This information could include 'as built' and 'as installed' drawings as well as operation and maintenance manuals. At the end of the project the cdm co-ordinator has to hand over the health and safety file to the client.

Information contained in the file needs to include that which assists persons carrying out construction work on the structure at any time after completion of the current project and may include:

(a) record or 'as built' drawings and plans used and produced throughout the construction process along with the design criteria

(b) general details of the construction methods and materials used

(c) details of the installation's equipment and maintenance facilities

(d) maintenance procedures and requirements for the installation

(e) manuals produced by specialist contractors and suppliers which outline operating and maintenance procedures and schedules for plant and equipment installed as part of the installation

(f) details on the location and nature of utilities and services, including emergency and fire-fighting systems.

10.3   Content

BSRIA Guide BG1/2007: *Handover, O&M manuals and project feedback toolkit*[4] provides detailed guidance on the content and quality of operation and maintenance manuals and will generally satisfy the requirements of the CDM Regulations. The presentation of information within the manual does not need to follow a rigid format but should cover the range of topics listed in BSRIA BG1/2007[4]. All manuals, however small, should contain a contents list and a comprehensive index. BG1/2007 suggests the following presentation of information:

— how to use the manual

— contractual and legal duties

— overall purpose (including design parameters)

— system descriptions, including control concepts

— equipment schedules and reference numbers

— spares policy and recommended spares lists

— commissioning records and data

— operation instructions

— maintenance instructions

— modification information

— disposal instructions

— record drawing schedules (including the location of the drawings)

— emergency information

— manufacturers' literature relevant to the installation (including directory of names and addresses).

BSRIA BG1/2007[4] also gives recommendations on the depth of detail required when preparing operation and maintenance manuals.

10.4   Manufacturers' literature

Manufacturers' literature is often unavailable or not sufficiently explicit. It should be made a condition when placing orders that explicit and specific operation and maintenance instructions for the item of equipment be supplied. This will avoid the issuing of basic and general literature covering ranges and types of equipment other than that supplied. It should also be a condition that date-stamped and certified 'as built' drawings are provided, together with recommended spares lists and disposal instructions. The manufacturer's literature and certified 'as built' drawings may both be available in electronic format should this be preferred.

10.5   Computer-based information systems

The use of computer technology enables most, if not all, of an operation and maintenance manual to be presented in electronic format. These computer-based systems provide a direct replacement for hard-copy manuals, and allow the user to view text and graphics on-screen. Several systems make use of sophisticated software tools which allow the user to navigate around documents by links or user-definable searches. This can help overcome the problem of handling and searching large amounts of information. Computer-based format for O&M manuals can provide a highly flexible and dynamic information medium which can include the added benefit of tools which help manage assets and maintenance activities. They can also offer a means of storing information through specialist service providers who can take responsibility for managing the information and making it available to specified users through the internet.

It is also possible to incorporate direct links to computer aided design (CAD) record drawings, building energy management system (BEMS) graphics, word-processed control strategies, and word-processed testing and commissioning results. CAD-prepared record drawings are convenient for preparing, storing, updating and viewing part or whole areas of building services installations. This flexibility, however, should not be allowed to override the importance of recording full details of any changes to drawings.

Computer-based information systems offer the option to print all or selected sections of the operating and maintenance manual in a hard copy format.

Procuring and implementing a computer-based O&M manual can be a challenging task for users and specifiers, particularly where they are unfamiliar with the technology. Deciding upon the most appropriate system to meet the specific need will require appreciation of the various software systems and types of products that are available. Further information is available in BSRIA Guide BG2/2004: *Computer-based operating and maintenance manuals*[5].

10.6 Maintenance management systems

An obvious advantage of well-produced record documentation to the end user of a building services installation will be the ease of transferring the documentation into a building maintenance management system. This provides an automated method of planning, controlling, recording, costing and monitoring operation and maintenance activities during the life of the installation.

10.7 Updating

There has always been a need to update documents if engineering plant is to be properly operated and maintained, to take account of developments in knowledge and technology. The CDM Regulations[1] (see also chapter 16) include a duty to update documents during the life of the installation. The updates should also take into account knowledge gained through operational experience.

Furthermore, the Health and Safety at Work etc. Act 1974[6] (paragraph 2.1.c) refers to the duty of every employer in the 'provision of such information, instruction, training and supervision as is necessary to ensure, so far as is reasonably practicable, the health and safety at work of his employees.' This can be interpreted as requiring the regular updating of manuals to include details of all modifications to plant and systems as and when they occur.

Unfortunately, whilst there is a recognised need to keep manuals up to date, this may be given a low priority. One reason given for this is that if they are provided initially to an unsatisfactory and poor standard, there is no incentive

to consider them as the important source of reference they represent.

Options for updating O&M manuals include:

— making updates the responsibility of the installation contractor making particular alterations

— making the updating a separate contract to an appropriate specialist.

10.8 Preparation

The requirement and responsibility for producing the operation and maintenance manuals may well justify the engagement of a specialist organisation with the requisite engineering and information technology skills to produce high quality comprehensive documentation to an appropriate quality standard.

Under the CDM Regulations[1] the client has a statutory requirement to make sure the health and safety file is kept secure and ready for inspection by any person who may need access to the information. This approach should also be applied to the operation and maintenance manuals. It is important that the client considers how the information should be prepared and managed as well as appointing responsibility for revisions.

Working copies should be kept of all important documentation. The originals (including a copy of the operation and maintenance manual) must be kept in a safe location, preferably off-site.

A model specification for preparation of O&M manuals is provided in BG1/2007: *Handover, O&M manuals and project feedback toolkit*[4]. This includes a table identifying the division of responsibilities for procurement of information required within the manuals, which is reproduced here as Table 10.1 (page 10-4).

References

1   The Construction (Design and Management) Regulations 1994 (London: The Stationery Office) (1994)

2   *Conservation of fuel and power in existing buildings other than dwellings* Building Regulations Approved Document L2B (London: NBS/RIBA Enterprises) (2006)

3   *Building log book toolkit* CIBSE TM 31 (London: Chartered Institution of Building Services Engineers) (2006)

4   *Handover, O&M manuals and project feedback toolkit* BSRIA BG 1/2007 (Bracknell: BSRIA) (2007)

5   *Computer-based Operating and Maintenance Manuals* BSRIA BG 2/2004 (Bracknell: BSRIA) (2004)

6   Health and Safety at Work etc. Act 1974 (London: The Stationery Office) (1974)

Bibliography

Managing health and safety in construction. Construction (Design and Management) Regulations 2007 (CDM) Approved Code of Practice (London: HSE Books) (2007)

Table 10.1 Division of responsibilities for the procurement of O&M manuals (reproduced from BSRIA BG1/2007[9], by permission of BSRIA)

Activity	Client	Employer/occupier	Design team	Main contractor	Services installation contractor	Specialist author
Brief	Use occupant surveys and design quality tools to identify user needs, such as space, comfort, storage, and controls usability	Provision of information and agreement with the design team	Set energy targets based on installed loads and expected hours of occupation			
O&M manual specification		Approval as submitted by the design team	Preparation of O&M manual specification			
Pre-contract planning			Target dates for information to be available to the specialist author, and manuals made available			
Contract documentation			Produce contract documentation for manuals			
Subcontract tenders		Approval of tender list	Compilation of tender list; insist on high standard of jargon-free English; consider adopting a style guide			
Production information		Consider occupant guidance, training helpdesk services, and labelling for user controls such as lighting and blinds	Specify information for construction, and provide to specialist author	Agree subcontractor programme for the release of information to specialist author	Issue copy orders and manufacturers' details to specialist author	Progress information from designers, installers and manufacturers
Construction	Insist on periodic reality-checking of the design as it develops, and match against the original design intent		'Reality-check' the design, revise energy targets based on altered specifications and/or expected hours of use			Installation familiarisation, site inspection, continued acquisition of information
Contract planning				Provision agreement and monitoring of subcontractors and specialist programmes		Preparation and agreement of programme for issue of draft and final documentation
Setting to work			Receive and comment on draft manuals	Receive and distribute draft manuals for use and approval	Operate and maintain plant and equipment in accordance with draft manuals	Make draft manuals available to main contractor; continue familiarisation to confirm draft procedures
Regulations	Fulfil requirements for energy labelling					Receive comments on draft manuals and update

Table 10.1 Division of responsibilities for the procurement of O&M manuals — *continued*

Activity	Client	Employer/occupier	Design team	Main contractor	Services installation contractor	Specialist author
Testing					Operate and maintain plant and equipment in accordance with draft manuals	Collect all testing and commissioning results; prepare final format for manual
Handover	Extract system concepts from the manuals and re-package information in formats that occupants can understand (e.g. mouse mats etc.)	Receive final manuals, issue to relevant staff			Handover installation to client and/or maintenance organisation	Issue final manuals; confirm date for issue of plans and drawings
Fine-tuning through post-handover support	Use empirical feedback methods to refine building controls and solve user problems; systems and avoid dysfunction, waste and alienation	Monitor building performance for the good of the client, and for design team education			Modify O&M manuals to reflect results of fine tuning and record results of surveys	

11 Risk assessment and management procedures

Summary

The range of risks that require assessment are divided into four categories.

Business risks affecting the operation of an enterprise are discussed and range from loss of a building service to an act of God.

Design and installation risks are detailed and the need for design standards, standby plant and equipment, and the relevance of insurance provisions are dealt with.

Operation and maintenance risks in the early stages of a new installation, together with warranties and the liability for defects and risks in an ongoing operation, are considered.

Risks associated with the disposal of obsolete plant or equipment that has reached the end of its economic life are outlined.

Risk assessment and management are important as any organisation is exposed to a complex range of risks. Some will be obvious or known but their potential impact may be underestimated, others may be undetected through lack of awareness. For the organisation to survive, exposing and controlling risks will be essential. Risk assessment is part of risk management and enables risk identification and clarification. It also helps with the preparation of contingency plans for when an emergency situation arises.

For all but the most basic buildings, the built environment relies to a large extent on the building services engineering installations. The risks associated with these installations have to be assessed and managed at all stages, from concept to dismantling and disposal. This is to ensure that the risks are acceptable within the parameters defined by the overall requirements of the client, statutory obligations and good practice. The effective loss of a building is a growing concern, and loss of the engineering services is the most likely and immediate cause.

In this context, risk can be defined as the chance or possibility of loss or undesirable consequences, or the possibility of incurring misfortune or loss. The financial services have defined operational risk as 'the risk of loss, resulting from inadequate or failed internal processes, people and systems, or from external events'.

Enlightened property operators are now beginning formally to address the risk potential associated with the operation of their building services.

Risks can be classified into categories, according to the area they derive from or affect:

— *business*: those risks that help to determine the specification for the building engineering service

— *design and installations*: those risks that have to be considered when looking at the options for design and installation

— *operation and maintenance*: those risks involved in running the plant and equipment

— *disposal*: risks that are likely to be similar to the operation and maintenance risks but worth considering separately.

These risks are shown in Figure 11.1.

11.1   Assessing the risks

The risks associated with each category need to be identified at the appropriate stage in the project life, the implications assessed, and the methods of addressing each risk determined. Ideally this should be an iterative process as shown in Figure 11.2 throughout the life of the project, learning from experience whether the risk assumptions were correct and modifying the procedures as necessary. To be able to do this, it is important that written records are made of the process, preferably identifying those undertaking the assessment and those responsible for the subsequent management.

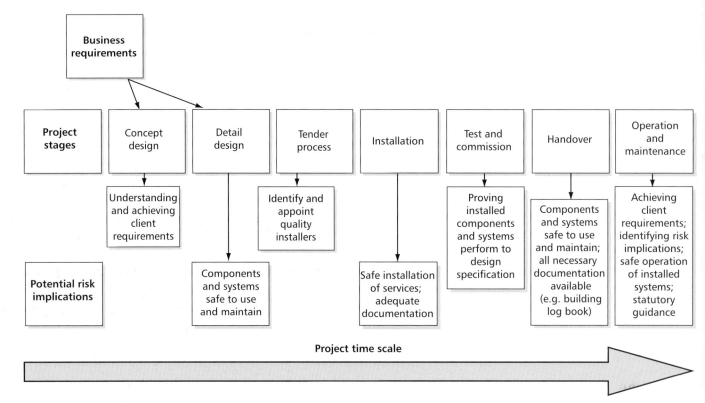

Figure 11.1 Risks arising during the project life

Figure 11.2 The assessment process

11.2   Business risks

11.2.1   Defining the operation, process or business

Business risks are related to the function carried out by the organisation and will influence the design of the building services from initial concept to final detail.

Examples of high risk operations are: continuous manufacturing processes, hospital operating theatres, broadcasting networks, computer and data centres, finance house dealing rooms, communications facilities and transportation systems. In air traffic control, for example, the overall reliability required may be higher than 99.9% and the mean time between failures (MTBF) for the

building services will therefore need to be of the same order as the equipment providing the air traffic control service. The risk to life may be the highest priority in some of these examples, but all will include some measure of financial risk, either direct or consequential. Some components of the building services will be more critical than others to the overall risk to the business.

Risks to businesses by way of environmental accidents or disasters can be categorised as follows:

— *external*: flood, fire, breach of security and destruction of facilities, e.g. an interruption to externally provided services and utilities

— *internal*: flood, fire and interruption of services through inadequate design or installation.

The design (including the location of plant and equipment), installation, security, operation and continuing maintenance of the building service should be subjected to a risk assessment based on the requirements of the business. This assessment should take into account both external and internal risks and is best carried out by the client or prospective building user with guidance from the building services designer. Such an assessment could include dependency modelling (see section 11.6) to identify potential plant and system failures which could affect the business function. Specialist professional advisors are available to undertake this role. An example of a dependency model is shown in Figure 11.3.

11.2.2   Performance brief and outline specification

The client's performance brief can be developed from the risk assessment and environmental requirements. The brief should state the limits within which the building services will be expected to operate, taking into account

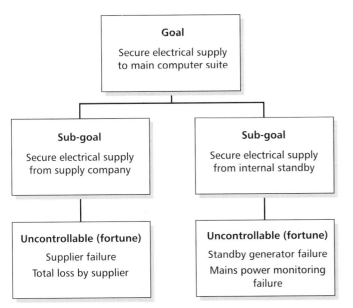

Figure 11.3 Example of a dependency model

both external and internal risks and the operating and maintenance regime necessary for the installation to continue to operate within the stated limits.

Depending on the procurement route it may be necessary for this brief to be presented in two parts i.e:

(a)   design/installation

(b)   operation/maintenance.

The performance brief may also require a value engineering assessment as part of the design. The outline specification will include the performance brief and recommendations on proven plant configurations or limitations known to apply to the design in hand. (See section 11.7 for more information on system resilience and section 11.8 for system redundancy.)

11.2.3   Procurement, delivery and service options

Procurement risks include those associated with the specification, design, delivery, installation, testing and commissioning, and subsequent operation and maintenance of the plant. They also include contractual risks, especially where a number of subcontractors are involved.

Specified manufacturers must be able to support the maintenance of plant with the provision of a range of spares, ideally for the full life of the installation. Delivery must be to an agreed installation programme within the relevant construction milestones. The installation must fit in with the way the plant has been designed, taking into account access and location problems and including ease of access for maintenance.

Within the procurement process, testing and commissioning needs to be given adequate consideration from the early design stage. Full implementation of commissioning procedures can be adversely affected by programme pressures. With installations that are technically complex, or where the design intent has not been clearly described, the risk of some systems or components not being fully or properly operational at handover needs to be assessed.

(The 2002 Building Regulations Part L2[1] introduced the requirement for a report by a suitably qualified person which included a commissioning plan and confirmed that the installed services met the approved design. Without this being in place there is a risk that Building Control may not allow handover to take place.)

Contractual arrangements can influence risk. A contractual chain which includes many subcontractors is particularly vulnerable because it distances the manufacturers and installers from the client. Private finance initiatives (PFIs) (see section 4.3) seek to allocate risks for design, funding, installation and operation to those best able to manage them, leaving the service user to get on with its business while service providers get on with theirs.

11.3   Design and installation risks

11.3.1   Design standards

The designer will need to confirm that the final design complies with agreed standards. For example, the design may need to take account of particular standards required by the client in addition to basic British Standards and CIBSE recommendations. Life cycle cost considerations should also influence the design as much as initial costs and may affect operational risk. (See chapter 13 on economic life factors)

Design decisions will need to address ease of access for maintenance and servicing, the provision of lifting arrangements for replacing components[2,3], safe procedures for handling oil (e.g. fuel and lubricants) and the collection of refrigerants[4].

11.3.2   Insurance and inspection implications

The designer will need to research fully the insurance requirements for the building services and include these in the design and specification, identifying any risk implications. This is of particular importance where an existing installation is extended. The role of the 'competent person' to undertake an assessment and prepare a written scheme of examination should be addressed during the installation process.

11.3.3   Reducing operational risks at the design stage

The level of business risk will determine the amount of investment required to design and install back-up or duplicate systems for the building services. Out of this will come the decision to provide standby plant and whether an automatic changeover is necessary (see section 11.8 on system redundancy).

Duplication of systems will introduce the requirement to assess common node failure points. The necessity for, and level of, monitoring and control by a building energy management system (BEMS) will need to be agreed. All alarms may be important, but only some will be of the highest priority and therefore in need of more than routine attention. Critical alarms may be further reduced by specifying modular plant (e.g. boilers, water chillers) so that the failure of a single unit will not reduce the plant output below the required level; this would minimise out-of-hours attendance.

11.4 Operation and maintenance risks

The management of operational risk is becoming increasingly important across all business sectors, particularly manufacturing and the financial services industries. Increasing industry regulatory requirements, protection of business reputation and concerns about profitability in a competitive environment are compelling organisations to develop systems and internal controls for identifying, understanding and managing operational risk.

Building managers will be well aware of the teething problems associated with the handover of new installations and the risks involved. Ideally the handover should be preceded by a thorough training and familiarisation period for those who are to be responsible for the ongoing operation and maintenance. An ideal time is during final installation and commissioning (see chapter 9 on handover procedures, which identifies when this should be provided).

Warranty and defects liability arrangements also need to be spelt out. On large installations, maintenance during the defects liability period may be included as part of the contract for the installation contractor. This avoids any misunderstanding over responsibility for failure of components.

Provision for storing and updating of information on the installation needs resourcing. Record drawings, commissioning data, test sheets, and operation and maintenance information can soon be destroyed or lost if data control systems are not provided. Without this information it is almost impossible to maintain and/or recalibrate the installation to its original design standard (see chapter 10 on operation and maintenance manuals). Such information should be recorded and kept up to date in the building log book (see CIBSE TM 31[5]).

Development and implementation of appropriate operational risk management controls, applicable to the buildings, facilities and resources which support the business, represents a significant challenge to an organisation. Management controls for business-critical environments need to address and evaluate four major elements: people, plant, process and facility; fully encompassing a broad range of both 'hard' (e.g. operation and maintenance of engineering plant and equipment) and 'soft' (e.g. cleaning, security, catering, grounds maintenance) services.

Figure 11.4 illustrates the main elements of operational risk.

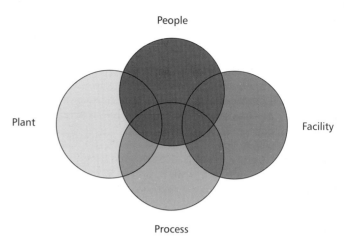

Figure 11.4 Major elements of operational risk

In addition to the requirements under duty of care in law and statutory regulations, it is imperative that all facilities services staff, consultants and contractors fully understand their respective responsibilities towards 'the client'. When carrying out their duties, they must all exercise duty of care by not introducing any additional unmanaged risks to the client's business operations.

In order to demonstrate appropriate management and control, operational risks must first be identified. Once identified, action can be taken to mitigate the risk and/or implement appropriate management control procedures and processes, to reduce the risk to an acceptable level. When assessing the 'operational risk' of a facility and the quality of the operation and maintenance services provided, the status of the elements shown in the checklist in Appendix 11.A2 should be considered and kept under review.

The maintenance programme will need to be developed from an assessment of statutory requirements, manufacturers' recommendations and operational risk. To over maintain is expensive; to under maintain is not cost effective as it leads to a deterioration of plant and service.

11.4.1 Areas of high risk

Installations such as high voltage or steam systems require special operating and maintenance skills, procedures and training, with the use of managed permit-to-work and access requirements. Method statements or written procedures will be required for less critical situations. Evaporative cooling towers are particularly associated with the risk of Legionnaires' disease, which can be controlled only within the framework of a formal and properly managed and audited programme of operation and maintenance (see CIBSE TM13[6]).

11.4.2 Audit requirements

Plant performance and maintenance standards and procedures should be audited continuously or at regular intervals against the maintenance programme, plant output and staff or contractor performance. A system of bench marking should also be established. Graphic records are useful for clearly indicating trends in plant operation and performance (see also chapter 14: *Maintenance audits*).

11.5　Disposal risks

A time will come with any installation when it needs to be disposed of or replaced. The plant should not represent a higher risk at this time than when it is in use. Regulations now exist for the control of hazardous substances such as asbestos and refrigerant gases. The Construction (Design and Management) Regulations 1994[7] (CDM Regulations) include those for 'the removal of a structure or part of a structure or of any product of waste resulting from demolition or dismantling of a structure or from disassembly of prefabricated elements which, immediately before disassembly, formed a structure'. The Waste Electrical and Electronic Equipment Directive[8] (WEEE Directive), which came into effect on 1 July 2006, restricts the use of certain hazardous materials in electrical and electronic equipment and places responsibilities on their safe disposal.

Removing plant and equipment from occupied areas presents its own special risks, especially if operational status (e.g. a production process) is to be maintained. Work needs to be carefully planned and coordinated to contain the risks. At such times other risks (for example, from fire and flooding) are increased and additional precautions and adequate contingency plans should be in place.

Complications can arise where later additions to the original installation or building restrict access to the installation, making it difficult to dismantle or maintain the plant. This can result in considerable cost above that required for the main task.

11.6　Dependency modelling

In order to demonstrate appropriate management and control, operational risks must first be identified. Once identified, action can be taken to mitigate the risk and/or implement appropriate management control procedures and processes, to reduce the risk to an acceptable level. Such an assessment could include dependency modelling to identify problem areas and system weaknesses which have the potential to disrupt business operations. This process maps the dependencies within an organisation and provides a visual tool to aid the prioritization of resource to address key problems. Specialist professional advisors are available to undertake this.

In addition to the areas shown in Appendix 11.A1, which are recommended for regular review, it is essential that the installed building plant, services and engineering systems be reviewed in detail. Similar dependency modelling techniques can be employed to map the systems configuration, capacity and status, to assess the installation suitability in supporting the client's business requirements.

11.7　System resilience

Critical business facilities are reliant upon services availability and system resilience. The impact to a client's business through the loss of a critical building or facility is a growing concern, and loss of the engineering services is the most likely and immediate cause. Whereas the engineering systems may only appear to be critical to the facility in which they are housed, failure of these systems may have far reaching business implications if many of 'the client's' business processes, IT support systems and applications are affected as a consequence. It is therefore necessary that an overall view of the 'the client's' business activities and reliance on supporting engineering and IT services be considered, in order that support system interdependency and resilience can be fully understood. The resilience of these support systems must be adequate to satisfy the full business needs.

It is of fundamental importance that the critical plant and systems supporting 'the client's' business operations, including IT equipment, systems and communication equipment be identified and the role it plays in supporting the business operation established.

A critical facility supporting business operations needs to be provided with an infrastructure of power systems and environmental controls which are robust and have been designed with the resilience, standby and redundant capacity necessary for 'the client's' needs. Decisions in relation to the design, operation and maintenance of facilities are therefore inextricably linked in satisfying this requirement.

11.8　System redundancy

For critical mechanical and electrical systems to support the business operations with a high degree of resilience, all critical systems must be configured such that there is minimum occurance of single points of failure. A single point of failure (SPOF) can be described as the 'base requirement' (N) of an operational system without any standby or alternative support arrangements. N will normally support the full load (electrical power or cooling) of the services it is designed to provide.

An improvement on N would be a system configured to $N+1$, where standby plant or equipment is employed to provide the same level of support should the N provision fail. This is better illustrated in the common arrangement of a 'run' and 'standby' pump set, where one pump is the duty pump and the other remains available to support the system load should the duty pump fail. $N+1$ will not always provide 100% redundancy. For example, a 1000 kVA uninterruptible power supply (UPS) comprising four 250 kVA modules may only have one further 250 kVA module ($N+1$), which provides redundancy to any one of the four modules should one fail.

A '$2N$' system will be a complete duplicate of N in respect of all critical components/assets. A facility with systems configured to a $2N$ level of redundancy will provide a stable and much improved business operating environment, where system resilience allows for critical plant and systems to be taken out of service for short periods, to carry out essential planned maintenance, without interruption to the business operation. Plant and equipment taken out of service reduces the reslilience of the systems and thus increases the risk to the business. However, this would be considered a 'managed risk' as this period of reduced resilience is planned and normally well communicated.

In brief, a $2N$ facility provides enhanced levels of resilience and operational integrity to mitigate the effects of unplanned outages to systems and allows for maintenance to be carried out without interruption to the business. For systems that are critically important and *must not fail* when called upon to operate, these should be designed as $2N$ plus a spare for maintenance, e.g. a pump arrangement with three pumps each able to operate as 'duty', 'standby' or be 'shutdown for maintenance'.

11.9   Supporting the business

The client needs to establish the most important overall performance of the systems that are critical to the business operations. Maintenance of these critical systems must be able to satisfy the overall performance objectives that support the business. That is the systems must be available to satisfy the demands made on them by the business.

11.10   Availability data

In assessing any maintenance strategy it is necessary to have 'availability data' about failure rates and repair times. If good and consistent data are not available for critical systems over a significant period, then planned preventive maintenance (PPM) should be adopted. The data need to be in the form of mean time to repair (MTTR) and the mean time between failures (MTBF).

These data are used to generate the 'up-time' or availability information of a system. The information about availability is then used to stretch the PPM activities to a point that failures increase to an unacceptable level. The PPM spans are then reduced slightly to reduce failure rates and allow for margins of error. For non-critical systems the data can be used to determine when 'fix on break' or 'replace on break' strategies are to be used.

Obtaining and monitoring MTTR and MTBF data is part of any good maintenance operation. However, it is not captured by most PPM activities because of the lack of resolve to capture the data and/or the lack of basic knowledge on the part of the maintainers on how to do this work. Effective control over the spans between PPM activities cannot be achieved without adequate MTTR and MTBF 'availability data', gained from actual experience of the systems.

References

1   *Conservation of fuel and power* Building Regulations 2000 Approved Document L2 (London: The Stationery Office) (2002)

2   The Lifting Operations and Lifting Equipment Regulations 1998 Statutory Instruments 1998 No. 2307 (London: The Stationery Office) (1998)

3   The Provision and Use of Work Equipment Regulations 1992 Statutory Instruments 1992 No. 2932 (London: The Stationery Office) (1992)

4   *REFCOM: Register of companies competent to handle refrigerants in the UK* (website) (Penrith: REFCOM) (http://www.refcom. org.uk) (accessed March 2008)

5   *Building log book toolkit* CIBSE TM31 (London: Chartered Institution of Building Services Engineers) (2006)

6   *Minimising the risk of Legionnaires' disease* CIBSE TM13 (2002)

7   The Construction (Design and Management) Regulations 1994 Statutory Instruments 1994 No. 3140 (London: Her Majesty's Stationery Office) (1994)

8   Directive 2002/96/EC of the European Parliament and of the Council of 27 January 2003 on waste electrical and electronic equipment (WEEE) — Joint declaration of the European Parliament, the Council and the Commission relating to Article 9 *Official J of the European Union.* **L037** 24–39 (13.02.2003)

Bibliography

Five steps to risk assessment HSE INDG 163 (rev. 2) (Health and Safety Executive) (2006) (http://www.hse.gov.uk/pubns/indg163.pdf) (accessed March 2008)

The Restriction of the Use of Certain Hazardous Substances in Electrical and Electronic Equipment Regulations 2005 Statutory Instruments 2005 No. 2748 (London: The Stationery Office)

BS 25999-1: 2006: *Business continuity management. Code of practice* (London: British Standards Institution) (2006)

BS 25999-2: 2007: *Business continuity management. Specification* (London: British Standards Institution) (2007)

BIP 2033: 2003: *Risk Assessment. Questions and answers. A Practical approach* (London: British Standards Institution) (2003)

BIP 2060: 2004: *Management of risk. Guidance for practitioners* (London: British Standards Institution) (2003)

Dallas M F *Value and risk management — a guide to best practice* (Oxford: Blackwell Publishing) (2006)

Website

—   The Uptime Institute: http://uptimeinstitute.org

Appendix 11.A1: Overall risk checklist

Business risks

— External to facility:
  — electrical supply
  — fuel for mechanical services
  — flood
  — fire
  — security breach

— Internal to facility:
  — electrical supply
  — fuel for mechanical services
  — flood
  — fire
  — security breach

Performance risks

— System failure
— Partial system failure
— Environmental conditions not satisfactory
— Water quality
— Occupant health
— Security

Procurement and delivery risks

— Quality of brief
— Contract terms
— Materials availability
— Materials quality
— On-going support for specified plant and equipment

Design and installation risks

— Health and safety
— Budget constraints
— Legislation
— Testing and commissioning

Operation and maintenance risks

— Scope of service provided
— Training
— Organisation and staffing
— Skills and competencies
— Performance measurement
— Critical risk awareness
— Emergency response provision
— Relationship with client
— Disposal risks
— Health and safety
— Environmental implications
— Access
— Availability of installation information

Disposal

— Health and safety
— Environment

Legislation

— Access
— Original installation information

Appendix 11.A2: Operational risk checklist

Aspect	People	Plant	Process	Facility
Scope of service:				
— operating requirements		●	●	●
— schedule of defects		●		
— water treatment		●		
— statutory inspections		●		
— harmonic series		●		
— thermography		●		
— vibration analysis		●		
— power discrimination		●		
— energy management		●	●	●
— drainage		●		●
Organisation and staffing:				
— labour loading	●		●	
— shift pattern	●			●
— organisation model	●			●
— minimum staffing	●		●	
— client and site induction	●			
— on- and off-site management	●		●	
— succession planning	●			
— insurance		●	●	●
Human factors:				
— skills assessment	●			
— needs assessment		●	●	●
— hiring practices	●			
Training:				
— training induction	●			
— training systems	●	●	●	
— training assessment	●	●	●	●
— scenario training	●		●	
— training plan	●			●
Performance measurement:				
— key performance indicators (KPIs)	●		●	●
— response	●		●	
— quality control	●	●	●	
— service level agreements (SLAs)	●		●	
— performance reports	●	●		
— availability reporting	●	●		
— incident tracking	●	●	●	●
Critical awareness:				
— asset register		●		●
— risk awareness		●	●	
— controlling work on critical systems	●	●	●	
— critical plant impact assessments		●	●	
— critical alarm logs	●	●	●	
— site log books	●	●		●
— change of management	●	●	●	
— duty of care	●			●
Client relationship:				
— reporting critical success	●		●	
— customer focus	●			●
— customer satisfaction			●	●
— facilities/IT relationship	●			
Emergency response:				
— emergency procedures	●	●	●	
— emergency notification and escalation	●		●	
— communication methods	●		●	
— preparedness	●	●	●	●
Operator functions:				
— help desk	●	●	●	●
— operational procedures	●		●	
— key control	●	●	●	
— colour coding	●			●
— plant housekeeping	●			●

12 Owning and operating costs

Summary

This section provides important information on the financial aspects of owning and operating building services installations and is relevant to both designers and building operators. It includes information on cost data and how it can be used to manage the maintenance of building services. It also covers practical aspects of benchmarking, basic accountancy and cost predictions associated with refurbishment or new construction.

12.1   Cost data

Reasons for the collection of cost data are twofold: first, to ensure that payments claimed by suppliers or contractors are fair and reasonable and, secondly, to help in planning and budgeting the building's expenditure. Care should be taken to ensure that the cost of collecting and logging data does not outweigh its usefulness.

There are four main types of cost data: utilities, consumables and spares, specialist services and labour.

12.1.1.   Utilities

The simplest forms of cost data to collect are those that appear in invoices which the building operator receives for goods or services. Of these, the simplest to collect are the data contained in utility invoices, e.g. for electricity, gas, fuel oil and water. All building operators should keep their own records of meter readings to ensure that the utility providers are invoicing correctly. The availability of this historical information will become more important as energy display certificates become accepted practice. Readings should be taken with, at the very least, the same frequency as the utility company bills, for example, monthly or quarterly. Sub-metering of different areas within a building or significant energy-using equipment and plant can provide useful information relating to how and where energy is being used. Since April 2006, sub-metering is a requirement under Part L of the Building Regulations[1]. Sub-metering is also useful when determining the operational rating of a property. Further information on sub-metering is provided in CIBSE TM39: *Building energy metering*[2].

Care must be taken in evaluating the invoices due to the complexity of differing contract or tariff arrangements. Building operators should, therefore, have a thorough understanding of the utility supply contract, especially penalties payable for increased consumption. Utility-use cost data are relatively simple to analyse against a number of performance indicators or targets. This is due in part to the formalised presentation of the information with little variation between companies, CIBSE Guide F: *Energy efficiency in buildings*[3] provides detailed information on this. However, building operators should be aware that energy supply companies are likely to issue estimated readings at some point due to logistical problems of getting meters read accurately and this may produce bill data at significant variance to data recorded by the building operator.

Some buildings will have meters which produce half hourly readings which can be very useful and available in spreadsheet format from the energy supplier. Where such data are considered to be useful it should be a specified requirement during refurbishment.

Vigilance in recording and monitoring meter readings will provide an early indication of potential problems in plant performance causing unnecessary use of energy.

12.1.2   Materials, spares and consumables

The next type of cost data is associated with invoicing for the supply of materials, consumables, spare parts and replacement equipment. This form of cost data is an important component of the operating costs of a building and must be clearly identifiable if performance indicators are to be produced and to ensure financial probity in the ordering of and paying for goods.

Each invoice should be clearly identifiable with an order. Unfortunately, the need for spares is often urgent — for example in emergency maintenance — and the paperwork associated with a verbal order is not always completed. Also the presentation of information on invoices often follows no particular form. Building owners should therefore develop their own records associated with such costs. These records could be incorporated as a database or spreadsheet related to a particular period, e.g. monthly or quarterly. A minimum series of data is listed below:

(*a*)   name of supplier

(*b*)   order number

(*c*)   date of order

(*d*)   quoted/estimated cost

(*e*)   date of supply

(*f*)   invoice number

(*g*)   invoiced amount

(*h*)   amount of any variation and reason(s).

To simplify the comparison of cost trends, the building owner should endeavour to place replacement orders for particular items on a regular basis.

12.1.3   Specialist services

Cost data associated with specialist services — for example, water treatment companies supplying materials, specialist labour and water quality analyses — are more complex. In these cases the costs can be a mixture of fixed and variable costs, changing with each visit to the building. Even more care is needed in collecting and checking such data.

A minimum series of data is:

(*a*)   name of specialist

(*b*)   date of site visit

(*c*)   estimated cost (based on original contract)

(*d*)   estimate of materials/spares used in visit

(*e*)   invoice number, date and value

(*f*)   comments.

In some cases the provision of specialist services is based on a 'fixed contract value' and it may be treated as any other material.

12.1.4   Maintenance and operation labour

This type of cost data can be for either directly employed labour or labour provided by a contractor. In the case of the contractor, it is relatively simple to collect cost data in terms of an hourly, daily or other time-based rate, differing rates applying for different trades and skill levels. The same approach should be taken as with materials in that invoices for labour supplied must be checked against what was actually provided. This can be

the source of much dispute, especially in the provision of 'call-out' response where there may be additional charges associated with responses to an emergency situation.

With directly employed labour, it is often difficult to obtain accurate cost data as details of an individual's wages or salary details are considered confidential and are not dealt with by the maintenance and operations management. At the very least, the hours worked by each grade of staff must be collected to allow planning and control. Ideally, for each trade and skill level an inclusive rate should be determined which incorporates the full cost of employment including all overheads. For example, this may include National Insurance and pension contributions, allowances for cover for holiday, sickness and training (either by overtime by others or temporary staff), the cost of staff facilities, an allowance for personnel management, safety management, any other support function they make use of and any additional corporate benefits such as subsidised travel.

12.2   Benchmarking

The object of benchmarking is to be able to compare any particular activity with other samples from a peer group to determine whether performance is above or below a selected datum level. It is important to differentiate whether the peer group used in the benchmark is a simple average, best practice or an acceptable minimum.

One of the major disadvantages with benchmarks is the difficulty in ensuring that the comparison being drawn is truly equitable. In the case of a single organisation making comparisons based upon internally generated data this should be simple to achieve. Where a broad, general benchmark is used, extreme care needs to be taken to ensure that the correct data are used.

With regard to the range of activities associated with producing a satisfactory working environment, the following are suggested headings which should be adapted to suit local requirements.

(*a*)   utilities costs

(*b*)   air conditioning costs

(*c*)   maintenance costs, subdivided into:

—   building fabric

—   fixtures and fittings

—   mechanical services

—   electrical services

—   lifts

—   fire systems

—   cyclic redecorations

—   environmental monitoring.

It is important that equipment upgrades, refurbishment and the maintenance of production and process equipment and systems are excluded from such cost centres as these are not relevant to facilities management activities and in many instances may be considered as exceptional costs.

It is recommended that at least five samples are required for internal comparison and, for external comparisons, a minimum of 20 data sets are obtained.

12.3 Cost data attributes

When analysing building services maintenance costs in detail, the data should have certain attributes:

— easy and cheap to collect and manipulate

— reliable, i.e. difficult to make mistakes in recording, calculating and presenting

— compatible with overall organisation objectives

— provide early indicators of poor performance and likely consequences

— known limitations to their use are apparent

— suitable for analysis to provide indication of remedial measures required.

12.4 Levels of information

In being able to plan and control expenditure, operation and maintenance information can be considered to exist on three levels, as follows.

12.4.1 Global maintenance

The uppermost level of information is that concerned with the building characteristics — for example, size, use and occupancy — and the overall totals of maintenance and operational expenditure. The collection of these may be used to provide useful benchmarks for comparisons with, for example, other buildings or maintenance contractors. They will also allow cost analyses to be carried out and highlight any deficiencies in the planned maintenance regime or in the energy efficiency of the operation. Collection of much of the data will be a one-off exercise or, where they vary annually, available within an organisation's accounting systems.

Possible information details to be collected for the building or premises are:

(a) postal address

(b) site exposure

(c) orientation of building

(d) aspect ratio and number of floors of building

(e) type and use of building

(f) type of construction

(g) age of building

(h) age of building services

(i) floor area of building (whatever factor is used in assessing the value of the building, i.e. nett lettable area or gross floor area)

(j) building population, type(s) and number

(k) building occupation pattern(s)

(l) building services system types

— heating and hot water service system

— air conditioning system(s) if applicable

— electrical distribution system

— lift installations, type and number

— utility supply details

— renewables

— IT infrastructure

— public health systems

(m) number of staff engaged in maintenance work, trades and levels/grades

(n) contract maintenance arrangements: level of risk assigned to contractor by contractual conditions and value

(o) maintenance policy pursued: this may differ between systems (see chapter 3)

(p) annual maintenance cost totals (note that the subtotal of planned and unplanned work should equal the subtotal of labour, materials and contract costs) for:

— planned maintenance

— unplanned maintenance

— labour

— materials

— contract

(q) utility cost totals (total consumption and any sub-metering):

— *electricity*: total costs including standing charges, units consumed, cost per unit, maximum demand, connection charge, availability charge etc.

— *gas*: as for electricity where applicable

— *oil*: as for electricity where applicable

— *other fuels*: as for electricity where applicable

— *water*: consumption and disposal costs.

The specific needs of the building operator will determine the precise requirements for information to be collected.

The division between planned and unplanned maintenance and the division between utilities used to produce the environment and that used in process consumption is very important but may be difficult to segregate.

One of the most influential factors on maintenance costs is the level of service required by the building occupier, which is difficult to identify objectively. The level of service depends primarily on the type of maintenance response to a contingency and the speed with which this is made. These factors, in turn, can be influenced by the organisation of the occupier and its managerial policy with respect to the service personnel. Many building services maintenance organisations perform functions, such as small works, in addition to specific maintenance tasks.

12.4.2   Systems and assets

The second level of information concerns the characteristics of the systems and plant items. The collection of these data is normally a one-off exercise and will lead to an essential understanding of the relative importance of items of plant and the building function which, in turn, should be used to determine appropriate maintenance policies.

The information should consist of a list of the building services systems installed, ranked according to the relationship between the system and the building function. For example, the electrical distribution system may be considered to be the most crucial to the building function and would, therefore, have the highest ranking.

A sublist of plant items within a building services system is often referred to as an asset list and is essential when considering maintenance approaches to individual items. It should contain information about each item used within each system and upon which maintenance, planned or unplanned, may be carried out. Ductwork, pipework, electrical distribution etc. can also be considered as plant items.

Care must be taken not to create too large a database of information by considering individual items to a very detailed level. At the initial stage it is unlikely that a building would be considered to have more than 100 types of plant item: it may have multiples of certain items, such as room terminal devices, but is not always necessary to identify these individually.

This asset list should detail:

(a)   the plant item function

(b)   the geographical location within the building

(c)   the manufacturer's/supplier's name and address

(d)   model description/type

(e)   model number

(f)   rating or capacity or certified performance data

(g)   number installed

(h)   cost of purchase

(i)   cost of installation

(j)   date of installation

(k)   factor used in any capitalisation scheme

(l)   factor relating the plant item's importance in relation to the system/building function.

This information is the backbone to creating a planned maintenance system and may be developed to whatever level of detail suits organisational needs. It can form the basis of building a service history and will be of use in valuing a building throughout its life and in ensuring that information concerning the building services is accessible to the whole of the occupying organisation and not in the sole possession of a few individuals. The list of items of plant and their relationship with the building function would also be helpful to the facilities manager when discussing forward planning and costings with non-engineering personnel and could also be used in contract negotiations with, for example, maintenance contractors when setting priorities.

This listing of the installed plant and systems will also be valuable when plant reaches the end of its economic life and needs to be replaced. At this point plant size, performance, operational need and system efficiency needs to be addressed. The tax advantages available through the Enhanced Capital Allowances scheme for using more efficient plant should be considered (details of currently applicable plant are available at http://www.eca.gov.uk).

Enhanced Capital Allowances (ECAs) enable a business to claim 100% first-year capital allowances on their spending on qualifying plant and machinery. The two most applicable schemes for ECAs are:

—   energy-saving plant and machinery

—   water conservation plant and machinery.

Businesses can write-off the whole of the capital cost of their investment in these technologies against their taxable profits of the period during which they make the investment. This may allow up to a 5% reduction in capital cost compared with plant not covered by the scheme. This can deliver a helpful cash flow boost and a shortened payback period

12.4.3   Maintenance tasks

The third level of information deals with the actual maintenance work that is carried out on individual systems and items of plant (the information for the asset list must exist before that for maintenance is compiled). Collection of this can produce considerable quantities of data and careful thought must be given to the value of the information produced and the uses it may be put to compared with the cost of collecting, collating and presenting it.

The information to be collected relates to planned and unplanned maintenance work. It is considered unlikely that any one item of equipment will have more than 10 individual maintenance work 'packages' carried out in any one year and that unplanned or breakdown work may be related to one or more causes.

For the majority of maintenance work much of the cost is labour related and it is therefore necessary to know the employment costs of that labour. Where actual employment data are not available, a nominal hourly rate for each labour grade which works with that item of equipment must be used if the efficacy of that equipment is to be assessed in terms of reliability, cost to maintain, value to an organisation etc.

For each maintenance task, planned or unplanned, the minimum level of detail would be:

(a)   item of plant being worked upon

(b)   job/maintenance procedure applied

(c)   time taken

(d)   grade of operative(s)

(e)   cost of materials.

The amount of information that would be produced at this level can be considerable and the use of a computer database is recommended.

It is important to be able to differentiate between planned and unplanned expenditure; in many cases, unplanned expenditure exceeds that which is planned.

The planned maintenance can be considered in relation to the frequency at which each task is carried out and will be predominantly based on regular (for example, yearly, quarterly, monthly, weekly) inspection, cleaning and replacement of consumables and irregular tasks associated with remedial work, replacement or redundancy. Care must be taken in selecting general job titles to allow later manipulation of the data. A range of titles could be:

—   inspection

—   cleaning

—   safety checks

—   testing

—   performance assessment against stated criteria

—   calibration

—   replacement of consumables

—   replacement of parts

—   refurbishment of plant

—   replacement of plant.

Note that fault finding/diagnosis is a combination of inspection and testing.

Unplanned work can be considered in relation to the cause. Again general titles should be used and a typical short list might be:

—   wear/corrosion/other progressive deterioration

—   manufacturing defect

—   material defect

—   design defect

—   installation defect

—   inadequate maintenance

—   maintenance reassembly defect

—   maintenance adjustment defect

—   operational mistake

—   malicious damage.

If information is collected at this level, the total cost of the individual maintenance items should equal the total expenditure and could be a useful corroboration between budget costings and actual expenditure. Correctly manipulated, the database will rapidly identify poor workmanship (i.e. repeated breakdowns), unreliable plant, plant that is costly to maintain, specific deficiencies in the regular planned work and many other useful items of maintenance management information. Most importantly it will allow improved accuracy of forward planning and realistic maintenance budgets to be set and justified.

12.5   Utilisation of labour

The following provides a systematic approach to identifying core activities of maintenance operatives so that comparisons may be drawn between buildings, contractors or even individual technicians or craftsmen. Careful analysis of such labour utilisation will also produce indicators of the effectiveness of maintenance management and the actual work carried out. It is important to be able to distinguish between planned and unplanned expenditure; in many cases, unplanned expenditure can equal or even exceed the planned expenditure.

Each of the main work categories are broken into ten subheadings, including one for 'other' work. If this catch-all heading occupies significant operative time to keep the plant in working order, an in-depth investigation of the maintenance system is warranted as the other headings typify most of the maintenance activities.

12.5.1   Planned activities

These include the following:

(a)   replenishment/replacement of consumables

(b)   inspection

(c)   functional testing

(d)   safety testing (e.g. electrical, gas, water, lifts, updating risk assessments such as fire and *legionellae*)

(e)   repairs, resulting from (b) to (d)

(f)   supervision/receiving particular instructions

(g)   procurement of materials, tools, spares and equipment

(h)   travelling, cleaning and tidying

(i)   minor new or improvement work initiated by maintenance management

(j)   other planned activities (including training, administration, record keeping, compliance).

12.5.2   Unplanned activities

These include:

(a)   response to complaints to assess situation

(b)   remedial work which results from (a)

(c)   attendance to unforeseen failure including fault diagnosis

(d)   emergency repairs associated with (c)

(e)   minor new or improvement works initiated outside maintenance organisation

(f)   major new works (not strictly maintenance activities but often involve maintenance operatives directly or indirectly)

(g)   dedicated travelling time (this is often significant in unplanned work)

(h)   tidying and cleaning following contingency and/or unplanned work.

(*i*) materials, tools and equipment procurement (often involves significant time to identify precise requirement)

(*j*) other unplanned activities (includes attendance time for other trades, visitors etc.).

12.6 Backlog of maintenance

It is an unfortunate fact that planned maintenance (and hence expenditure) must often be deferred or even dropped as a result of expenditure cuts to meet overall operating cost limits. Many non-engineering management personnel view maintenance activities as an optional luxury that produces no tangible benefit. It is important to record not only the work dropped (and the reasons for this) but the consequential results of not doing the work. With the increasing emphasis on health and safety legislation and risk assessments, this information may be needed in any court proceedings arising from an accident that occurs as a result of maintenance deferred or not carried out.

Conversely, unnecessary maintenance activities should be identified from the use of benchmarks or other means of comparative assessment and maintenance programmes suitably adjusted to redeploy or reduce resources.

12.7 Data priorities

Owning and operating cost estimates are, typically, generated by the design team with the major inputs from the system designer while the main user of the data is the system operator. Each party has differing priorities. The importance of accurate and realistic assessments of utility costs is increasing as Building Regulations require such information.

For the designer, the ability to produce accurate predictions of the capital and life cycle costs are paramount so that the engineering design decisions have the backing of financial justification. In the past, the new works sector has been concerned principally with first costs; the designer's major priority has therefore been the estimation of the capital cost of major items of plant — the cost of materials and installation. As a result of both Private Finance Initiative (PFI) projects (see section 4.3) and the need to improve energy efficiency, it is increasingly important for the designer to be able to estimate accurately energy use and other operating costs (a requirement under the Building Regulations Part L[1]), further information is available in CIBSE Guide F: *Energy efficiency in buildings*[3]. The use of modern thermal modelling software should facilitate energy consumption costing and improve its accuracy. Estimating the maintenance costs is far more difficult as there are no wide-coverage databases of information publicly available to allow comparisons; section 12.8 gives details of some areas to be considered. However, modelling techniques may be appropriate to develop and analyse design options and associated costs which should address not only initial capital costs but also operation, maintenance, energy use, replacement frequency and replacement cost. Example

information is provided in *Whole-life economics of building services*[4].

For the building operator the priorities are different. First, the data collected should be able to demonstrate financial probity and, secondly, it should enable the operator to evaluate whether value for money is being achieved. This is the balance between the effectiveness of the maintenance in support of the business function of the building and the acceptability of the costs. This involves collecting data that permit the examination of trends in expenditure while facilitating historical comparisons and highlighting performance indicators.

12.8 Cost predictions for new buildings and designs

Cost predictions for engineering services in the course of design have to be based on historical data derived from similar installations or components and need to take into account various factors that will be specific to the proposed scheme. Some of these factors will be difficult to express in financial terms.

In addition to the obvious criteria such as building footprint, major plant items, and rule-of-thumb installation costs, cost predictions will need to address:

— Quality of the environment required: this is a complex measure taking into account the airtightness of the building envelope, type and size of fenestration, and the degree of control required for temperature and humidity.

— Environmental impact, both on the building (e.g. due to climate change) and due to the building and the potential cost implications of these impacts.

— Operational cost implications of complying with Building Regulations Part L[1], which requires buildings to minimise energy use.

— Operational cost implications of using renewable energy sources.

— Budget limits and constraints set by the client: at this stage of the prediction it is important to understand fully the client's financial status given that almost all projects overrun their original budgets. It is tempting to use broadbrush unit floor costs but these should be used only as very broad guides.

— Systems suggested: this involves understanding the client's need for the building and what is acceptable in terms of floor and ceiling space devoted to building services. In addition to likely capital and installation costs, it will be necessary to know the relative merits and limits of each system in terms of its likely energy effectiveness (and hence energy consumption) and maintenance costs (routine repetitive replacement of consumables, such as filters, together with an allowance for a number of breakdowns and replacement of subassemblies).

— Weather conditions specific to the site: this will affect the quality of plant exposed on rooftops etc., the need for frost protection and likely energy consumption.

— Occupant type and their expectations: this relates to the quality of environment to be achieved and the required response of the maintenance personnel to occupant complaints.

— Occupancy patterns: these can affect both energy consumption and the costs of maintenance in terms of when plant can be taken out of service for carrying out maintenance. Changes to the planned intervals between inspections may be necessary to account for increased running hours if occupancy hours are extended and an 'hours run' maintenance policy is applied.

— Maintenance policy to be applied: whether a 'do nothing', a time-based or condition-based policy is to be operated. This cost will also be influenced by the degree of reliability required from the systems and plant, which clients often do not define. (Note that a building owner operating a 'do nothing' maintenance policy could be open to action from the Health and Safety Executive in the event of an accident resulting from the absence of inspections or servicing.)

— Specialist requirements of the plant for maintenance: whether, for example, water treatment costs or building management system maintenance need to be taken into consideration.

— Geographical location: this is especially important in terms of availability of local labour (for installation and maintenance) and transport logistics.

Once the scheme design is finished, more detailed maintenance cost estimates may be built up based on the knowledge of the engineering services and plant to be installed. Much of this is concerned with:

— numbers and capacities of the principal items of plant, e.g. heat generators, chillers, calorifiers, controls and pumps

— extent and complexity of control system

— extent of distributed plant and equipment, e.g. number of room terminal units, total length of pipe and ductwork systems.

There are a various sources of data for carrying out rule-of-thumb cost calculations, including:

(a) Building Cost Information Service (BCIS)* (see Table 12.1 for sample data)

(b) *Spon's mechanical and electrical services price book*[5]

(c) Published examples: cost models have been published in *Building Services Journal* as follows:

  — commercial offices (urban environment)[6]

  — commercial offices (non-urban environment)[7]

  — shopping centres[8]

  — structured cabling[9]

  — standby generation[10]

  — schools[11]

  — swimming pools[12]

  — combined heat and power (CHP)[13]

  — hospitals[14]

  — private hospitals[15]

  — commercial restaurants (provincial city centres)[16]

  — museums and galleries[17,18]

  — lifts and escalators[19]

  — building energy management systems[20]

  — wind and the global warming imperative[21]

Table 12.1 Indicative annual maintenance and utilities costs (based on fourth quarter, 2005) (information provided by and with the kind permission of Building Cost Information Service[28])

Building type	Estimated maintenance cost / (£/100 m^2)	Estimated utilities cost / (£/100 m^2)
Administration building (local)	1250	2150
Ambulance station	800	1900
Bank/building society	2100	3000
Call centre	2300	5100
Cinema	1050	1950
Computer building	2300	3650
Factory	700	1200
Fire station	1050	2250
Health centre	950	1900
Hospital	1700	2150
Hotel	1450	1400
Laboratory	2050	2950
Law courts	1600	2150
Library	1600	1750
Museum	1350	2450
Nursing home	1050	1800
Offices:		
— general	1650	2550
— air conditioned	2150	3600
— non-air conditioned	1250	1600
Police station	1200	2300
Prison (closed; without laundry)	1400	2200
Restaurant	1750	4700
Retail warehouse	950	1350
Shopping centre:		
— air conditioned	900	2150
— non-air conditioned	700	800
Sports centre	1350	2000
Supermarket	1450	5200
Theatre	1050	1950
School		
— primary (no swimming pool)	1200	800
— secondary (no swimming pool)	950	800
University	1500	1650
Warehouse	650	1050

* Building Cost Information Service, 12 Great George Street, Parliament Square, London, SW1P 3AD (http://www.bcis.co.uk)

- — chiller technology[22]
- — office air conditioning[23]
- — renewable energy[24]
- — ground water cooling[25]
- — combined heat and power[26]
- — IT cabling[27]

(d)   Specialist cost consultants.

12.9   Simple accounting techniques

Double entry book-keeping is a system that reports what profit the business has made, how much the business owes and how much is owed to the business.

Modern accounting falls broadly into two categories:

- — *financial accounting*: which is concerned with the supply of information to an owner as to how well the business is doing

- — *management accounting*: which is concerned with the supply of information to a manager for use in planning and in controlling the business.

The task of dealing with owning and operating costs is largely one of management accounting, particularly with regard to ensuring that the building's services are effective in achieving the right internal environment for the occupying business and are doing so efficiently. The two main branches of management accounting relevant to owning and operating costs are budgetary control and capital investment appraisal.

12.9.1   Budgetary control

Before control can be exercised, a budget must be drawn up. The Chartered Institute of Management Accountants (CIMA) defines a budget as:

> A plan expressed in money. It is prepared and approved prior to the budget period and may show income, expenditure and the capital to be employed.

A maintenance budget should be drawn up as 'zero-based'; that is, working from basic principles and not just incrementing the previous period's figures. This encourages the independent assessment of each activity followed by a suitable combination of the whole range of activities to match available funds. In reality, for an existing building some cognisance of historical financial performance will be taken but must be tempered by what needs to be done in the future together with a careful assessment of the scope for improvement.

The essential features of a maintenance budget are as follows:

- — Its objectives are achieved. This means operating and maintaining the plant in such a way and with such staff as are necessary to achieve an acceptable level of availability. It includes the funding and planned replacement of plant that can no longer be economically repaired, is obsolete, is too ineffi-

cient, or is rendered redundant due to legislative or other action.

- — It contains quantitative and financial data, which are formally documented.

- — It covers a defined future period of time.

Once the budget exists, it may be used for control purposes. Budgetary control may be summarised as:

- — clearly defining the financial responsibilities of the relevant management

- — detailing a plan of action within the manager's sphere of responsibility; this may be in terms of labour, materials and new equipment

- — ensuring the manager adheres to the budget

- — monitoring the performance and comparing the results at relevant intervals with the budgeted figures

- — considering, recommending and approving corrective action if actual results differ

- — investigating any such variances that are unaccounted for

- — permitting deliberate departures from the budget only if approved by senior management.

In building services terms, the budget for owning, operating and maintaining is likely to be only one part of a master budget for a business. The nature of building use can change or failures may occur which cannot be accurately forecast when the budget is compiled. Budgets for operating buildings, therefore, must have a degree of flexibility to cope with such changes. This may be identified as a contingency sum or the nature of the organisation may be such that it can deal with changes to the budget during the budget period. In either case, such changes must be justified.

Table 12.2 provides a checklist for preparing a budget for maintenance.

12.9.2   Capital investment appraisal

In undertaking a capital investment appraisal it is important to understand the difference between capital expenditure (CAPEX) and revenue or operating expenditure (OPEX). Capital expenditure is defined as the cost of acquiring, producing or enhancing fixed assets. Revenue expenditure is defined as expenditure on the supply and manufacture of goods and the provision of services charged in the accounting period in which they are consumed. This includes repairs and depreciation of the fixed assets as distinct from the provision of those assets.

Generally, capital expenditure has some important characteristics that must be taken into account in the appraisal. For example, it is likely to include substantial expenditure, the benefits could be spread over many years, the benefits may be difficult to predict, it will have an impact on the organisation's employees and it will help the organisation achieve its objectives.

However, not all aspects of these definitions are applicable to owning and operating buildings. Capital expenditure

Table 12.2 Maintenance budget checklist

Category	Item
Labour	In-house trades: supervision, management and training
	Contract: mobile, resident, supplementary for labour-intensive tasks (e.g. tank and domestic water system chlorination, and checking of electrical connections)
	Specialist subcontractors: for specialist tasks (e.g. controls, lifts, uninterruptible power supplies and lifting equipment)
Materials	Replenishment (e.g. oils, greases and fuel oils)
	Replacement: routine (e.g. filters and belts)
	Replacement: non-routine (e.g. pipework, cables and lamps)
Equipment	Replacement of life-expired plant
	Replacement of plant that has suffered catastrophic failure
	Replacement of worn parts
	Repair of misuse and abuse damage
	Energy efficiency improvements (e.g. light fittings and controls)
	Enhancements in aid of maintenance efficiency improvements (e.g. condition monitoring modifications)
	Disposal of redundant plant
Specialist resources	Consultants for auditing and change management (e.g. planning system improvements, and energy and safety audits
	Specialist contractors (e.g. cooling tower maintenance, lift re-roping and water treatment)
Management	Planned maintenance system (e.g labour to implement and operate hardware and software consumables such as disks, tapes and paper)
	Legal compliance (e.g. documentation)
	Insurance
	Training
Diagnostics	Development of feedback mechanisms, condition monitoring, one-off investigations (e.g. failure of complex plant)
	Environment: air quality surveys, disposal of cleaning and water treatment chemicals
Utilities	Electricity consumption and connection charges (contract re-negotiation): lighting, small power, HVAC, lifts/transportation, catering
	Gas: heating, catering and hot water production
	Water: supply, sewerage, fire, treatment, rebate for evaporative use (e.g. cooling towers)

will typically be for replacing worn-out or obsolete plant or for the partial or complete replacement of systems to enhance the environmental control within the building or improve energy efficiency (for example, investment in CHP plant). It may also include the removal of redundant plant that will have some secondhand or substantial scrap value. Capital expenditure for new or replacement may be eligible for tax allowances under the Enhance Capital Allowances scheme (see section 12.4.2).

In the case of manufacturing industry, the benefit from capital investment is often easy to quantify in, say, increased output or reduced production costs, both of which affect the outcome of the appraisal. When it comes to capital investment in building services, however, there are often no tangible benefits in terms of increased profitability. The benefit from installing air conditioning in a heated-only building will be increased occupant comfort and, possibly, increased productivity; against this there is likely to be increased energy consumption and increased maintenance requirements. The advantages are difficult to evaluate financially, while the disadvantages are very easy to cost. Capital appraisal is most influenced by items that have an accurate monetary value.

There are five basic techniques for capital appraisal:

— payback

— discounted payback

— accounting rate of return

— net present value

— internal rate of return.

Of these, only two — payback and net present value — have direct relevance to owning and operating costs.

12.9.2.1 Payback

This is a very simple technique of deciding how long it will take for net profit on a project to pay off the original investment. It can be rapidly calculated to assess and compare a number of projects and will indicate how long each option will take to recoup the investment. For use in the context of operating buildings, there has to be some tangible return from the project such as a reduction in energy consumption, a decrease in maintenance effort leading to labour and/or materials savings or a change of fuel leading to reduced fuel costs.

The technique consists of evaluating the net cashflow of the project, taking the original investment and reducing the total by the savings (minus any installments paid on the amount borrowed) in each relevant period (say annually) until the net sum outstanding is reduced to zero. The time taken to offset the investment is expressed in years and is termed the 'payback period'.

The disadvantages of this technique is that it does not take account of:

— changing value of money with time (e.g. the effect of inflation)

— the stage in the payback period when the major proportion of the investment is recovered; (a short payback period option may recover most of the investment in the latter stages and this may represent a risk)

— the profit made once the payback is achieved; a project with the shortest payback period may be selected even though there may be other options with longer payback periods that, in the longer term, would be more profitable

— the actual amount of the original investment; a high-cost project with high future profitability may be rejected in favour of a lower-cost project with a short payback.

12.9.2.2   Net present value

This is accepted by financial concerns as the most appropriate method of capital investment appraisal as it can take into account the value of money over time, the profitability of a project and the return on the investment. It is important to understand that this technique produces only a figure to evaluate the financial desirability of a number of project options; there may be many factors other than cost that must be taken into account in the final selection.

The main disadvantage is that of selecting an appropriate rate of interest to apply as, over time, interest rates vary considerably in a way that is not predictable.

The technique consists of combining the original investment with each of the future costs and incomes associated with an option that will occur over a specific period of time and calculating their value in terms of a single point in time (using the same principles as involved in compound interest).

Discount factor tables

To enable future one-off payments or savings to be evaluated in terms of the single point in time, discount tables can be used to determine the value of money invested or discounted. Table 12.3 contains a series of discount factors derived from the formula:

$$f = 1 / (1 + I)^n$$

where f is the discount factor, I is the interest or inflation rate (expressed as a decimal) and n is the number of years. In practical terms, the discount factors may be used to determine the single sum of money that must be invested

now to yield a specific value at a certain point in the future assuming a constant rate of interest.

Example: a payment of £100 is due in 10 years' time and the assumed inflation rate is 10%; what is the present or equivalent value of money?

$$100 \times [1 / (1 + 0.1)^{10}] = £38.55$$

Cumulative discount factors

An alternative view might be to determine the sum of money that must be invested to yield £100 in 10 years' time, assuming an interest rate of 10% per annum. If the payment is repeated and constant, a similar factor can be calculated to determine the present value of all such payments. Table 12.4 gives a series of cumulative discount factors derived from the formula:

$$c = \{1 - [(1 + I)^{-n}]\} / I$$

where c is the cumulative factor, I is the interest or inflation rate (expressed as a decimal) and n is the number of years over which an annual payment will be made.

Cumulative discount factors may be used to determine a single value today representing regular payments for a fixed time at a fixed interest rate. For example, a single value today can be calculated for the payments for planned maintenance visits over the life of the plant or the purchase of regular consumables such as disposable air filters.

Example: an annual payment of £10 is made for 10 years at a constant inflation rate of 10%; what is the present value of all those payments?

$$10 \times \{1 - [(1 + 0.1)^{-10}]\} / 0.1 = £61.45$$

Each of the components of a project can be similarly adjusted to their net present value so that an overall value of the project can be determined and compared with, say, the benefit of investing the same sum of money elsewhere.

12.9.2.3   Investment appraisal

The three remaining techniques for the capital appraisal all have major disadvantages that invariably make them unsuitable for assessment of building services projects:

— *Discounted payback*: while it does take account of the value of money over time, it concentrates only on the cash recovery of the investment and ignores what happens after the payback period. The payback period using this technique is always longer than that for simple payback.

— *Accounting rate of return*: compares the profit made with the capital invested expressed as a percentage. This is inappropriate for most building services projects as very few make a clearly quantifiable profit.

— *Internal rate of return*: very similar to net present value but seeks to determine what rate of return would be required to ensure the total net present value equals the total initial cost. As income from

Table 12.3 Discount factor table: present value of £1.00, received after n years, discounted at $I\%$: $f = 1/(1+I)^n$

Year										Discount factor for stated annual interest rate (%)										
	1	2	3	4	5	6	7	8	9	10	11	12	13	14	15	16	17	18	19	20
1	0.9901	0.9804	0.9709	0.9615	0.9524	0.9434	0.9346	0.9259	0.9174	0.9091	0.9009	0.8929	0.8850	0.8772	0.8696	0.8621	0.8547	0.8475	0.8403	0.8333
2	0.9803	0.9612	0.9426	0.9246	0.9070	0.8900	0.8734	0.8573	0.8417	0.8264	0.8116	0.7972	0.7831	0.7695	0.7561	0.7432	0.7305	0.7182	0.7062	0.6944
3	0.9706	0.9423	0.9151	0.8890	0.8638	0.8396	0.8163	0.7938	0.7722	0.7513	0.7312	0.7118	0.6931	0.6750	0.6575	0.6407	0.6244	0.6086	0.5934	0.5787
4	0.9610	0.9238	0.8885	0.8548	0.8227	0.7921	0.7629	0.7350	0.7084	0.6830	0.6587	0.6355	0.6133	0.5921	0.5718	0.5523	0.5337	0.5158	0.4987	0.4823
5	0.9515	0.9057	0.8626	0.8219	0.7835	0.7473	0.7130	0.6806	0.6499	0.6209	0.5935	0.5674	0.5428	0.5194	0.4972	0.4761	0.4561	0.4371	0.4190	0.4019
6	0.9420	0.8880	0.8375	0.7903	0.7462	0.7050	0.6663	0.6302	0.5963	0.5645	0.5346	0.5066	0.4803	0.4556	0.4323	0.4104	0.3898	0.3704	0.3521	0.3349
7	0.9327	0.8706	0.8131	0.7599	0.7107	0.6651	0.6227	0.5835	0.5470	0.5132	0.4817	0.4523	0.4251	0.3996	0.3759	0.3538	0.3332	0.3139	0.2959	0.2791
8	0.9235	0.8535	0.7894	0.7307	0.6768	0.6274	0.5820	0.5403	0.5019	0.4665	0.4339	0.4039	0.3762	0.3506	0.3269	0.3050	0.2848	0.2660	0.2487	0.2326
9	0.9143	0.8368	0.7664	0.7026	0.6446	0.5919	0.5439	0.5002	0.4604	0.4241	0.3909	0.3606	0.3329	0.3075	0.2843	0.2630	0.2434	0.2255	0.2090	0.1938
10	0.9053	0.8203	0.7441	0.6756	0.6139	0.5584	0.5083	0.4632	0.4224	0.3855	0.3522	0.3220	0.2946	0.2697	0.2472	0.2267	0.2080	0.1911	0.1756	0.1615
11	0.8963	0.8043	0.7224	0.6496	0.5847	0.5268	0.4751	0.4289	0.3875	0.3505	0.3173	0.2875	0.2607	0.2366	0.2149	0.1954	0.1778	0.1619	0.1476	0.1346
12	0.8874	0.7885	0.7014	0.6246	0.5568	0.4970	0.4440	0.3971	0.3555	0.3186	0.2858	0.2567	0.2307	0.2076	0.1869	0.1685	0.1520	0.1372	0.1240	0.1122
13	0.8787	0.7730	0.6810	0.6006	0.5303	0.4688	0.4150	0.3677	0.3262	0.2897	0.2575	0.2292	0.2042	0.1821	0.1625	0.1452	0.1299	0.1163	0.1042	0.0935
14	0.8700	0.7579	0.6611	0.5775	0.5051	0.4423	0.3878	0.3405	0.2992	0.2633	0.2320	0.2046	0.1807	0.1597	0.1413	0.1252	0.1110	0.0985	0.0876	0.0779
15	0.8613	0.7430	0.6419	0.5553	0.4810	0.4173	0.3624	0.3152	0.2745	0.2394	0.2090	0.1827	0.1599	0.1401	0.1229	0.1079	0.0949	0.0835	0.0736	0.0649
16	0.8528	0.7284	0.6232	0.5339	0.4581	0.3936	0.3387	0.2919	0.2519	0.2176	0.1883	0.1631	0.1415	0.1229	0.1069	0.0930	0.0811	0.0708	0.0618	0.0541
17	0.8444	0.7142	0.6050	0.5134	0.4363	0.3714	0.3166	0.2703	0.2311	0.1978	0.1696	0.1456	0.1252	0.1078	0.0929	0.0802	0.0693	0.0600	0.0520	0.0451
18	0.8360	0.7002	0.5874	0.4936	0.4155	0.3503	0.2959	0.2502	0.2120	0.1799	0.1528	0.1300	0.1108	0.0946	0.0808	0.0691	0.0592	0.0508	0.0437	0.0376
19	0.8277	0.6864	0.5703	0.4746	0.3957	0.3305	0.2765	0.2317	0.1945	0.1635	0.1377	0.1161	0.0981	0.0829	0.0703	0.0596	0.0506	0.0431	0.0367	0.0313
20	0.8195	0.6730	0.5537	0.4564	0.3769	0.3118	0.2584	0.2145	0.1784	0.1486	0.1240	0.1037	0.0868	0.0728	0.0611	0.0514	0.0433	0.0365	0.0308	0.0261
21	0.8114	0.6598	0.5375	0.4388	0.3589	0.2942	0.2415	0.1987	0.1637	0.1351	0.1117	0.0926	0.0768	0.0638	0.0531	0.0443	0.0370	0.0309	0.0259	0.0217
22	0.8034	0.6468	0.5219	0.4220	0.3418	0.2775	0.2257	0.1839	0.1502	0.1228	0.1007	0.0826	0.0680	0.0560	0.0462	0.0382	0.0316	0.0262	0.0218	0.0181
23	0.7954	0.6342	0.5067	0.4057	0.3256	0.2618	0.2109	0.1703	0.1378	0.1117	0.0907	0.0738	0.0601	0.0491	0.0402	0.0329	0.0270	0.0222	0.0183	0.0151
24	0.7876	0.6217	0.4919	0.3901	0.3101	0.2470	0.1971	0.1577	0.1264	0.1015	0.0817	0.0659	0.0532	0.0431	0.0349	0.0284	0.0231	0.0188	0.0154	0.0126
25	0.7798	0.6095	0.4776	0.3751	0.2953	0.2330	0.1842	0.1460	0.1160	0.0923	0.0736	0.0588	0.0471	0.0378	0.0304	0.0245	0.0197	0.0160	0.0129	0.0105
26	0.7720	0.5976	0.4637	0.3607	0.2812	0.2198	0.1722	0.1352	0.1064	0.0839	0.0663	0.0525	0.0417	0.0331	0.0264	0.0211	0.0169	0.0135	0.0109	0.0087
27	0.7644	0.5859	0.4502	0.3468	0.2678	0.2074	0.1609	0.1252	0.0976	0.0763	0.0597	0.0469	0.0369	0.0291	0.0230	0.0182	0.0144	0.0115	0.0091	0.0073
28	0.7568	0.5744	0.4371	0.3335	0.2551	0.1956	0.1504	0.1159	0.0895	0.0693	0.0538	0.0419	0.0326	0.0255	0.0200	0.0157	0.0123	0.0097	0.0077	0.0061
29	0.7493	0.5631	0.4243	0.3207	0.2429	0.1846	0.1406	0.1073	0.0822	0.0630	0.0485	0.0374	0.0289	0.0224	0.0174	0.0135	0.0105	0.0082	0.0064	0.0051
30	0.7419	0.5521	0.4120	0.3083	0.2314	0.1741	0.1314	0.0994	0.0754	0.0573	0.0437	0.0334	0.0256	0.0196	0.0151	0.0116	0.0090	0.0070	0.0054	0.0042

Table 12.4 Cumulative discount factors present value of a series of n regular annual payments, at an interest rate of I%: $c = \{1 - [(1 + I)^{-n}]\} / I$

| Years | \multicolumn{15}{c}{Discount factor for stated annual interest rate (%)} |
	1	2	3	4	5	6	7	8	9	10	11	12	13	14	15
1	0.9901	0.9804	0.9709	0.9615	0.9524	0.9434	0.9346	0.9259	0.9174	0.9091	0.9009	0.8929	0.8850	0.8772	0.8696
2	1.9704	1.9416	1.9135	1.8861	1.8594	1.8334	1.8080	1.7833	1.7591	1.7355	1.7125	1.6901	1.6681	1.6467	1.6257
3	2.9410	2.8839	2.8286	2.7751	2.7232	2.6730	2.6243	2.5771	2.5313	2.4869	2.4437	2.4018	2.3612	2.3216	2.2832
4	3.9020	3.8077	3.7171	3.6299	3.5460	3.4651	3.3872	3.3121	3.2397	3.1699	3.1024	3.0373	2.9745	2.9137	2.8550
5	4.8534	4.7135	4.5797	4.4518	4.3295	4.2124	4.1002	3.9927	3.8897	3.7908	3.6959	3.6048	3.5172	3.4331	3.3522
6	5.7955	5.6014	5.4172	5.2421	5.0757	4.9173	4.7665	4.6229	4.4859	4.3553	4.2305	4.1114	3.9975	3.8887	3.7845
7	6.7282	6.4720	6.2303	6.0021	5.7864	5.5824	5.3893	5.2064	5.0330	4.8684	4.7122	4.5638	4.4226	4.2883	4.1604
8	7.6517	7.3255	7.0197	6.7327	6.4632	6.2098	5.9713	5.7466	5.5348	5.3349	5.1461	4.9676	4.7988	4.6389	4.4873
9	8.5660	8.1622	7.7861	7.4353	7.1078	6.8017	6.5152	6.2469	5.9952	5.7590	5.5370	5.3282	5.1317	4.9464	4.7716
10	9.4713	8.9826	8.5302	8.1109	7.7217	7.3601	7.0236	6.7101	6.4177	6.1446	5.8892	5.6502	5.4262	5.2161	5.0188
11	10.3676	9.7868	9.2526	8.7605	8.3064	7.8869	7.4987	7.1390	6.8052	6.4951	6.2065	5.9377	5.6869	5.4527	5.2337
12	11.2551	10.5753	9.9540	9.3851	8.8633	8.3838	7.9427	7.5361	7.1607	6.8137	6.4924	6.1944	5.9176	5.6603	5.4206
13	12.1337	11.3484	10.6350	9.9856	9.3936	8.8527	8.3577	7.9038	7.4869	7.1034	6.7499	6.4235	6.1218	5.8424	5.5831
14	13.0037	12.1062	11.2961	10.5631	9.8986	9.2950	8.7455	8.2442	7.7862	7.3667	6.9819	6.6282	6.3025	6.0021	5.7245
15	13.8651	12.8493	11.9379	11.1184	10.3797	9.7122	9.1079	8.5595	8.0607	7.6061	7.1909	6.8109	6.4624	6.1422	5.8474
16	14.7179	13.5777	12.5611	11.6523	10.8378	10.1059	9.4466	8.8514	8.3126	7.8237	7.3792	6.9740	6.6039	6.2651	5.9542
17	15.5623	14.2919	13.1661	12.1657	11.2741	10.4773	9.7632	9.1216	8.5436	8.0216	7.5488	7.1196	6.7291	6.3729	6.0472
18	16.3983	14.9920	13.7535	12.6593	11.6896	10.8276	10.0591	9.3719	8.7556	8.2014	7.7016	7.2497	6.8399	6.4674	6.1280
19	17.2260	15.6785	14.3238	13.1339	12.0853	11.1581	10.3356	9.6036	8.9501	8.3649	7.8393	7.3658	6.9380	6.5504	6.1982
20	18.0456	16.3514	14.8775	13.5903	12.4622	11.4699	10.5940	9.8181	9.1285	8.5136	7.9633	7.4694	7.0248	6.6231	6.2593
21	18.8570	17.0112	15.4150	14.0292	12.8212	11.7641	10.8355	10.0168	9.2922	8.6487	8.0751	7.5620	7.1016	6.6870	6.3125
22	19.6604	17.6580	15.9369	14.4511	13.1630	12.0416	11.0612	10.2007	9.4424	8.7715	8.1757	7.6446	7.1695	6.7429	6.3587
23	20.4558	18.2922	16.4436	14.8568	13.4886	12.3034	11.2722	10.3711	9.5802	8.8832	8.2664	7.7184	7.2297	6.7921	6.3988
24	21.2434	18.9139	16.9355	15.2470	13.7986	12.5504	11.4693	10.5288	9.7066	8.9847	8.3481	7.7843	7.2829	6.8351	6.4338
25	22.0232	19.5235	17.4131	15.6221	14.0939	12.7834	11.6536	10.6748	9.8226	9.0770	8.4217	7.8431	7.3300	6.8729	6.4641
26	22.7952	20.1210	17.8768	15.9828	14.3752	13.0032	11.8258	10.8100	9.9290	9.1609	8.4881	7.8957	7.3717	6.9061	6.4906
27	23.5596	20.7069	18.3270	16.3296	14.6430	13.2105	11.9867	10.9352	10.0266	9.2372	8.5478	7.9426	7.4086	6.9352	6.5135
28	24.3164	21.2813	18.7641	16.6631	14.8981	13.4062	12.1371	11.0511	10.1161	9.3066	8.6016	7.9844	7.4412	6.9607	6.5335
29	25.0658	21.8444	19.1885	16.9837	15.1411	13.5907	12.2777	11.1584	10.1983	9.3696	8.6501	8.0218	7.4701	6.9830	6.5509
30	25.8077	22.3965	19.6004	17.2920	15.3725	13.7648	12.4090	11.2578	10.2737	9.4269	8.6938	8.0552	7.4957	7.0027	6.5660

building services projects often does not occur, this method is not appropriate.

12.9.2.4   More advanced techniques

In addition to the techniques described in the previous sections there are many more complex methods used by accountancy experts. A number of these allow risk to be taken into account. One method, the 'capital asset pricing model', relates the risk of a particular course of action to the return on a similar investment in relatively stable sections of the financial markets. It requires knowledge of the general level of risk acceptable to, say, a maintenance contractor so that the effect of accepting a higher level of risk for a new activity can be estimated. Details of advanced techniques can be found in the *Handbook of management accounting*[29].

Another technique takes account of a private company's mix of debt and equity and its gearing (the ratio of long-term debt to capital employed). This can be used to calculate a weighted average cost of capital (WACC), which in turn can be used to determine a discount rate for investments of average risk and adjusted to reflect projects that represent different risks[30].

12.10   Life cycle costs

Life cycle costs are the combined total of capital and revenue costs for an item of plant or equipment throughout its useful life. Established life cycle costs for particular items have a number of uses, including:

—   to aid design decisions regarding the selection of systems and their components

—   to aid decisions as to whether to repair or replace specific plant items

—   to appraise the effectiveness of a plant or system at the end of its life with a view to future replication of the desirable features, e.g. 'designing out' maintenance activities, reducing or eradicating unplanned downtime, improving reliability and avoiding excessive maintenance expenditure.

The capital costs of building services systems will be a combination of the initial capital costs, the discounted replacement costs and any residual value (scrap) of items of equipment or other components of the system. The revenue costs are made up of the energy costs, the planned maintenance costs, the unplanned maintenance costs and the costs associated with consequential losses resulting from plant failure, such as loss of occupant productivity or production plant downtime.

Obviously some elements of life cycle costs for specific systems cannot be accurately predicted and certain assumptions will always have to be made. It is unfortunate that very few data are available for typical failures and reliability of equipment and system components or for the maintenance costs associated with different systems. Some information is available in BSRIA AG3/2004: *Business focused maintenance*[31] and BSRIA BG7/2004: *Business focused maintenance toolkit*[32]. Information on the expected life of a large selection of building services plant and systems is provided in chapter 13, Appendix 13.A1.

References

1   *Conservation of fuel and power* Building Regulations 2000 Approved Document L (London: NBS/Department for Communities and Local Government) (2006) (available from http://www.planningportal.gov.uk/england/professionals/en/111 5314110382.html) (accessed March 2008)

2   *Building energy metering* CIBSE TM39 (London: Chartered Institution of Building Services Engineers) (2006)

3   *Energy efficiency in buildings* CIBSE Guide F (London: Chartered Institution of Building Services Engineers) (2004)

4   *Whole-life economics of building services* (Bromley: International Facilities and Property Information) (2005)

5   *Spon's mechanical and electrical services price book* (London: Taylor & Francis) (published annually)

6   Building cost survey: Urban commercial offices *Building Serv. J.* **21**(2) 13–15 (February 1999)

7   Building cost survey: Commercial offices (non-urban environment) *Building Serv. J.* **17**(11) 15–16 (November 1995)

8   Shopping centres (cost model) *Building Serv. J.* **24**(7) 16 (July 2002)

9   Building cost survey: Structured cabling *Building Serv. J.* **21**(8) 21–22 (August 1999)

10   Standby generation (cost model) *Building Serv. J.* **16** 50–52 (April 2005)

11   Schools (cost model) *Building Serv. J.* **24**(1) 14–15 (January 2002)

12   Building cost survey: Swimming pools *Building Serv. J.* **18**(11) 15–16 (November 1996)

13   Combined heat and power (cost model) *Building Serv. J.* **26**(10) 20–22 (October 2004)

14   Hospitals (cost model) *Building Serv. J.* **24**(3) 28–30 (March 2002)

15   Building cost survey: Private hospitals *Building Serv. J.* **19**(3) 13–14 (March 1997)

16   Building cost survey: Restaurants *Building Serv. J.* **19**(8) 13–14 (August 1997)

17   Museums (cost model) *Building Serv. J.* **28**(9) 68–75 (September 2006)

18   Cost model: Museums and galleries *Building Serv. J.* **26**(6) 24–26 (June 2004)

19   Lifts and escalators (cost model) *Building Serv. J.* **27**(12) 44–46 (December 2005)

20   Cost model: Building management systems *Building Serv. J.* **26**(1) 20–22 (January 2004)

21   Cost model: Wind and the global warming imperative *Building Serv. J.* **28**(6) 71–74 (June 2006)

22   Cost model: Chiller technology *Building Serv. J.* **28**(4) 65–66 (April 2006)

23   Cost model: Office air conditioning *Building Serv. J.* **28**(2) 48–50 (February 2006)

24   Cost model: Renewable energy *Building Serv. J.* **27**(8) 52–54 (August 2005)

25   Cost model: Ground water cooling *Building Serv. J.* **27**(6) 57–59 (June 2005)

26   Cost model: Combined heat and power *Building Serv. J.* **26**(10) 20–22 (October 2004)

27   Building cost survey: IT cabling *Building Serv. J.* **18**(3) 11–13 (March 1996)

28   *Review of maintenance costs May 2006* BMI Special Report (London: Building Cost Information Service) (2006)

29   Innes J *Handbook of management accounting* (London: Chartered Institute of Management Accountants/Gee Publishing) (2004)

30   Ferry D J O and Flanagan R *Life cycle costing — a radical approach* CIRIA Report 122 (London: Construction Industry Research and Information Association) (1991)

31   *Business focused maintenance* BSRIA AG3/2004 (Bracknell: Building Services Research and Information Association) (2004)

32   *Business focused maintenance toolkit* BSRIA BG7/2004 (Bracknell: Building Services Research and Information Association) (2004)

Bibliography

Energy management (ch. 35); Owning and operating costs (ch. 36); Operation and maintenance management (ch. 38) in ASHRAE Handbook: *HVAC Applications* (Atlanta GA: American Society of Heating, Refrigeration and Air Conditioning Engineers) (2003)

Energy estimating and modelling (ch. 32) in ASHRAE Handbook: *Fundamentals* (Atlanta GA: American Society of Heating, Refrigeration and Air Conditioning Engineers) (2005)

IESNA Lighting Handbook (New York NY: Illuminating Engineering Society of North America) (2000)

Code for lighting (London: CIBSE/Society of Light and Lighting) (2006)

Whole-life costing and cost management Achieving excellence in construction — Procurement Guide 07 (London: Office of Government Commerce) (2003)

BS 3811: 1993: *Glossary of terms used in terotechnology* (London: British Standards Institution) (1993)

BS 3843: 1992: *Guide to terotechnology (the economic management of assets)*: Part 3: *Guide to available techniques* (London: British Standards Institution) (1992)

Smith M H *Maintenance and utility costs: results of a survey* BSRIA TM3/91 (Bracknell: Building Services Research and Information Association) (1991)

Dyson J R *Accounting for non-accounting students* (London: Financial Times/ Prentice Hall) (2003)

Williams B *Facilities economics* (CD-ROM) (Bromley: International Facilities and Property Information) (2005)

Service charge analysis for offices Office Service Charge Annual Review (OSCAR) (website) (London: Jones Lang LaSalle) (http://www.oscar.joneslanglasalle.co.uk/office/index.html) (accessed March 2008)

13 Economic life factors and end of economic life

Summary

The tabulated data for this chapter comprise estimates of the economic life of constituent components.

The sources and derivation of the economic life estimates are detailed and a number of factors that can influence the life are explained.

Arrangements for the allocation of funding for plant replacement by the sinking fund method and a commercial refinement of this are described.

A graphical illustration and explanation of the staged, partial replacement of plant is provided together with details of depreciation and statutes covering capital allowances.

Economic life factors are an integral part of life cycle costing and should be used when:

(*a*)   comparing alternative design solutions

(*b*)   replacing plant items and components at intervals which, for the purpose of prediction, should be the economic life factors; a system may comprise many plant items and components with various individual life cycles and this approach should ensure that a system operates at optimum performance

(*c*)   commencing a new design, improvement or refurbishment, to consider the total cost including design, safety, installation, testing, commissioning, satisfactory level of handover, maintenance, review of performance following handover, subsequent replacement and disposal.

Specialist industrial refrigeration plant and refrigeration equipment used in supermarkets and public houses for food and drink are not covered.

The economic life factors scheduled in this section are for initial reference and guidance only. Detailed information should always be obtained from the supplier, distributor, manufacturer, installer or professional adviser.

Whole life costing (WLC) is a valuable technique that is used to assist in assessing the cost performance of constructed assets. It is used as a tool to identify options where there are alternative means of achieving the client's objectives and where those alternatives differ not only in their initial costs but also in their subsequent operational and life care costs.

The life cycle phases for a system are:

—   acquisition

—   use and maintenance

—   renewal and adaptation

—   disposal.

Figure 13.1 Phases in the life of a system

The relationship between these phases is illustrated in Figure 13.1.

The design life should be defined in the client's brief and the estimated service life should be at least as long as the design life. Maintenance will be required for certain items to achieve the predicted/estimated life. Service life replacement dates are an important variable in WLC. The estimation of service life takes account of the period during which the asset is intended to be used for its function or business purpose. Frequently this period will dictate the period of analysis of the WLCs and may dictate the design life for major assets and components.

13.1   Background

To establish the economic life factors used in this section, information in published material[1–10] was reviewed. In addition, advice and comments from the sources listed in the acknowledgements for this Guide were considered and, where appropriate, used in the text or economic life factor tables. In reviewing such a large amount of information a certain degree of flexibility has been necessary in the description of the equipment items. Where there is considered to be a need to review any particular item in greater detail, reference to the original source is recommended.

Readers should note that the economic life factors scheduled in this chapter are derived from a broadly based survey of generic plant and equipment. Users of the data may, however, wish to adjust the factors given based on their own experience or, in the case of particular proprietary equipment, to take advice from the manufacturer.

Kirk and Dell'Isola[11] define economic life, technological life and useful life of an item as:

— *economic life*: the estimated number of years until that item no longer represents the least expensive method of performing its function

— *technological life*: the estimated number of years until technology causes an item to become obsolete

— *useful life*: the estimated number of years during which an item will perform its function according to some established performance standard.

The above definition of economic life has been used for the purposes of the life factors in this section. The definitions for technological life and useful life are provided for use when comparing life factor schedules in other publications. It is important that contractual and legal documentation clearly define the basis of the life factors used to minimise misunderstanding and possible future disputes between the parties scheduled in the documentation.

The listed economic life factors assume that the following conditions apply:

— a good standard of maintenance (see chapter 3 of this Guide)

— a high standard of quality control at all levels during manufacture

— compliance with approved British and European standards and codes of practice

— installation, including testing and commissioning, carried out to good industry standards (see CIBSE Commissioning Codes[12–18])

— where plant and equipment are imported from outside the European Union, equivalent quality and safety standards are clearly specified and appropriate inspections made

— hours of plant operation (especially rotating plant): many buildings are now being used for longer periods of time as commercial pressures and international competition intensify; where duplicate or multiple plant is installed, the hours of each unit should be assumed to be nominally equal

— adequate space for safety, access, maintenance and removal of plant.

13.2 Predicting future life of existing plant

Preparation of long term maintenance and repair budgets for building services requires a forecast of the future life of existing plant and equipment, and when replacement in part or whole will be necessary. Economic life factors are sometimes used to determine whether and when existing plant and equipment should be replaced without reference

to records of the plant performance in use. Engineers may assume that once plant has reached the age indicated by the economic life factor it should be replaced. This is not necessarily the case and may lead to premature and unnecessary replacement. The economic life factors given in Appendix 13.A1 are intended primarily for life cycle costing and are likely to provide a conservative forecast, particularly when plant has been in use for some years and operational performance and service records are available.

Economic life is described in section 13.1 as that point in time when that item 'no longer represents the least expensive method of performing its function', i.e. it is less expensive to replace the item than to continue to repair it. There are, however, many other reasons why plant is replaced including that it may be approaching the end of its technological life or its useful life. Retaining plant until it reaches the end of its economic life may not be the best engineering solution if it has already exceeded its technological and useful life spans.

Economic life factors, average age at replacement and median service lives are all based on plant having been replaced for any reason which may include:

— anticipated or actual failure

— approaching the end of its useful life

— obsolescence (end of technological life)

— refurbishment of building

— changes in building use and required capacity

— changes in legislation

— improved efficiency of new plant

— marketing, i.e. more 'bells and whistles' on new plant.

The least likely reason is that an economic analysis has been carried out to determine if the plant is approaching the end of its economic life.

13.2.1 Typical life of building services plant

The 'bathtub' curve in Figure 13.2 is frequently used as a model to describe the reliability and likelihood of failure of products and plant over its life[19].

The curve is empirical and has been found to apply to composite products, systems or sub-systems with components that are subject to wear, such as rotating machinery.

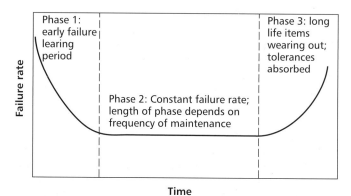

Figure 13.2 'Bathtub' curve

Other components may be subject to 'random' failures. These may increase with age or may continue to occur at a steady rate throughout an asset's life. With building services, the bath tub curve can be applied to entire systems and major plant such as chillers, boiler/burner units, air handling units, packaged air conditioning systems, heat pumps and lifts etc. Maintenance such as replacement of parts may reduce the impact of wear. There are typically three distinct phases in the life:

— *Phase 1: Decreasing failure rate*: this occurs when the system is new and is a consequence of teething problems such as design and installation errors, faulty components and manufacturing faults among other matters.

— *Phase 2: Constant failure rate*: in maintained systems, after the early failure period, the system will be in a settled state; random isolated faults and failures will occur, and parts that wear will need repair and/or replacement from time to time as part of preventive maintenance. Such parts typically include bearings, seals, printed circuit boards, control components, motors, heat exchanger components and compressors on packaged heat pumps/air conditioners or multiple compressor chillers.

— *Phase 3: Increasing failure rate*: this is the point where major components begin to fail and random failures increase with time. At this stage the cost of repair of plant and equipment begins to exceed the cost of replacement.

The useful life would be the period of time before the onset of phase 3, i.e. before there is any significant increase in the risk of failure rate.

13.2.2   Estimating future life expectancy

To assess the future life for an individual item of plant it is necessary to consider its condition, operating performance and service record to determine, as far as possible, whether the item of plant is in average, better than average, or worse than average condition for its age. This would normally be assessed by various measures including the following:

— a visual inspection of the physical condition and the plant in operation

— an assessment of whether the plant is performing an appropriate performance standard

— a review of service and maintenance records.

Such a review would indicate the condition of the existing plant by comparison with the average, and allow an engineer to make an estimate of the remaining period before there is any significant increase in the risk of failure rate.

Although there are only a limited number of items of plant where the median service life has been documented it is reasonable in the absence of such data to assume that the life factors represent a close approximation of the median service life and for engineers to project an assessment of future life based on typical survival curves.

13.3   Variation factors

Appropriate variation of the scheduled economic life factors can be made by applying a variation factor with a value greater or less than 1.0. A suggested range of conditions, together with typical examples that may require a variation factor to be applied, is listed below.

Condition 1: external environment

A factor should be applied in the following circumstances:

— urban developments where exposure to pollution and corrosion may occur

— roof top exposure to rain, snow and wind

— coastal conditions, such as wind and exposure to salt-laden air.

Condition 2: internal environment

Dry and corrosion-free conditions are required for plant, equipment and distribution systems. Where this condition has not been met a variation factor may be appropriate.

Condition 3: technology changes

Equipment design, manufacturing procedures and materials may all develop during the lifetime of installed plant and services, affecting their economic life (as defined in 13.1 above), particularly where reliability and efficiency of performance is significantly improved.

Condition 4: design and specification

Commercial buildings, especially those constructed in the 1980s, may show a marked divergence between the design specification and the actual conditions observed (for occupants) or measured (relating to lighting and small power loads). This results from the increased use of computers and other items of office equipment now operated in commercial premises.

Studies instigated by BSRIA[20] and Stanhope[21,22] highlighted the matter of overdesign or overspecification which can give rise to operational problems in achieving acceptable comfort conditions. If a building falls into this category it is assumed that the systems will be recommissioned to suit the actual conditions, otherwise the control system may not be able to compensate and provide effective regulation of performance. This, in turn, can lead to 'hunting' (i.e. cycling between maximum and minimum output) leading to poor energy efficiency and a shorter plant and equipment lifespan than expected.

The general quality of materials, components, plant and equipment should, as a minimum requirement, comply with relevant British and European standards and codes of practice; where this is in doubt, a variation factor should be applied.

To avoid overspecification it is recommended that an action plan be prepared, based on BSRIA TR21/95: *Over-engineering in building services*[23] and, for commercial developments, the British Council for Offices' *Best practice in the specification for offices*[24].

Condition 5: unoccupied and closed-down buildings

Where a building has been unoccupied or closed down for a number of years and is required to be used again, a condition survey is recommended (see chapter 15). Where appropriate, plant and systems should be repaired or refurbished and recommissioned to a satisfactory standard. Where this is not allowed, a factor variation for the residual life of the plant may well be appropriate.

Note that a condition survey may be relevant for both new and used plant and systems, especially where the purchase or lease of a building is under consideration.

Condition 6: maintenance

Where the standard of maintenance provided does not meet the criteria set out in chapter 3 of this Guide, a variation factor should be applied.

Condition 7: hours of operation

The reference standard assumes a 12-hour operational period (Monday–Friday) and 8 hours during the weekend. If operating hours are higher or lower, a variation factor may be appropriate.

Condition 8: installation

The reference standard assumes that a high standard of installation quality control has been applied, approved British and European standards and codes of practice followed, and testing and commissioning have taken place[12–18]. A variation factor may be appropriate where there is some doubt that all these have occurred.

Condition 9: adequate space

Allowing adequate space for maintenance and plant replacement is very important; where the particular reference standard is in doubt, or plant and equipment have been 'shoe-horned' into a space, a variation factor should be applied.

Worked example

Assume that the reference standards for conditions 6 and 9 above have not been complied with, and variation factors of 0.95 and 0.92 have been adopted, the estimated economic life factor would be calculated as follows:

Reference economic life factor = 20 years

Estimated economic life factor = 20 × 0.95 × 0.92

= 17.48 years

It is important to appreciate that this method is subjective, and relies on assessment by trained and experienced engineers. Nevertheless, it provides a logical approach for estimating purposes. Furthermore, the means of arriving at the chosen life factor is clearly defined and demonstrable.

Appendix 13.A1 provides a schedule of economic life factors. It should be noted that this is not exhaustive, and there will always be scope for additions and the need to recognise changes in technology.

13.4 Applications

13.4.1 Sinking fund

An approach to allocating funds for future plant and system replacement is to set up a sinking fund. In practice, this approach will need specialist accounting, tax and legal advice. This section concentrates on the calculations involved and ignores all possible effects of tax and inflation.

A sinking fund can be considered as a method of depreciation. At the end of the asset's life, the investment will provide cash equal to the cost of the asset. The general formula is:

$$\text{AR} = (\text{RC} \times I) / \{[(1 + I)^n] - 1\}$$

Where AR is annual recovery (£), RC is replacement cost (£), I is annual interest rate (%) and n is life period (years).

Consider the replacement cost of boiler plant and system in 20 years' time at 4% yearly interest. The estimated cost is £37 400. The annual recovery and contribution to the sinking fund can be calculated as:

$$\text{AR} = (37\,400 \times 0.04) / \{[(1 + 0.04)^{20}] - 1\} = £1256$$

It is important to demonstrate reasonably reliable economic life factors and the effect on the annual recovery should the factors be inaccurate. For example, if the actual life period were 13 years rather than 20 years, using the same calculation procedure for 13 years, the annual recovery would have been set at £2249. This would result in a shortfall in the fund to replace the boiler plant of £993 per annum.

13.4.2 Commercial method

For commercial purposes a more practical approach is required than simple sinking fund calculations. The method, as used in the property industry, is detailed as a worked example in Table 13.1. It covers a six-year period to illustrate the method in tabular form, using the same data as the example in section 13.3.

The principles of this practical, commercial method are:

(a) Depending on the level of inflation and market conditions, valuations should be obtained at periodic intervals from independent engineers to establish the likely replacement cost and should include a review of the original estimated life period (factor) for the plant and systems. These figures should be adjusted to allow for fees for professional advisors and value-added tax (VAT). The time period between valuations will typically be 2–3 years if inflation levels are high and 5–7 years if inflation is stable and reasonably low. Between valuations, appropriate yearly cost inflation indices should be obtained from independent sources based on their detailed knowledge of the

Table 13.1 Example calculation using commercial method

Year ending	Life (years)	Past life (years)	Interest rate (%)	Inflation rate (%)	Replacement cost (£)	Reserve (£)	Past recovery (£)	Annual recovery (£)	Interest allowance (£)	Contribution (£)
2001	20	1	5.00	6.00	37 400	1 870	—	1870	—	1870
2002	20	2	3.80	4.00	38 896	3 890	1 870	2020	71	1949
2003	20	3	2.30	3.80	40 374	6 056	3 890	2167	89	2077
2004	20	4	2.59	3.00	41 585	8 317	6 056	2261	157	2104
2005	20	5	3.00	4.00	43 249	10 812	8 317	2495	250	2246
2006	20	6	3.00	4.00	44 979	13 494	10 812	2681	324	2357

industry, type of plant and system. These indices should then be compared with the retail prices index (RPI), which is well established and understood fully by financial professionals.

(b) The replacement cost of each plant item and system should be multiplied by the expired life period and divided by the expected life period to produce the expected provision. The provisions actually recovered to date should be deducted from the expected total provision to give a value representing the amount that has to be set aside to provide an adequate sum for the future replacement of the specific plant and system.

(c) The replacement costs should be adjusted each year for inflation based on independent advice. An annual contribution should be obtained by subtracting the expected provision from the previous year's provision figure.

(d) A notional interest allowance should be made on the previous year's expected provision, which represents the cumulative payments expected to have been received. This interest amount should then be deducted from the annual provision and the remaining balance recovered from the tenants.

(e) A gross rate of interest allowance is calculated on the average bank base rate and is subject to tax deduction to meet the following conditions:

— the replacement provision is recovered as additional rent, which is taxable

— interest can be earned only on amounts retained after deducting the appropriate rate of corporation tax

— tax will then be applied again on interest received (i.e. two levels of tax need to be applied).

(f) Replacement provisions should be retained in a general provision account and not be treated as part of company income.

(g) When a plant and system replacement becomes due the landlord will, in general, be required to make good any shortfall in funds (which can arise as a result of unlet spaces, lease defects, service charge capping and the like).

(h) Shortfalls relating to tenants in occupation at the time of replacement would be included in the service charge in the year following replacement of the plant and system.

(i) Where there is an overprovision of funds, nothing more is collected until the reserve and replacement cost balance (based on revaluation criteria) come near to convergence.

(j) Where there is an underprovision of funds, it may be necessary to try to recover the shortfall in the year of revaluation. This would be subject to commercial considerations and may be spread over two or three years.

13.4.3 Partial replacement during expected life period

Figure 13.3 illustrates how the value of plant and systems will change should early replacement be introduced due to changes in technology and energy management. The

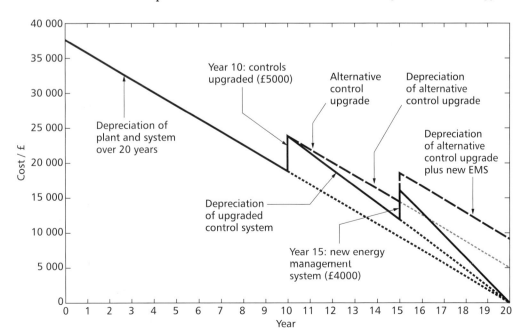

Figure 13.3 Changing value of plant resulting from early replacement

following data are used in conjunction with the example in section 13.3.

(*a*)   The plant and system are assumed to reduce in value on a linear basis over a 20-year period with zero value at the end of the life period.

(*b*)   In year 10, the control system is upgraded at a cost of £5000 with a high probability of upgrading again in a further 10 years, indicated by the solid line. The dashed line indicates an upgrade with extended life after 10 years.

(*c*)   In year 15, a new energy management system is introduced at a cost of £4000 which is likely to last for a further 5 years, indicated in black, before work will be required again. The dashed line indicates an upgrade with extended life after 5 years.

This is a simple model but could be developed to introduce non-linear yearly changes in value and inflation by extending the life period beyond 20 years with the introduction of modernisation and refurbishment. This approach could satisfy the need for reducing operating and maintenance costs and keeping plant and systems as modern and energy efficient as possible.

13.4.4   Depreciation

Accounting standards define depreciation[25], but for all practical purposes the following details must be determined for each item of plant or equipment before any assessment can be made:

—   the total cost (£)

—   economic life (years)

—   salvage value (£)

—   a method of depreciation which is systematic and rational.

The building services engineer can establish values for total cost, economic life and salvage value while the accountant decides the depreciation method. Various depreciation methods are scheduled as follows:

—   straight line

—   sum of the year's digits

—   fixed percentage

—   compound

—   declining balance

—   sinking fund

—   repair reserve

—   revaluation

—   manufacturing unit.

13.4.5   Investment appraisal

Investment appraisal is dealt with in section 12.9.2 but economic life factor input is needed before any meaningful appraisal can be made.

13.4.6   Capital allowances and the Finance Act 1997

When machinery or plant is purchased for a business, the cost of each item is added to a pool (motor vehicles are treated separately). A yearly capital allowance of 20% on a reducing balance basis is applied for each tax year to the pool and claimed as a writing-down allowance. Schedule 13 of the Finance Act 1997[26] amended the Capital Allowances Act 1990 by introducing the case of machinery or plant that is new or, when new, would have a useful economic life of at least 25 years; a 10% capital allowance then applies on the reducing balance basis. There are exclusions to this rule and reference should be made to the Finance Act 1997 for further information. Current investment allowances made in budgets subsequent to the Act should also be identified and applied.

The items of machinery or plant that qualify for capital allowances can be complex and assessing them requires the expertise of tax, quantity surveying and engineering professionals.

The tax advantages available through the Enhanced Capital Allowances scheme for using more efficient plant should be considered (details of currently applicable plant are available at http://www.eca.gov.uk).

Enhanced Capital Allowances (ECAs) enable a business to claim 100% first-year capital allowances on their spending on qualifying plant and machinery. The two most applicable schemes for ECAs are:

—   energy-saving plant and machinery

—   water conservation plant and machinery.

Businesses can write off the whole of the capital cost of their investment in these technologies against their taxable profits of the period during which they make the investment. This may allow up to a 5% reduction in capital cost compared with plant not covered by the scheme. This can deliver a helpful cash flow boost and a shortened payback period

Other engineering input to the above considerations would involve the assessment of economic life periods and, where appropriate, the provision of assessments for the Inland Revenue inspector.

References

1   *Transportation systems in buildings* CIBSE Guide D (London: Chartered Institution of Building Services Engineers) (2005)

2   Comparison of service life estimates (Table 4) in *Owning and operating costs* (ch. 36) in ASHRAE Handbook: *HVCA Applications* (Atlanta GA: American Society of Heating, Refrigerating and Air Conditioning Engineers) (2007)

3   *Periods of use and maintenance costs, based on the fundamentals of Sanitar Und Heizungstechnik* Publication 2067 of the VDI (German Society of Engineers) BSRIA Translation No. 256, Report 76230/1 (Bracknell: Building Services Research and Information Association) (1985)

4   Oughton D R and Hodkinson S *Faber and Kell's heating and air-conditioning of buildings* (9th edn.) (Oxford: Butterworth-Heinemann Ltd) (2001)

5   *Maintenance of mechanical services* (London: Department of Education and Science/The Stationery Office) (1990)

6   *Maintenance of electrical services* (London: Department of Education and Science/The Stationery Office) (1992)

7   *BLP Building services component life manual* (Oxford: Blackwell Science) (2001)

8   *Anticipated economic life expectancy of MPS building services* MPS Report M.203 (London: Metropolitan Police Service, Property Services Department Surveying and Engineering Division) (1996)

9   Jønsson A and Lindgren S *The longevity of building services installations Stage 1: Inventory of operating experiences for estimating longevity* Report 811662 4/80s of Swedish Building Research Council BSRIA Translation No 252 (Bracknell: Building Services Research and Information Association)

10   *BLP Construction Durability Database* (website) (London: Building Life Plans) (2004) (http://www.componentlife.com) (accessed April 2008)

11   Kirk S J and Dell'Isola A J *Life cycle costing for design professionals* (New York: McGraw-Hill) (1995)

12   *Air distribution systems* CIBSE Commissioning Code A (London: Chartered Institution of Building Services Engineers) (1996)

13   *Boiler plant* CIBSE Commissioning Code B (London: Chartered Institution of Building Services Engineers) (2002)

14   *Automatic controls* CIBSE Commissioning Code C (London: Chartered Institution of Building Services Engineers) (2001)

15   *Refrigerating systems* CIBSE Commissioning Code R (London: Chartered Institution of Building Services Engineers) (2002)

16   *Water distribution systems* CIBSE Commissioning Code W (London: Chartered Institution of Building Services Engineers) (2003)

17   *Lighting* CIBSE/SSL Commissioning Code (London: Chartered Institution of Building Services Engineers/Society of Light and Lighting) (2003)

18   *Commissioning Management* CIBSE Commissioning Code M (London: Chartered Institution of Building Services Engineers) (2003)

19   *Maintenance of mechanical services* Maintenance and Renewal in Educational Buildings Bulletin No. 70 (London: Department of Education and Science) (1990)

20   Hejab M and Parsloe C *Small power loads* BSRIA TN8/92 (Bracknell: Building Services Research and Information Association) (1992)

21   LoPinto A, Farnfield T and Eames J *An assessment of small power loads for commercial office buildings* Stanhope Position Paper (London: Stanhope Properties) (1993)

22   Katsikakis D and Laing A *An assessment of occupation density levels in commercial office buildings* Stanhope Position Paper (London: Stanhope Properties) (1993)

23   Parsloe C J *Over-engineering in building services* BSRIA TR21/95 (Bracknell: Building Services Research and Information Association) (1995)

24   *Best practice in the specification for offices* (Reading: British Council for Offices) (2005)

25   Wood F and Sangster A *Business accounting 2* (10th edn.) (London: Pearson Books) (2005)

26   Finance Act 1997 (London: The Stationery Office) (1997)

Bibliography

BS ISO 15686-1: 2000: *Buildings and constructed assets. Service life planning. General principles* (London: British Standards Institution) (2000)

BS ISO 15686-6: 2004: *Buildings and constructed assets. Service life planning. Procedures for considering environmental impacts* (London: British Standards Institution) (2004)

Hillier CC 'Determining equipment service life' *ASHRAE J.* (August 2000)

Lovvorn N and Hillier CC 'Heat pump life revisited' *ASHRAE Trans.* Paper 4560 (2002)

Abramson B, Won L-S and Herman DL 'Service life data from an interactive web-based owning and operating cost database' *ASHRAE Trans.* Paper 4830 (RP-1237) (2006)

Appendix 13.A1: Indicative life expectancy factors

Equipment item	Indicative life / years	Remarks	BCIS cost group	HVCA SFG/20 reference
(a) Heating source				
Boiler plant:				
— cast iron sectional boilers (MTHW/LTHW)	25		5E	05-14; 05-23
— condensing boilers (MTHW/LTHW)	20		5E	05-04; 05-12
— domestic boilers (combination)	10		—	—
— domestic boilers (condensing)	15		—	—
— electrode/electric boilers (MTHW/LTHW)	25	Water treatment is very important	5E	05-22
— electrode/electric boilers (steam and HTHW)	25	Water treatment is very important	5E	05-19; 05-20
— modular boilers	15		5E	05-11
— shell and tube boilers (MTHW/LTHW)	20	Water treatment is very important	5E	05-14; 05-23
— shell and tube boilers (steam and HTHW)	20	Water treatment is very important	5E	05-19; 05-20
— steel boilers (MTHW/LTHW)	20		5E	05-14; 05-23
— water tube boilers (MTHW/LTHW)	25	Water treatment is very important	5E	05-14; 05-23
— water tube boilers (steam and HTHW)	25	Water treatment is very important	5E	05-19; 05-20
Boiler plant auxiliaries:				
— boiler electrodes	8		5E	05-22
— chimney (brick or concrete) (outside)	40		5E	24-01
— chimney (brick or concrete) (inside)	50		5E	24-01
— chimney (steel) (outside)	30	Depends on thickness of metal and corrosion protection	5E	24-01
— combustion controls	12		5E	05-(15-20)
— dosing pots	15		5E	65-10
— fans (high temperature)	15		5E	20-08
— feed pumps	15		5E	45-04
— flue (mild steel)	15	Depends on thickness of metal and corrosion protection	5E	24-01
— flue (stainless steel)	30	Check quality of stainless steel	5E	24-01
— gas burners (atmospheric)	20		5E	05-(03-04); 06-01
— gas burners (forced air)	15		5E	05-(10-12); 06-03
— gas distribution system for boiler plant	40		5E	40-10
— instrumentation	10		5E	05-(15-18)
— oil burners (pressure jet)	15		5E	05-13; 06-(04-06)
— oil distribution system for boiler plant	40		5E	40-10
— oil storage tanks (external protection)	20	Depends on thickness of metal and corrosion protection	5E	56-05
— oil storage tanks (inside building)	30		5E	56-05
— oil storage tanks (underground)	15	Depends on thickness of metal and corrosion protection	5E	56-05
— water treatment equipment	15		5E	65-(01-10)
— solid fuel handling plant	15	Conveyor system up to 20 years	5E	05-(05-08)
(b) Cooling source				
Ancillaries:				
— refrigerant leak detector	10		5F	46-01
— trace heating	20		5F	40-03
Chillers (medium to large):				
— absorption	25	Depends on availability of refrigerant	5F	09-05
— centrifugal	20	Depends on availability of refrigerant	5F	09-02; 12-03
— reciprocating	20	Depends on availability of refrigerant	5F	09-02; 12-01
— screw	25	Depends on availability of refrigerant	5F	09-02; 12-02
External heat rejection for refrigeration plant:				
— air blast dry air coolers (epoxy treated metal)	20		5F	13-02
— air blast dry air coolers (plastic coated metal)	25	Consider thickness, bonding and quality of plastic coating	5F	13-02
— air blast dry air coolers (galvanised metal)	20	Consider thickness and quality of galvanising	5F	13-02
— air cooled condensers	20		5F	13-02
— evaporative condensers	20		5F	19-01; 13-02; 30-03

Equipment item	Indicative life / years	Remarks	BCIS cost group	HVCA SFG/20 reference
(b) Cooling source (*continued*)				
Open type cooling towers:				
— ceramic	35		5F	30-02
— epoxy treated metal	15			
— galvanised metal	12	Consider thickness and quality of galvanising	5F	30-02
— plastic coated metal	25	Consider thickness, bonding and quality of plastic coating	5F	30-02
— plastic construction	20	Consider thickness and quality of plastic	5F	30-02
— stainless steel	30	Consider quality and thickness of stainless steel	5F	30-02
— timber construction	10	Quality of timber preservation can extend life	5F	30-02
(c) Water and fuel installations				
Storage vessels:				
— chilled water storage vessel (copper)	20		5D (water)	56-02
— chilled water storage vessel (galvanised)	15	Not suitable for soft water or softened water	5D (water)	56-02
— chilled water storage vessel (mild steel)	20		5D (water)	56-02
— fuel oil storage tank (external, above ground)	20	Depends on thickness of metal and corrosion protection	5E	56-05
— fuel oil storage tank (external, below ground)	15	Depends on thickness of metal and corrosion protection	5E	56-05
— ice storage	15		5D (water)	56-02
— water cisterns (cast iron)	35		5D (water)	56-02
— water cisterns (galvanised)	15		5D (water)	56-02
— water cisterns (mild steel, treated)	25	Not for domestic or drinking water purposes	5D (water)	56-02
— water cisterns (plastic)	25	High quality structural support is necessary	5D (water)	56-02
(d) Calorifiers/heat exchangers				
Calorifiers:				
— copper	25		5D	32-(05-07)
— mild steel	20		5D	32-(05-07)
Heat exchangers:				
— plate	15	Subject to regular cleaning	5D	29-(05-07)
— shell and tube	25		5D	32-(05-07)
(e) Pumps				
Base mounted pumps	20		—	45-
Boiler feed pumps	15		—	—
Centrifugal pumps	20		—	45-03
Circulating pumps:				
— commercial (dual type)	20		—	45-02
— domestic	10		—	—
Condensate pumps	10		—	—
Glandless pumps	10		—	45-
Pipework mounted pumps	15		—	45-
Sump and well pumps	12	Consider mechanical damage and expansion	5D	45-10
(f) Pressurisation systems				
Chilled water pressurisation unit	20		5F	45-12
Combined heating/chilled water	20		—	45-12
Expansion vessel (unvented hot water)	15		—	—
Heating pressurisation unit	20		5E	45-12
(g) Water boosters				
Domestic booster	15		5D	45-11
Hose reel booster	20		—	23-02
Mains cold water booster	15		5F	45-12

Equipment item	Indicative life / years	Remarks	BCIS cost group	HVCA SFG/20 reference
(g) Water boosters (continued)				
Sprinkler	20		—	23-14
(h) Pipework systems and components				
Bellows:				
— expansion (steel)	10		—	—
— flexible (rubber)	8		—	—
— flexible (steel)	10		—	—
Condensate pipework system	12	Consider type of material, wall thickness and water treatment	5F	40-(04-06)
Condensate collecting vessel	12	Consider type of material, wall thickness and water treatment	5F	40-(04-06)
Expansion vessels:				
— open	10		—	—
— closed (with membrane)	15		—	—
Fuel pipework:				
— gas	50		—	—
— oil	50		—	—
Heating pipework system (plastic)	35		5E	40-01
Pipework systems (closed):				
— copper	45	Consider tube thickness and quality of copper	5E	40-01
— steel	25		5E	40-01
— steel (galvanised)	35		5E	40-01
Pipework systems (open):				
— copper	45	Consider tube thickness and quality of copper	5E	40-01
— steel	25		5E	40-01
— steel (galvanised)	25		5E	40-01
Refrigerant pipework systems	30		5F	46-01
Steam pipework system	25		5E	40-11
Water softeners:				
— base exchange	30		—	—
— de-alkalisation	20		—	—
— de-ionisation	20		—	—
Water treatment plant	15		—	65-(01-10)
Water treatment control and measurement equipment	10		—	65-(01-10)
(i) Insulation (pipework)				
Pipework thermal insulation:				
— moulded type	30	Consider fire and smoke rating	—	35-01
— blanket type	30	Consider fire and smoke rating	—	35-01
Vessel thermal insulation:				
— moulded type	30	Consider fire and smoke rating	—	35-01
— blanket type	30	Consider fire and smoke rating	—	35-01
Tank thermal insulation:				
— moulded type	30	Consider fire and smoke rating	—	35-01
— blanket type	30	Consider fire and smoke rating	—	35-01
Ductwork thermal insulation (blanket type)	30	Consider fire and smoke rating	—	35-01
Fire insulation (intumescent) for pipes and ducts	20	Inspection for damage required at frequent intervals	—	—
(j) Valves				
Commissioning valves	25		—	61-01
Draw-off taps	20		—	—
Fuel shut-off valves	25		—	61-01
Motorised control valves	15		—	62-(01-07)
Motorised control valve actuators	10		—	01-(01-08)
Shower mixer and head	10		—	61-05

Equipment item	Indicative life / years	Remarks	BCIS cost group	HVCA SFG/20 reference
(j) Valves (continued)				
Supply-side shut-off valve	25		—	—
Valves:				
— cast iron	30		—	—
— copper	30		—	—
— glandless	20			61-01
— glands	15			61-01
— mild steel	25		—	—
(k) Terminal units (wet systems)				
Ceiling heating:				
— hot water	25		5E	—
— electric	15		5E	—
Fan coil units (heating only)	15		5E	28-01
Natural convectors:				
— water	20		5E	—
— electric	10		5E	—
Radiant heaters:				
— steam and hot water	20		5E	28-01
— electric	10		5E	28-01
Radiators:				
— aluminium	20	Water condition and materials in the system are important	5E	28-01
— cast iron	25		5E	28-01
— steel	20	Water condition is important	5E	28-01
— steel (2 mm thick)	20	Water condition is important	5E	28-01
Radiator painting	5	Use correct type of paint	5E	28-01
Storage heaters (electric)	10		5E	—
Underfloor heating:				
— electric	20		5E	—
— plastic pipes (concrete encased)	30	Suggest a long-term bonded warranty is obtained; consider quality of plastic pipe	5E	—
— steel pipes (concrete encased)	25	Suggest a long-term bonded warranty is obtained; corrosion prevention required for steel pipes	5E	—
Unit heaters:				
— steam and hot water	15		5E	28-01
— gas and electric	10		5E	28-01
(l) Air handling and ventilation				
Air conditioning terminal units:				
— chilled ceiling panels	25	Flexible water pipework connections 10 years (depending on type)	5F	—
— chilled beams	20	Flexible water pipework connections 10 years (depending on type)	5F	—
— computer room air conditioning	15		5F	—
— double duct terminal units	15		5F	59-
— fan coil units (heating and cooling)	15		5F	59-06
— induction units	20		5F	59-05
— split systems	10		5F	—
— terminal reheat units	20		5F	59-(01-03)
— VAV terminal units (bellows type)	15		5F	59-(01-03)
— VAV terminal units (box type)	15		5F	59-(01-03)
— ventilated ceilings	25		5G	—
— VRV units	10		5F	—
— VVT fan powered terminal units	15		5F	—
Fans:				
— axial	15	Life likely to be reduced if fan motor in air stream	5E	20-04
— centrifugal	20	Life likely to be reduced if fan motor in air stream	5E	20-03
— centrifugal (heavy duty)	25	Life likely to be reduced if fan motor in air stream	5E	20-03
— extract (e.g. domestic)	10		—	—

Equipment item	Indicative life / years	Remarks	BCIS cost group	HVCA SFG/20 reference
(*l*) Air handling and ventilation (*continued*)				
Fans (*continued*):				
— high temperature (boiler combustion)	15		5E	—
— propellor	10		5E	20-05
— roof mounted units	15		5E	20-07
Ductwork:				
— galvanised (rectangular and circular)	40		5G	16-(01-04)
— plastic	15	Expansion and risk of mechanical damage and need to be considered	5G	16-(01-04)
— flexible (circular)	15	Risk of mechanical damage and cleaning difficulties needs to be considered	5G	16-(01-04)
Ductwork Ancillaries:				
— attenuators	25	Consider type of lining, adhesive and fixing of acoustic material	5G	16-04
— coils (aluminium fins) (cooling)	15	Consider quality and thickness of aluminium fins and exposure to adverse and wet external conditions	5E; 5F; 5G	29-01
— coils (aluminium fins) (heating)	15	Consider quality and thickness of aluminium fins and exposure to adverse external conditions	5E; 5F; 5G	29-01
— coils (copper fins) (cooling)	25	Consider operational duty (wet surfaces)	5E; 5F; 5G	29-01
— coils (copper fins) (heating)	25		5E; 5F; 5G	29-01
— coils (electric)	10		5G	29-02
— coils (galvanised) (heating	12		5E; 5F; 5G	29-01
— dampers (manual)	20		5G	16-03
— dampers (automatic)	15		5G	16-03
— eliminators (galvanised)	10		5G; 5F; 5G	16-02
— eliminators (plastic)	15		5G; 5F; 5G	16-02
— eliminators (stainless steel)	20		5G; 5F; 5G	16-02
— external louvres (anodised aluminium)	25	Regular cleaning is important to avoid possible breakdown of surface coating	5G	—
— external louvres (steel painted)	20	Early signs of corrosion must be dealt with	5G	26-02
— filters (automatic) (excluding media)	15		5G	21-02
— filters (panel) (excluding media)	20		5G	21-02
— filters (primary) (washable)	10	8 hours/day; 5 days/week	—	—
— filters (primary) (disposable)	0.5	8 hours/day; 5 days/week	—	—
— filters (secondary) (pleated and bag types)	1	8 hours/day; 5 days/week	—	—
— filters (electrostatic)	15		5G	21-03
— filters (activated carbon) (excluding media)	15		5G	21-02
— filters (high efficiency particulate air (HEPA))	2	8 hours/day; 5 days/week	5G	21-02
— fire dampers (curtain type)	10		5G	16-03
— grilles and diffusers (anodised aluminium)	25		5G	26-01
— grilles and diffusers (painted metal)	30		5G	26-01
— hoods	30		5G	—
— insulation (ductwork systems)	30		—	35-01
— plate recuperator	20		5G	29-03
— spray cooler coils (copper electro-tinned) and washers	15		5G; 5F; 5G	29-01
— thermal wheels	15		5G	29-04
Humidifiers:				
— chemical dehumidifiers (excluding medium)	15		5G	—
— pan type humidifier	10	Early signs of corrosion must be dealt with	5G	33-01
— steam (direct)	10	Maintenance is very important	5G	33-02
— steam (electrically generated)	8	Maintenance is very important	5G	33-02
— water spray	15	Early signs of corrosion must be dealt with	5G	33-01
Insulation (ductwork and vessel) (blanket type)	30	Consider type of fixing and risk of mechanical damage	5F; 5G	35-01
Packaged air handling/conditioning units:				
— external	15	Consider type of corrosion protection	5F; 5G	03-01
— internal	20		5F; 5G	03-01
Terminal units (air systems)	25			26-01
(*m*) Miscellaneous mechanical equipment and plant				
Air compressor	20		5M	40-08
Compressed air receiver	20		5M	40-09

Equipment item	Indicative life / years	Remarks	BCIS cost group	HVCA SFG/20 reference
(m) Miscellaneous mechanical equipment and plant (*continued*)				
Computer room air conditioning	15		5F	—
Domestic gas fired appliances:				
— warm air heaters	15		5E	—
— boilers	10		5E	—
— combination boilers	10		5E	—
— hot water (storage and continuous)	12		5E	—
— gas fires	8		5E	—
Drinking fountains	10		5D	—
Fire protection (pipes and ducts)	20	Damage to fire protection should be examined at frequent intervals	—	—
Food/container waste disposal	5		—	—
Furnaces (gas or oil fired)	15	Selection of heat exchanger material is important	5E	—
Hand dryers	5		—	—
Incinerators	15		—	—
Kitchen (cooking and support systems)	15		5B	—
Laundries (equipment and support systems)	20		5B	—
Sanitary towel disposal	10		—	—
Stair/lobby ventilation	20		5G	16-03
Tea rooms (equipment and support systems)	15		5D	—
Vending machines	8		—	—
Waste paper shredders/disposal	10		—	—
Water features	15	Water treatment is very important	5D	25-01
(n) Controls				
Building management systems (BMS):				
— head end (supervisor)	5		—	—
— outstations	10		5M	14-(01-16)
— plant controller	10		—	—
— operating system	5		5M	—
— remote display panels	10		5M	—
— communications network (hardwiring)	25	Should be 'future proofed' with additional cable wireways	5M	—
Electric/electronic controls:				
— electric controls	20		5M	14-(01-16)
— electronic controls	10		5M	14-(01-16)
— sensors	8	Periodic loop tuning and calibration should be considered	5M	50-(01-11)
— control valves	15		5M	62-(01-07)
— control dampers	15		5M	16-03
— hydraulic valve actuators	10		5M	01-05
— variable speed drives	15		—	—
Pneumatic controls:				
— air compressor	20		—	—
— pneumatic controls	20		5M	—
— pneumatic valve actuators	15		5M	01-04
— dryer (pneumatic controls)	20		—	—
— receiver	20		—	—
— valves, connections	20		—	—
— electronic/pneumatic interfaces	10		5M	—
— hydraulic valve actuators	10		5M	01-05
Leak detection:				
— gas	10		—	—
— refrigerant	10		—	—
— water	15		—	—
(o) Electrical installations				
Batteries and power storage:				
— battery chargers	20		5H	18-01
— lead–acid batteries (sealed)	5		5H	18-01
— nickel–alkaline batteries (vented)	20		5H	18-01

Equipment item	Indicative life / years	Remarks	BCIS cost group	HVCA SFG/20 reference
(o) Electrical installations (continued)				
Mains cable (permanent installations):				
— mineral insulated	35		5H	18-01
— paper insulated	35		5H	18-01
— thermoplastic	30		5H	18-01
— thermosetting (fire performance)	35		5H	18-01
Mains power supplies:				
— HV switchgear (external)	30		—	—
— HV switchgear (internal)	30		—	—
— LV switchgear (internal)	25		—	—
— main supply switchgear and distribution	30		5H	18-01
— transformers (dry type)	30		5H	18-01
— transformers (oil-filled type)	30		5H	18-01
Motors:				
— motor rating < 7.5 W	10		5H	18-01
— motor rating 7.5 W to 75 kW	15		5H	18-01
— motor rating > 75 kW	20		5H	18-01
Motor drives (variable speed)	15		5H	18-01
Power generation:				
— combined heat and power (CHP) (gas fired)	20		—	—
— combined heat and power (CHP) (diesel powered)	15		—	—
— continuously rated gas/oil engines (frequent use)	15		5H	18-01
— continuously rated gas/oil engines (standby)	25		5H	18-01
— continuously rated steam engines (frequent use)	25		5H	18-01
— continuously rated steam turbines (frequent use)	25		5H	18-01
— standby alternator plus prime mover	30		—	—
Protective installations:				
— earth bonding (major)	30		5H	18-01
— earth bonding (domestic)	25		5H	18-01
— lightning protection	25		5H	18-01
Sub-main distribution:				
— consumer units	20		5H	18-01
— distribution boards	20		5H	18-01
— feeder pillar	20		5H	18-01
— final circuits and outlets	20		5H	18-01
— inverter	20		5H	18-01
— lighting installations (luminaires) (external)	15		5H	18-01
— lighting installations (luminaires) (internal)	20		5H	18-01
— miniature circuit breaker (MCB)	20		—	—
— moulded case circuit breaker (MCCB)	25		—	—
— power distribution unit (PDU)	20		5H	18-01
— residual current breaker (RCB)	20		—	—
— switched socket outlet (SSO)	15		—	—
Uninterruptible power supplies (UPS)/back-up power:				
— battery chargers	20		5H	18-01
— lead–acid batteries (sealed)	5		5H	18-01
— nickel–alkaline batteries (vented)	20		5H	18-01
(p) Lighting				
Lamps:				
— compact fluorescent lamps	3	10 000 hours (based on 10 h/day, 6 days/week, 52 weeks/year	5H	36-(01-04)
— fluorescent tubes	2	7500 hours (based on 10 h/day, 6 days/week, 52 weeks/year	5H	36-(01-04)
— metal halide lamps	3	9000 hours (based on 10 h/day, 6 days/week, 52 weeks/year	5H	36-(01-04)
— SON lamps	4	12 000 hours (based on 10 h/day, 6 days/week, 52 weeks/year	5H	36-(01-04)
Lighting systems:				
— emergency lighting	25		5H	37-(01-02)
— lighting and luminaires (external)	15	Lamp life depends on usage	5H	36-(01-04)
— lighting and luminaires (internal)	20	Lamp life depends on usage	5H	36-(01-04)
— switches	10		—	—

Equipment item	Indicative life / years	Remarks	BCIS cost group	HVCA SFG/20 reference
(q) Drainage and sanitation				
Above ground rainwater drainage (plastic)	25	Includes guttering	5A	—
Below ground drainage:				
— salt glazed	40	Consider possibility of damage and structural movement	5A	—
— cast iron	45	Consider possibility of ground and structural movement	5A	—
— plastic	40	Consider mechanical damage	5A	—
Internal waste, foul and rainwater drainage:				
— cast iron	35		5C	—
— copper	40		5C	—
— plastic	20	Consider possibility of mechanical damage and requirements for expansion	5C	—
Sanitary ware	25		5A	—
(r) Metering and measurement				
Electricity	20		5M	14-03
Gas	20		5M	14-03
Water	20		5M	14-03
(s) Protection systems (fire and security)				
Access control	15		—	—
Call points (break glass)	15		5M	—
Closed circuit television (CCTV):				
— external	15		—	—
— internal	20		—	—
Computer room fire extinguishing system	15	Consider environmental impact and possible phasing out of fire extinguishing agent	—	23-05
Control panel	15		—	—
Dry risers	25		—	—
Fire alarms:				
— battery support	20		—	22-01
— electrical	20		—	22-01
Fire dampers (curtain type)	15		—	16-03
Fire protection (pipes and ducts)	20	Damage to fire protection should be examined at frequent intervals	—	—
Foam systems	15		—	23-07
Heat detectors	20		—	—
Hose reels (fire)	15		—	23-03
Hydrants (fire)	30		—	23-04
Infrared lighting	10		—	
Intruder detection	15		—	
Intruder system control panel	20		—	
Portable fire appliances	8		—	23-(08-13)
Risers:				
— dry	25		—	—
— wet	20		—	—
Smoke and heat detectors	10		—	—
Smoke curtain	20		—	—
Smoke ventilation systems	30		—	16-03
Wet risers	20		—	—
Sounder (bell)	15		—	—
Sprinklers:				
— alternate wet and dry	20	Consider corrosion	—	—
— wet	25	Consider corrosion	—	23-14

Equipment item	Indicative life / years	Remarks	BCIS cost group	HVCA SFG/20 reference
(s) Protection systems (fire and security) (continued)				
Sprinkler heads	30		—	—
(t) Miscellaneous electrical equipment and plant				
Air conditioner:				
— commercial ('through-the-wall' unit)	10		5H	—
— residential (single or split packaged unit)	10		5H	—
Batteries:				
— battery chargers	20		5H	—
— lead–acid batteries (sealed)	5		5H	—
— nickel–alkaline batteries (vented)	20		5H	—
Clock systems	15		5H	—
Closed circuit television (CCTV) and video	10		5H	—
Communication systems	20	Voice and data	5H	—
Continuous flow electrical heaters	12		5H	—
Electric floor heating	25		5H	—
Electrical heater (on peak)	8		5H	—
Electrical storage heaters with ventilation	20		5H	—
Electrical water heaters	12		5H	—
Heat pumps:				
— air-to-air (residential)	10		5H	—
— air-to-air (commercial)	15		5H	—
— water-to-air (commercial)	15		5H	—
Intruder alarms and intercommunications	10		5H	—
Lighting control and management systems	15		5H	—
Lightning protection	25		5H	—
Public address systems	20		5H	—
Television and satellite systems	15		5H	—
Uninterruptible power supply (UPS) systems	20		5H	—
Water cooled air conditioner	15		5H	—
Window unit air conditioner	8		5H	—
(u) Vertical and horizontal transportation				
Brake assembly	20		—	—
Car and landing cills	15		—	—
Car and landing door panels	10		—	—
Car door safety devices	15		—	—
Car frame	30		—	—
Controllers	15		—	—
Door operator	15		—	—
Electric traction lifts	20		—	—
Electric traction lifts (packaged)	15		—	—
Entrance doors:				
— two panel (with obstacle detector)	15		—	—
— single opening door (with obstacle detector)	20		—	—
Escalators (commercial, e.g. office, retail)	30		—	—
Floor selector	20		—	—
Governor rope	10		—	—
Guide rails	35		—	—
Hydraulic lifts:				
— lift installation	15		—	—
— hydraulic cylinder	15		—	—
— hydraulic oil	5	With filtration	—	—
— oil cooling system	10		—	—

Equipment item	Indicative life / years	Remarks	BCIS cost group	HVCA SFG/20 reference
(*u*) **Vertical and horizontal transportation** (*continued*)				
Machines:				
— geared	15		—	—
— gearless	20		—	—
Motor–generator	20		—	—
Motors (for drive units):				
— squirrel cage	10		—	—
— DC	25	Check for vibration	—	—
Suspension ropes	12		—	—
Traction sheave	15	Can be recut	—	—
Transportation systems:				
— airport terminal, bus or rail station	25		—	—
— high density mass transit	20		—	—
(*v*) **Lifting equipment**				
Atrium gantry	30		—	—
Eye bolt	30		—	—
Fork lift truck	10		—	—
Lifting beam	20		—	—
Pallet truck	15		—	—
Window cradle	25		—	—
(*w*) **Other**			—	—
Photovoltaic panels	25		—	53-01
Solar panels (water heating)	25		—	—
Swimming pool filtration system	20		—	—
Wind turbines	20		—	57-03

14 Maintenance audits

Summary

A technique for auditing maintenance contract performance is described in detail. It entails an assessment of performance under the headings of management, maintenance, communications, health and safety, technical proficiency and invoicing.

A qualitative scoring method is proposed and a procedure for conducting the audit is outlined.

An example maintenance audit check sheet is provided.

This section is intended to provide a formal framework to allow clients, maintenance contractors and professional advisers to work together to improve the quality of performance of engineering maintenance. It may also be used as a means of auditing a direct labour force.

A maintenance audit is always likely to be based on subjective assessments but the intention is that, by developing a standard format for the assessment document and describing the content of each item, the process can be made more objective. This should increase the benefit of the audit to all the parties concerned. If a client has any concerns about understanding or completing the maintenance audit document, it is strongly recommended that professional advice be obtained.

14.1 Audit document

A maintenance audit document is illustrated in Appendix 14.A1. More detailed information is provided in BSRIA AG13/2000: *Toolkit for building operation audits*[1]. The document should be completed by or in close cooperation with the client. The services of a professional adviser should be used where appropriate, for example where the client feels the need for an independent review or detailed technical support.

The initial information includes, for record purposes:

— details of the client

— type of maintenance contract

— contract start date

— building function, size, location and principle engineering services installed

— date of the assessment

— name of maintenance contractor

— name of assessor.

Types of maintenance contract are detailed in chapter 4. They can include, for example: labour only, planned maintenance, call-out only, service level agreement, performance based, fixed price, measured, semi-comprehensive, fully comprehensive and inspection-only contracts.

The audit document addresses the topics outlined below. These are not intended to be definitive, and the user may wish to modify the headings to suit a specific application.

14.2 Audit details

14.2.1 Management

This has two elements:

— relationship with client including contract conformity

— management of staff (either contractor or direct labour).

The first addresses how the contract is being complied with, whether reports are submitted as required, whether the building log book[2] is provided, on site and up-to-date, whether meetings are scheduled and kept to, and how productive and positive these are. Contractors should be aware of their role in ensuring that buildings remain functional.

The second element, addressing as appropriate contractor or direct labour staff, considers their competence, skills, quality, management and supervision, conduct and appearance, housekeeping, response to work requests, call-outs and emergencies, and standards of training. It is important for maintenance operatives to keep up-to-date with technical developments, safety awareness and practical training on the wide variety of plant likely to be encountered. A significant indicator of a competent contractor is the provision of adequate opportunities for, and the implementation of, recognised training together with records of training. Where service provision is through a maintenance contractor, membership of HVCA would be a good indicator of conforming with this criterion.

14.2.2   Maintenance service

This element assesses whether effective work planning is being applied, the maintenance is being carried out at the stated intervals and all the tasks are being achieved to an acceptable quality standard. An important aspect of the contractor's management is to ensure that the maintenance periodicity is under continuous review to minimise tendencies towards either under- or over-maintenance. Where planned preventive maintenance (PPM) is being applied, this will entail the systematic investigation at predetermined intervals of all the plant items listed on the asset register.

In practical terms, it is recommended that the client or his/her adviser makes periodic inspections of plant rooms, the major occupied areas and equipment of significant importance to the normal building operation to monitor that satisfactory maintenance standards are being achieved. The inspections should include regular checks that all control equipment is within calibration. Records of such inspections together with appropriate comments, could be made in the building log book.

The performance element also addresses whether the expected level of service is provided, the required plant availability is achieved, the level of complaints from the building occupants is acceptable, the response time to work requests and emergencies is satisfactory, and work is carried out in a positive manner. The latter includes showing an innovative, flexible approach, including initiative and perseverance.

Computer-based maintenance management systems (CMMS) can provide considerable information in summarised format to demonstrate both that maintenance has been carried out and, by using data analysis techniques, that it has been effective. The availability and routine analysis of such information should score highly on the audit.

14.2.3   Communication

Maintenance review meetings allow the client and contractor to develop a mutual understanding of their respective objectives and requirements. Minutes of each formal meeting should be produced for reference and to ensure that agreed actions are carried out. It may be appropriate for the contractor to prepare cost forecasts for some or all such meetings to demonstrate the anticipated progress of the contract.

Regular meetings should prevent situations getting out of hand by fostering improved working relationships. Typically, these meetings should take place at least quarterly (more frequently in the early stages of a contract). A typical agenda should include an indication of the current status of all maintenance work, a summary of all instructions for additional work received in the last period and a report on work completed.

Communications should cover both those between client and contractor and with the occupants of the building.

Ideally, occupant complaints should be recorded formally; this may be through a 'help desk', possibly manned by the maintenance service provider. All communications need to be clear and concise. Response time to instructions can also be addressed under this heading.

This element should reflect the ability of both parties to raise problems or concerns and discuss them in an open and positive manner, with the expectation of a high level of professional advice and guidance from the contractor.

14.2.4   Health and safety

Although the client must accept ultimate responsibility for health and safety, the implementation of specific procedures may be placed with the contractor. This may extend to ensuring compliance with statutory requirements. These aspects should be clearly identified at the start of the contract and monitored to ensure that the work is being carried out satisfactorily. Health and safety policy statements should be available from both the client and the contractor. These should be exchanged at the start of the contract and any anomalies resolved, particularly in respect to demarcation of responsibility.

The contractor should be able to demonstrate the competencies of the operatives being employed on the particular contract and that these competencies are relevant to the work being undertaken.

The contractor should have clear and defined health and safety procedures[3], be actively training its employees in health and safety matters including general awareness, have a rigid safety management system in place and be able to support this with comprehensive records. The contractor should demonstrate a competent and pro-active approach to health and safety. Correct labelling and storage of chemicals and compliance with the Control of Substances Hazardous to Health Regulations[4] can provide some indication of the contractor's approach to safety. All operatives using access equipment such as mobile elevated working platforms (MEWPs) must have current certificates of training.

One particular aspect of safe operating procedures is the use of permits-to-work. These provide a controlled system of work in hazardous or sensitive areas. They are issued to suitably trained personnel by an authorised person. Where they are in use, the client should be aware of and understand their purpose and function.

The audit score may be influenced by whether appropriate risk assessments are in place and the demonstrable competencies of the operatives working on the particular contract.

See also CIBSE TM40: *Health issues in building services*[5].

14.2.5   Technical proficiency

All plant on the asset register should be maintained in accordance with agreed schedules which identify the extent of the work and the frequency. The HVCA's *Standard maintenance specification for building services*[6] provides a good starting point. The results of maintenance inspections and follow-up work need to be supported by detailed records compiled by the contractor together with other relevant documentation.

In many instances, the contractor will be operating an approved quality assurance system which, in turn, will require documentation to demonstrate that work has been completed as stated.

Spares, replacement parts and materials will be required during maintenance activities. There will be cost, reliability and quality implications for these, possibly also related to standards of performance or manufacture.

It may be deemed necessary for the contractor to draw up a list of essential spares which are to be retained on site to ensure ready availability. The list will need to be agreed by the client. There will be a cost associated with this provision of spares (initial purchase and ongoing storage). The client may consider that the availability and regular review of an essential spares list is an important element in the audit score.

The need for access to the building and its engineering services may require admittance of the contractor's personnel to controlled or secure areas. Adequate arrangements need to be in place and monitored. It may also be useful periodically to review who has access to plant areas and to ensure that, where necessary, arrangements exist for access out of normal hours.

Environmental aspects of maintenance and operation should also be addressed. All legislation should be complied with, good practice codes adopted where appropriate and all matters needing attention reported formally to the client.

14.2.6 Energy use and management

Normal plant operation should include monitoring to ensure that systems are performing efficiently, particularly in terms of energy use. It may be a client requirement to include, as part of maintenance review meetings, a routine report on energy use and opportunities to improve efficiency, possibly including details of energy consumption and costs. Further detailed information relating to energy efficiency is provided in CIBSE Guide F: *Energy efficiency in buildings*[7].

The maintenance service provider should be expected to be aware of the need to conserve energy, use it efficiently and identify opportunities for energy savings. This should also apply when the service provider is not tasked with managing the energy payment process.

14.2.7 Invoicing

Invoicing and payment procedures should be agreed between all parties at the start of the contract. They may include such matters as frequency of submission, payment terms, need for authorisation (e.g. for additional work) and expenditure limits (e.g. up to £200 value of essential work can be carried out without prior authorisation). An agreed format in which invoices are to be submitted should be established at the start of the agreement, although this may need to be reviewed as the contract progresses. The submitted invoices should be checked for accuracy and may be subject to a review procedure by the client's professional adviser, where appointed.

14.3 Scoring system

A simple, easily understood scoring system should be adopted at the start of the maintenance performance assessment process. A three-tier scoring system for the audit document, as shown in Appendix 14.A1, is proposed to provide an initial guide, see Table 14.1.

Table 14.1 Three-tier scoring system for maintenance performance

Assessed achievement	Score
Poor	1–3
Average	4–6
High	7–9

A five-tier scoring system would give greater scope for discrimination, provided that each performance category is adequately defined and understood fully.

It may be appropriate to apply different multipliers to each of the assessment headings to indicate their relative importance. For example, taking the norm multiplier as one, management might have a multiplier of 1.5, while invoicing could have a multiplier of 0.6. The multiplier is shown as the 'weighting factor' in the 'adjusted score' section in Appendix 14.A1. An example and sample method of presenting the information is also shown in the appendix.

The aggregate score can then be obtained by adding all the individual scores. While each individual audit may be difficult to analyse, noting trends in how the scoring changes over time will provide a useful indication of how standards are being maintained. Any deterioration in standards should be discussed fully at the following maintenance review meeting.

14.4 Recording comments

It is expected that comments will be produced during the audit, many of which may not need to be recorded. However, it will be useful for future reference to record anecdotal notes, special achievements or significant failings. Where scores of less than 3 or more than 7 are entered, they should be supported by explanatory comments.

14.5 Audit procedure

The audit procedure should consist of the following steps:

(*a*)   determine the audit date and instruct contractor to attend

(*b*)   arrange professional support if required

(*c*)   complete audit form

(*d*)   carry out inspections as required of plant rooms etc.

(e)   carry out inspections of the building log book, log sheets, reports, and supporting building documentation (see Table 14.2 for an indicative list)

(f)   attend audit meeting or maintenance review meeting and discuss situation with contractor (see Figure 14.1 for an outline agenda)

(g)   agree future action, including period until next audit

(h)   prepare formal record of meeting

(i)   monitor agreed action is being achieved.

Table 14.2 Checklist for building documentation

Type of document
Building log book (see CIBSE TM31: *Building log book toolkit*[2])
Records of fire detection and alarm tests
Sprinkler system test records
Smoke extract system test records
Escape route pressurisation system test records
Electrical system safety inspection records
Electrical earthing and insulation test records
Portable appliance test records
Emergency lighting system test records
Fire extinguisher and fire hose reel test records (see BS 5306-3[8])
Legionella risk assessment and routine inspection records (see CIBSE TM13: *Minimising the risk of Legionnaires' disease*[9])
Notification of cooling towers and evaporative condensers
COSHH[4] records
Lift insurance inspection reports
Lifting equipment insurance test reports and certificates
Pressure vessel and system test reports and certificates
Fume cupboard test reports and certificates
Operating and maintenance manuals
Waste disposal and handling procedures
Noise assessments
Asbestos awareness reports
General risk assessment
Gas safety inspection record

1.0	Introduction and overview of previous audit
2.0	Agreed objectives and extent achieved
3.0	Current audit assessments, trends and comments
3.1	Management
3.2	Maintenance service
3.3	Communication
3.4	Health and safety
3.5	Technical proficiency
3.6	Invoicing
4.0	Overall review
5.0	Concerns, future objectives and actions required
6.0	Other related matters
7.0	Date and time of next audit

Figure 14.1 Sample outline agenda for maintenance audit meeting

References

1   *Toolkit for building operation audits* BSRIA AG13/2000 (Bracknell: Building Services Research and Information Association) (2000)

2   *Building log book toolkit* CIBSE TM31 (London: Chartered Institution of Building Services Engineers) (2006)

3   Management of Health and Safety at Work Regulations 1999 Statutory Instruments 1999 Number 3242 (London: The Stationery Office) (1999)

4   Control of Substances Hazardous to Health Regulations 1999 Statutory Instruments 1999 No. 437 (London: The Stationery Office) (1999)

5   *Health issues in building services* CIBSE TM40 (London: Chartered Institution of Building Services Engineers) (2006)

6   *Standard maintenance specification for building services* HVCA SFG20 (electronic database) (London: Heating and Ventilating Contractors Association)

7   *Energy efficiency in buildings* CIBSE Guide F (London: Chartered Institution of Building Services Engineers) (2004)

8   BS 5306-3: 2003: *Fire extinguishing installations and equipment on premises. Code of practice for the inspection and maintenance of portable fire extinguishers* (London: British Standards Institution) (2003)

9   *Minimising the risk of Legionnaires' disease* CIBSE TM13 (London: Chartered Institution of Building Services Engineers) (2002)

Appendix 14.A1: Maintenance audit checklist for building services

14.A1.2   Blank checklist

Client:

Building:	Location (address):
Contract type:	Contract start date:
Contractor:	
Assessor:	Assessment date:

Part 1 Management

1A Contractor's relationship with client (e.g. contract compliance, reports, meetings, contractor role, client support)

Score:	1	2	3	4	5	6	7	8	9
Weighting factor (see paragraph 14.3):	0.7	0.8	0.9	1.0	1.1	1.2	1.3

Adjusted score (score × weighting factor): _____

Comments:

1B Contractor's staff (e.g. quality of resource, resource management/supervision, conduct, housekeeping, work requests, emergencies, training)

Score:	1	2	3	4	5	6	7	8	9
Weighting factor (see paragraph 14.3):	0.7	0.8	0.9	1.0	1.1	1.2	1.3

Adjusted score (score × weighting factor): _____

Comments:

Part 2 Maintenance service (e.g. planned preventative maintenance (PPM), service provided, response time, positive approach, dealing with complaints, flexibility and innovation, effectiveness of planning, service level)

Score:	1	2	3	4	5	6	7	8	9
Weighting factor (see paragraph 14.3):	0.7	0.8	0.9	1.0	1.1	1.2	1.3

Adjusted score (score × weighting factor): _____

Comments:

Part 3 Communication (e.g. clarity, concerns with client, with occupants [where appropriate], quality of advice, responding to queries/complaints)

Score:	1	2	3	4	5	6	7	8	9
Weighting factor (see paragraph 14.3):	0.7	0.8	0.9	1.0	1.1	1.2	1.3

Adjusted score (score × weighting factor): _____

Comments:

Part 4 Health and safety (e.g. general awareness, knowledge of regulations, management, procedures, training, permits-to-work, records)

Score:	1	2	3	4	5	6	7	8	9
Weighting factor (see paragraph 14.3):	0.7	0.8	0.9	1.0	1.1	1.2	1.3

Adjusted score (score × weighting factor):   8.4

Comments:

Notes:

Part 5 Technical proficiency (e.g. PPM performance, records and reports, quality assurance, materials and spares, security, energy efficiency, environmental matters)

Score:	1	2	3	4	5	6	7	8	9
Weighting factor (see paragraph 14.3):	0.7	0.8		0.9	1.0	1.1	1.2	1.3	

Adjusted score (score × weighting factor): _____

Comments:

Part 6 Energy use and management

Score:	1	2	3	4	5	6	7	8	9
Weighting factor (see paragraph 14.3):	0.7	0.8		0.9	1.0	1.1	1.2	1.3	

Adjusted score (score × weighting factor): _____

Comments:

Part 7 Invoicing (e.g. procedure, format, accuracy, timescale)

Score:	1	2	3	4	5	6	7	8	9
Weighting factor (see paragraph 14.3):	0.7	0.8		0.9	1.0	1.1	1.2	1.3	

Adjusted score (score × weighting factor): _____

Comments:

Summary

Audit criterion		Basic score	Factor	Score
1A	Contractor's relationship with client			
1B	Contractor's staff			
2	Maintenance service			
3	Communication			
4	Health and safety			
5	Technical proficiency			
6	Energy use and management			
7	Invoicing			

14.A1.2   Example of completed checklist

Client:	Loxley Financial Services		
Building:	Armville House	Location (address):	Armville House, Cubworth
Contract type:	Planned maintenance*	Contract start date:	9 November 2006
Contractor:	Weston Maintenance Ltd.		
Assessor:	J Armstrong	Assessment date:	10 March 2008

Part 1 Management

1A Contractor's relationship with client (e.g. contract compliance, reports, meetings, contractor role, client support)

Score:	1	2	3	4	5	⑥	7	8	9
Weighting factor (see paragraph 14.3):	0.7		0.8		0.9	⑴.⓪	1.1		1.2	1.3

Adjusted score (score × weighting factor):   6.0

Comments:

1B Contractor's staff (e.g. quality of resource, resource management/supervision, conduct, housekeeping, work requests, emergencies, training)

Score:	1	2	3	4	5	6	7	8	⑨
Weighting factor (see paragraph 14.3):	0.7		0.8		0.9		1.0		1.1		1.2	⑴.③

Adjusted score (score × weighting factor):   11.7

Comments:

Part 2 Maintenance service (e.g. planned preventative maintenance (PPM), service provided, response time, positive approach, dealing with complaints, flexibility and innovation, effectiveness of planning, service level)

Score:	1	2	3	4	5	6	7	8	⑨
Weighting factor (see paragraph 14.3):	0.7		0.8		0.9		1.0		1.1		1.2	⑴.③

Adjusted score (score × weighting factor):   11.7

Comments:

Part 3 Communication (e.g. clarity, concerns with client, with occupants [where appropriate], quality of advice, responding to queries/complaints)

Score:	1	2	3	④	5	6	7	8	9
Weighting factor (see paragraph 14.3):	⓪.⑦		0.8		0.9		1.0		1.1		1.2	1.3

Adjusted score (score × weighting factor):   2.8

Comments:

Part 4 Health and safety (e.g. general awareness, knowledge of regulations, management, procedures, training, permits-to-work, records)

Score:	1	2	3	4	5	6	⑦	8	9
Weighting factor (see paragraph 14.3):	0.7		0.8		0.9		1.0		1.1	⑴.②	1.3

Adjusted score (score × weighting factor):   8.4

Comments:

Notes:

Maintenance contract includes for all repairs costing less than £200 excluding VAT.

Weighting factors agreed with client prior to audit.

Part 5 Technical proficiency (e.g. PPM performance, records and reports, quality assurance, materials and spares, security, energy efficiency, environmental matters)

Score:	1	2	3	4	5	6	7	(8)	9
Weighting factor (see paragraph 14.3):	0.7	0.8	0.9	1.0	1.1	1.2	(1.3)		

Adjusted score (score × weighting factor):   10.4

Comments:

Part 6 Energy use and management

Score:	1	2	3	4	5	(6)	7	8	9
Weighting factor (see paragraph 14.3):	0.7	0.8	(0.9)	1.0	1.1	1.2	1.3		

Adjusted score (score × weighting factor):   5.4

Comments:

Part 7 Invoicing (e.g. procedure, format, accuracy, timescale)

Score:	1	2	3	4	5	(6)	7	8	9
Weighting factor (see paragraph 14.3):	0.7	0.8	(0.9)	1.0	1.1	1.2	1.3		

Adjusted score (score × weighting factor):   5.4

Comments:

Summary

Audit criterion		Basic score	Factor	Score
1A	Contractor's relationship with client	6	1.0	6.0
1B	Contractor's staff	9	1.3	11.7
2	Maintenance service	9	1.3	11.7
3	Communication	4	0.7	2.8
4	Health and safety	7	1.2	8.4
5	Technical proficiency	8	1.3	10.4
6	Energy use and management	6	0.9	5.4
7	Invoicing	6	0.9	5.4

15 Condition surveys

15.1	Types and frequency	
15.2	Thermal imaging	
15.3	Consistency of information	
15.4	Classifying priorities	
15.5	Data collection	
15.6	Updating information	
15.7	Future developments	
References		
Bibliography		

Summary

The application of condition surveys to various types of building services installations is described and the characteristics of different types of survey, ranging from a general overview to a thorough survey, are detailed.

The part that can be played by thermal imaging techniques is explained and the need for consistent presentation of information noted.

To improve the usefulness of the results of a survey to a client, the need for some form of prioritisation of actions is stressed and three categories are proposed.

Methods of data collection are described, ranging from simple, handwritten recording to sophisticated electronic methods. The need for updating of information is highlighted.

Condition appraisals, or condition surveys as they are more commonly called, can be defined as: 'the subjective assessment of the present condition of an individual component or complete system' or 'the compilation of data referring to the state of repair of a building and its engineering services'.

A condition survey may be called for by a building owner or occupier to provide comprehensive information on the current state of a building and its services or by someone considering the purchase or leasing of a premise and wishing to know the extent of the maintenance liability.

A client will undoubtedly expect his or her professional advisor on building services matters to provide clear and concise information on short and long term maintenance needs. When correctly undertaken, a condition survey will not only produce this information but will provide a profile of a building's maintenance requirement. Such a survey will allow a building owner, or whoever is responsible for the repair and maintenance of the building, to decide on what work should be done, when it should be carried out and the likely cost of the work to be undertaken.

If such exist, the building's health and safety file[1], operation and maintenance manual[2] and building log book[3] must be made available to the person carrying out the survey. Additional and valuable information is often obtained by monitoring plant and equipment in operation and by reading log books, invoices and servicing manuals or reports. Every effort should be made to seek out these documents because the information can be invaluable when making recommendations in the final survey report. Interviewing the servicing or maintenance contractor can also provide information not readily obtained from a purely subjective assessment.

In many instances, maintenance requirements are estimated from a visual inspection of the site. Even though the inspections may be undertaken annually they can overlook long term problems and fail to identify when items require replacement prior to failure. Encased or hidden services cannot be confidently assessed unless physically inspected. If a survey is to be non-invasive, all parties (client, contractor, surveyor etc.) need to be aware that plant and services will not be dismantled or opened-up for internal inspection.

It is usual for a survey to be restricted, and for inaccessible areas of structures and finishes not to be opened-up for inspection. Where removable covers are accessible, however, these should be removed to inspect the services they encase. Invasive surveys, because of the disruption they can cause, are difficult to undertake in an occupied building and should not be contemplated without the client's full agreement Even though condition surveys are normally non-invasive they should nevertheless be sufficiently thorough to ensure that the need for further inspections or tests is highlighted

Maintenance budgets often fall seriously short of what is required. In such cases it is important that accurate and meaningful information is available upon which decisions can be made. This information allows a maintenance manager or building owner to spread the budget wisely over a wide range of activities. When financial constraints are imposed, which is invariably the case, this method of working is often economically and professionally sound. However, because of the lack of adequate investment it may well be that this approach never totally resolves a particular maintenance problem, since year after year finance is allocated simply to keep pace with a problem rather than to resolve or eliminate it. In this situation a condition survey is a useful management tool assisting the maintenance manager to:

— set priority objectives

— plan short term expenditure

— justify long term investment.

15.1   Types and frequency

BS 8210[4] suggests that an in-depth survey is undertaken on a five-yearly cycle (quinquennial inspection) supplemented by a more superficial two-yearly inspection. This frequency can, of course, vary depending on the purpose of the survey and the condition of the services to be inspected.

Where an effective regime of maintenance meetings is operating (see section 14.2.3) it may be reasonable to relax the frequency of in-depth surveys. It would be necessary, however, to ensure that the routine reviews are predictive and do not simply respond to events as they occur.

Most professional services allow for choice and diversity. Engineering surveys are no exception, and there are several types of survey available to suit the short and long term property objectives of most clients. Costs can vary significantly depending upon the type of survey undertaken and the extent of detail of the report. It is widely recognised, however, that an inspection, in whatever form it takes, provides an ideal starting point in the assessment of maintenance priorities. It is extremely important, at the onset, to establish the precise limits of the client's brief, or the limitations of the survey to be undertaken. This will ensure there is no misunderstanding as to the information to be contained in the final survey report. The brief must identify for what purpose the report is required, what information is expected from the survey and how the information is to be presented and subsequently used. Photographs are a great help in highlighting specific issues of concern and can if necessary be used as an aide-memoir at some later date.

Further information on condition surveys is available from BSRIA AG4/2000: *Condition survey of building services*[5].

Typical types of surveys are indicated in the following sections.

15.1.1   Overview assessment

An overview assessment of the building services identifies immediate maintenance needs from observed data previously obtained from *ad hoc* visits and capitalises on the knowledge a surveyor may have of the site.

This type of survey will give clients a relatively accurate assessment of the financial commitment required in the forthcoming year, but will be of limited accuracy for subsequent years. A physical inspection of the site would not normally be undertaken unless of course the individual surveyor wished to inspect a known problem area in more detail to be certain that the nature of the defect was fully understood. An overview assessment can only be undertaken by someone who knows the site. If the surveyor is not familiar with the site a physical inspection will need to be carried out.

A schedule of repairs will be produced indicating the nature of the remedial works and their cost. If areas are identified as requiring attention beyond year one, the year in which the repair should be undertaken will be indicated wherever possible. If a surveyor has been making *ad hoc* visits throughout the year, he or she should have knowledge of any seasonal problems.

An energy report is not usually part of this type of survey.

15.1.2   Two year maintenance plan

A physical overview assessment identifying the immediate maintenance need and those required over the next two and possibly three years.

This level of survey, whilst being a distinct service, is somewhat of a 'halfway house' but will nevertheless provide a client with reliable information and a clear indication of the state of repair the building services are in. A physical inspection of the site would be made, noting expected repairs and the likely expenditure required during the next three years. An energy report is excluded, although obvious cases of excess energy consumption would need to be reported.

In addition to the schedule of repairs, a brief overview report would be prepared to give a medium term strategy for maintenance.

15.1.3   Full condition survey

There is always the risk that overview inspections will miss the more serious, less obvious, maintenance issues. Whilst the cost may prohibit a full, in-depth survey on a frequent basis, an annual overview inspection supplemented by a more thorough survey once every five years provides an ideal compromise. This approach will provide a client with a comprehensive assessment of maintenance needs for the short and medium terms, that is, 1–5 years. It should be noted that for many businesses, or for long term development reasons, clients will require a ten-year maintenance profile.

A full in-depth survey would generally contain the following information:

(*a*)   an executive summary of the site covering the salient points emerging from the survey

(*b*)   sub-reports relating to:

—   external services

—   incoming services

—   mechanical services

—   electrical services

—   control systems

—   achievement of performance parameters

—   energy management and environmental assessment.

Each sub-report would include an investment summary for that particular element, identifying the maintenance and remedial requirements, their cost and the year in which the work should be undertaken. Graphical investment profiles can also be presented in an appendix to illustrate a total and five year investment sum (see section 12.9). This provides accurate and useful information enabling a client to set, with confidence, priority objectives and plan both short- and long-term maintenance needs.

It is important to say that, from the client's point of view, the information will be incomplete if an engineering assessment is carried out in isolation. Without information on the building fabric, including the grounds and external works, the client will not be able to assess the total repair and maintenance requirement. It is also advisable that an energy and environmental assessment overview report be included. Only then will the complete maintenance picture unfold. This approach enables a comprehensive investment profile to be prepared and ensures that the works are complementary to each other and compatible in terms of timing when they are carried out.

It should be noted that risk assessment is a separate issue and falls outside the scope of a conventional condition survey. This must be pointed out to the client at an early stage because, if it is included, other professional experts may need to be engaged (see section 11). A condition survey, or a maintenance plan, will, however, if undertaken correctly, identify general health and safety issues together with all items of a repair and maintenance nature. The information collected will be of considerable help to a client in setting priority objectives and planning short-, medium- and long-term expenditure on maintenance works.

The surveyor should not only have the relevant experience but must also be capable of:

— surveying the site(s) within a reasonable time scale

— rapidly collecting and processing the maintenance data

— establishing or reviewing and revising the maintenance plan

— estimating the cost of the maintenance work required

— categorising data in a priority order

— creating a data base for maintenance backlog.

15.1.4   Dilapidation reports

Most engineering surveyors will be familiar with dilapidation reports. Such reports are usually attached to a conventional condition survey. Whilst the condition survey outlines the present condition of a building and its services, the dilapidation report takes into account the terms of a lease defining the responsibilities of the tenant and landlord for repair and maintenance and any building covenants. Schedules of dilapidations should be treated as a separate entity. If a schedule of dilapidations is prepared for a client at the end of a lease, it should identify any significant variations in the condition of the fabric and engineering services compared with their condition at the start of the lease. There would, therefore, be no need for a condition survey to be undertaken.

At the commencement of a lease, a dilapidations report should be prepared which identifies the condition of the fabric and its services at that time. This can be used as a benchmark in the future (for example when the building is vacated) to identify what, if any, deterioration or dilapidation has taken place. Photographs incorporated in the report, taken prior to the commencement of the lease, serve as a very useful *aide-mémoire* in the event of a dispute.

15.2   Thermal imaging

There are certain highly sensitive and critical installations that may require more than a subjective visual assessment of their present condition. In such a cases the cost of thermal imaging may well be justified compared with the consequential problems that could ultimately arise as a result of plant failure.

Thermal imaging is a technique for presenting a coloured representation of an elevation where different colours indicate the temperatures of the exposed surfaces. There is a distinct correlation between temperature and electrical resistance generated from faulty equipment, so any problems occurring due to faulty components, loose connections or corroded terminals will show up on the thermal image as 'hot spots'. Care must be taken, however, in interpreting the data. Conclusions formed should be based on trends rather than definitive temperatures because hot spots can result from inherent design irregularities and have nothing to do with loose terminals or corrosion.

Clearly, if the component under test involves live wires, it is essential that safe working practices are adhered to. Providing that adequate care is taken, thermal imaging, being non-conductive, is relatively safe to carry out, because it relies upon the amount of radiation emitted from the equipment being checked.

In recent years thermal imaging has become more widely used to assess the condition of electrical equipment in panels and similar items of plant[6]. In addition it can be used to highlight hot spots in mechanical services (due to poor bearings, deteriorated or poor insulation etc.) and to give a rapid assessment of shortcomings in the integrity of building fabric (inadequate or collapsed thermal insulation)[7,8]. The degree to which this is successful is primarily determined by the emissivity of the fabric surface and the ability of the camera to translate the information it receives into a pictorial image. Nevertheless this technique is a powerful way of identifying heat loss, or excessive loss due to badly installed or collapsed insulation without spending considerable time taking temperature readings.

As an alternative, single point measurement devices are available but whilst much cheaper to buy or hire, are unlikely to give the same level of results. It is also difficult to obtain consistent temperature readings from some surfaces.

15.3   Consistency of information

There is little doubt that individual buildings have their own particular maintenance requirements. These requirements will depend upon:

— the performance criteria for the building

— the age and type of the building engineering services

— the design and specification of building engineering services

— the maintenance history of the building services.

Where buildings on an estate are being considered by different surveyors (some major clients have hundreds of buildings), it is important to have a common and consistent recording and assessment system. It will be of enormous benefit if the surveyor has prior knowledge of the site and is therefore aware of the maintenance problems encountered over the previous years. Even with such knowledge, however, the judgement of priorities may be out of step with that of other colleagues undertaking similar surveys on other buildings of the estate unless there is a standard classification system.

When the engineering survey is undertaken in conjunction with a building fabric survey, care must be taken to ensure there is consistency in the management of the data collected. Location, block and room references have to be the same for each discipline if the data is to be meaningful. This will help to ensure all elements of the survey are ultimately carried out in a complimentary way by simply focusing on an exact location within the management data file. When duplicate plant or standby equipment is installed, it is clearly important to establish not only its exact location but also the specific item to which the surveyor is referring in the report.

A classification system for the major elements of the engineering services will need to be agreed with the client at the onset of the survey. The extent that the major elements are broken down into their constituent sub-elements will depend upon the client's requirements but must be defined. Table 15.1 indicates a classification system that could be adopted for major elements and their constituent sub-elements. These elements can be extended or reduced to suit the type of survey to be undertaken.

15.4   Classifying priorities

An organisation's building stock represents one of its most important assets and, generally, reflects many years of investment. This type of asset requires, and deserves, continuous care and protection yet, in spite of this requirement, it is astonishing to find that the level of financial investment in the care and protection of buildings and their services often falls seriously short of what is required.

There is often a danger that, when resources are scarce, long term investments are passed over for simpler and less expensive short term measures.

It is clearly wise to look at maintenance in relation to other property running costs since maintenance has to compete with other high priority demands such as heating, lighting and cleaning. However it can be argued

Table 15.1 Classification of engineering services elements

Major element	Sub-element	Plant items
Mechanical services	Heating services	Boilers, flues, pumps Pipework, valves and fittings Controls Radiators/heat emitters Lagging Others
	Hot/cold water services	Cylinders/heat exchangers Pipework, valves and fittings Storage tanks and equipment Mixers/blenders Others
	Gas distribution	
	Ventilation	
	Air conditioning	
	Others	
Electrical services	Incoming supply	
	Control gear	
	Power	Distribution boards Wiring Fittings
	Lighting	Wiring Fittings
	Fire alarms	
	Intruder alarms	
	Lightning protection	
	Communications systems	
	Lifts and hoists	

that a cut back in maintenance expenditure causes difficulty in other areas; for example, increased expenditure on energy, increased vandalism, reduced morale amongst the building occupants and the failure of equipment which, in turn, could undermine the economic life of the plant.

It is important, therefore, to spend a limited maintenance budget wisely. To help in this the following categories can be applied to help set priorities:

— *Priority A (urgent)*: work required to prevent immediate closure of premises, address serious health and safety issues and/or correct any serious breach of legislation.

— *Priority B (necessary/essential)*: work required to prevent the deterioration of other services or the building fabric and/or correct less serious health and safety issues or breach of legislation.

— *Priority C (desirable/recommended)*: environmental and sustainability considerations and low risk health and safety issues or minor breach of legislation.

— *Priority D (long term issues)*: that will need to be addressed beyond five years.

The effect of the current Building Regulations on priority must be carefully assessed. Many of the maintenance items may require a higher specification to meet current standards and achieve compliance. Many other regulations could have similar effect in terms of cost and priority.

Alternatively, a simple numerical coding can be used to classify the data obtained from a survey of the services as outlined in Table 15.2. This table can be used in conjunction with the priority ratings given above. In addition it would be of advantage to a client if the particular legislation which the maintenance defect contravened was indicated within the survey report (for example, 'Electricity at Work Regulations 1989'). Failure to meet statutory requirements will feature highly in any survey carried out and it is extremely important that the surveyor is up-to-date with current legislative requirements and codes of practice.

It is also important to note that the terms 'condition' and 'priority' do not have the same meaning: 'condition' relates to the present state of the individual component or

Table 15.2 Classification of data from services condition survey

Condition	Designation	Explanation
1	Hazardous	Requires urgent attention. Closure of building imminent. Presents a danger if left unattended.
2	Bad	Whilst not dangerous must receive a high priority because of its bad state.
3	Partly bad	Affected parts should receive a high priority.
4	Poor	Whilst unsatisfactory, presents no immediate risk of failure. Replacement or repair should be considered in the near future.
5	Reasonable	Satisfactory, operating as intended. Routine maintenance only required. Review at next opportunity.
6	Good	As new and requires no attention.

complete system whilst 'priority' determines when the identified work requires to be undertaken.

15.4.1 Asset management plans (AMPs)

Guidance on asset management plans for educational buildings is available from the Department for Children, Schools and Families (DCSF) as a series of five documents under the general title *Asset management plans for educational buildings*[9]. Section 3 deals with condition assessment and offers non-statutory guidance on a framework for assessing the condition of school premises. Section 3a, *Getting into condition*, has also been produced to complement section 3, *Condition assessment* (revised February 2003). These booklets are available through the DCSF's 'Teachernet' website (http://www.teachernet.gov.uk).

Other sections within the series are:

— Section 1: *Framework*

— Section 2: *Property Information Systems and School Premises Data*

— Section 4: *Suitability Assessment*

— Section 5: *Sufficiency Assessment*

It is interesting to note that the DCSF categorises priority numerically and condition alphabetically, the reverse of what is suggested in 15.4 above. Both categorisations are acceptable but, as always, the data collected must be comprehensive, accurate and consistent.

15.5 Data collection

The availability of accurate and meaningful information is a fundamental requirement of any data collection system. Basically, there are three distinct ways of collecting site data:

— manual (paper) systems

— optical markers or readers

— computers systems.

15.5.1 Manual (paper) systems

This method of collection still appears to be the one most commonly used by surveyors. This is possibly attributable to the fact that while information technology (IT) systems are numerous and readily available, they are somewhat misunderstood. With time, however, (IT) systems will undoubtedly take over.

Low-technology manual systems are very suitable for many small to medium installations, and walking around a site with a proforma data collection sheet is still popular with surveyors. In many instances the information collected is subsequently transferred to some form of computerised system for ease of amendment or updating. Proforma data sheets help to minimise the possibility of inconsistent information when more than one surveyor is involved. However, the proforma must be adequate for the purpose of the inspections to be carried out and the surveying team must receive adequate training on how to complete the form in a consistent way. When the survey is completed, large volumes of paper will probably need to be archived. As more surveys are undertaken this volume can become unmanageable.

When these facts are considered, together with the problems of typing, checking and subsequent updating of manually collected data, the use of IT systems would appear to be a sensible solution. Whilst initial set-up costs may be relatively higher, the long-term benefits are significant.

15.5.2   Electronic data collection

The development in computers has been significant in recent years and today many simple and relatively straightforward electronic data capture systems are available. Current IT applications, which are readily available from various sources, bring about a system of standardisation in terms of approach and format. They generally concentrate on a reduced narrative with an emphasis on alphanumeric references to define elemental condition and priority status. Information gathered on site, obtained by answering pre-set questions, can easily be directly downloaded into a computer back in the office. Many of the computer systems incorporate bar code readers which are ideal for creating an asset register and for tracking assets. This is not only suitable for plant and equipment but can be applied to portable appliance testing.

The systems available include the following:

—   *Optical mark readers*: these have been available for many years. Using one of these, a surveyor can quickly carry out a survey using an optical mark reader to answer pre-set questions on a proforma specially designed for the particular application. The answers are scanned directly into the reader. One of the main drawbacks of this system is that care must be taken to complete all the questions on the reporting form. Failure to answer one question may cause the system to fail.

—   *Hand-held computers*: these are robust, easy to carry around and relatively cheap to purchase. Their compact size generally means that they operate by a keypad using menu driven software. The lack of a full 'QWERTY' keyboard can, however, restrict their operation in terms of flexibility. Conversely, palm-top machines, whilst using a QWERTY keypad, are not as robust as hand-held machines.

—   *Tablet pen-based computers*: these are now available from several manufacturers. Being light in weight they are easy to carry around a site, and integrate easily with printers, bar code readers and scanners. The software is client-driven with the surveyor working from a list of user defined standard specifications, descriptions, areas etc. Many of these systems can be used as a desktop computer and are compatible with standard offices software packages. The pen facility allows text to be hand written. Computer-aided design (CAD) modules can also be used as a peripheral tool allowing record drawings to be updated on site.

The main benefits of such systems are:

—   low capital cost

—   flexible and ease of operation

—   little or no computer knowledge is required to operate the base systems

—   saving in administrative time

—   information is accurate and consistent

—   corrections can easily be made to the recorded data.

No one will doubt that IT applications are here to stay and have a considerable role to play in the future of property management. Such applications, when used for carrying out a condition survey, can easily dovetail into a client's property information system. With the right software a simple personal data assistant (PDA) can be used for collecting the raw data. The data can then be manipulated using Microsoft® Access or similar software.

There is much debate on the best and most cost effective way to collect data. Voice messaging straight into data population is currently being explored. This is more sophisticated than audio recording, which is then inputted by typing, but when readily available will avoid the relatively slow process of collecting, typing and converting survey information into a usable format.

15.6   Updating information

This is an important task and must be done on an annual basis. If neglected the impetus of the initiative will be lost and the information previously collected will quickly become out of date.

15.7   Future developments

Due to the lack of care and attention over a period of many years, numerous buildings throughout the country have fallen into a deplorable condition. With land and building values escalating, along with a strong desire by the nation to save old and dilapidated buildings, regeneration and restoration appear to be in vogue. Had those same buildings been given the care and attention they deserved during the period of decay, the high costs of restoration would have been avoided.

In addition, and until the mid-1970s, many buildings were constructed with little attention to future maintenance and running costs. Now, many years later, a large percentage of these buildings (and their engineering services) require major investment to restore their condition to a reasonable state. Where maintenance budgets fall substantially short of what is required, the gap between the financial provision and assessed need will undoubtedly widen.

The latest amendments to the Building Regulations are already having a financial impact on maintenance works and their cost. Adequate financial provision will need to be made available in order to comply with current legislation and keep pace with the maintenance need. Often maintenance budgets fall short of what is required, creating a bigger gap between provision and need. Provided adequate finance is made available to undertake this maintenance work, this gap can be minimised.

References

1 The Construction (Design and Management) Regulations 1994 Statutory Instrument 1994 No. 3140 (London: Stationery Office) (1994)

2 Hastings P, Pennycook K and Bunn R *Handover, O&M manuals, and project feedback — a toolkit for designers and contractors* BSRIA BG1/2007 (Bracknell: BSRIA) (2007)

3 *Building log book toolkit* CIBSE TM31 (London: Chartered Institution of Building Services Engineers) (2006)

4 BS 8210: 1986: *Guide to building maintenance management* (London: British Standards Institution)

5 Nanayakkara R *Condition survey of building services* BSRIA AG4/2000 (Bracknell: BSRIA) (2000)

6 Pearson C and Barnard N *Guidance and specification for thermal imaging of LV electrical installations* BSRIA FMS5/99 (Bracknell: BSRIA) (1999)

7 Pearson C *Thermal imaging of building fabric. A best practice guide for continuous insulation* BSRIA TN 9/2002 (Bracknell: BSRIA) (2002)

8 Barnard N and Pearson C *Guidance and the standard specification for thermal imaging of non-electrical building services installations* BSRIA FMS6/2000 (Bracknell: BSRIA) (2000)

9 *Asset management plans for educational buildings Section 3: Condition assessment* and *Section 3a: Getting into condition* (London: Department for Children, Schools and Families) (2003) (http://www.teachernet.gov.uk/management/resources financeandbuilding/schoolbuildings/premises/sbamps) (accessed March 2007)

Bibliography

Stock condition surveys — a guidance note (London: Royal Institution Of Chartered Surveyors) (1997)

Condition assessment surveys (London: RICS/Building Cost Information Service) (1995)

16   Legislation, compliance and good practice

Summary

This chapter provides an overview of key legislation relevant to building services. However, it does not claim to be comprehensive.

Requirements for inspection and testing are also considered. The appendix provides a summary of the requirements for compliance with legislation.

Building owners and operators have a significant challenge ensuring that the engineering services operate satisfactorily to achieve a safe and comfortable environment for building occupants. Coupled with this is the need to ensure security of supply of electricity, gas, water and other utility sources to enable the building to function.

This means that there is a need for regular inspection and maintenance to provide a measure of certainty that the plant and services will operate safely and reliably, as and when needed. In the past, failures to carry out the essential function of inspection and maintenance have resulted in instances of severe injury and even loss of life. This in turn has led to the formulation of statutory requirements and other recommendations relating to the management of building services.

A survey of facilities managers by BSRIA revealed that many had concerns about the ever-increasing volume of legislation, standards and codes of practice with which they had to comply. This chapter provides an overview of key legislation relevant to building services, although it cannot be fully comprehensive and it is not the intention to identify every item of legislation or code of good practice.

As well as ensuring that all appropriate legislation is being complied with, the necessary records and supporting information must be in place. This then provides a strong and defensible position should an incident occur.

16.1   Legislation

In many of the Acts and Regulations listed below, non-compliance can result in prosecution. A summary of selected compliance requirements is given in Appendix 16.A1.

Health and Safety at Work etc. Act 1974

This legislation was the first that applied to all work locations. The act places responsibility on employers and employees to work together to find solutions to problems. It is known as an 'enabling' act, for all British legislation relating to health and safety. Amongst many requirements, the act requires the provision and maintenance of safe systems of work by employers.

Building Regulations 2000

The legal framework is provided by the Building Act 1984 and relates to the design and construction of buildings. Where the planned building, or building extension, is subject to the regulations (and this applies to almost all buildings), then a set procedure must be followed to comply, in conjunction with the local authority building control office. Where buildings governed by these Regulations already exist, then copies of completion certificates must be on file. See also the Construction Regulations, below.

The Building Regulations are being used to provide the route to implementation of some important elements of the EU directive on the energy performance of buildings[1], for example, Article 3 (methodology for calculating the energy performance of buildings), Article 4 (setting of energy performance requirements), Article 5 (new buildings to meet minimum energy performance requirements) and Article 6 (existing buildings over 1000 m^2 undergoing major renovation to have energy performance upgraded to meet minimum requirements).

Confined Spaces Regulations 1997

Where entry by employees or others to a confined space is unavoidable, the appropriate risk assessments and arrangements for rescue in an emergency are mandatory.

Construction Regulations

The Construction Regulations apply to the broadest possible range of work from the most minor internal task to the largest building project and includes general building and engineering work, refurbishment and maintenance. The regulations are grouped under three headings: Construction (Design and Management)

Regulations 2007 ('CDM Regulations'), Construction (Head Protection) Regulations 1989 and the Construction (Health, Safety and Welfare) Regulations 1996. The CDM Regulations were revised following a consultation process by Health and Safety Executive (HSE) in 2002 and new regulations and guidance provided in 2007. These recognised the need to reduce the bureaucratic implications and replaced the Planning Supervisor with the CDM co-ordinator.

Control of Asbestos at Work Regulations 2002

Compliance is mandatory. The approach to dealing with suspect material can be summarised as follows:

— check type of asbestos (use a professional analyst)

— check concentration and extent

— arrange for an approved contractor to strip out the offending material or, if appropriate, seal or encase.

Full records must be kept and the asbestos register shown to all contractors who may work on the fabric of buildings, where asbestos may be found.

See also the HSE's *A short guide to managing asbestos in premises*[2].

Control of Substances Hazardous to Health Regulations 2002 (COSHH)

These regulations apply to all business and work related activity where hazardous substances are used. An employer or his/her representative (e.g. facilities manager), has a responsibility to assess all work situations to establish if employees might be exposed to a hazardous substance, be it a solid, liquid, vapour, dust, gas or biological agent. COSHH data sheets are available from all suppliers of hazardous substances.

Electricity at Work Regulations 1989

The regulations require that electrical systems should be constructed and maintained at all times to prevent danger or injury, as far as is reasonably practicable. However, some provisions within the regulations are absolute. It is, for example, the employer's responsibility to assess the risks of any tasks utilising electricity or electrical equipment and any tasks on or in the vicinity of electrical power supplies or systems. In certain situations it is stipulated that technical knowledge and experience are a prerequisite to avoiding danger or injury, and there is an obligation placed on the 'duty holder' (usually the facilities manager) to ensure that any electrical operatives employed (even if they work for another company under a contract) are competent to do the required work These regulations provide an example of where, in general terms, compliance can be achieved by observing the requirements of a British Standard, in this case BS 7671[3] (the *IEE Wiring Regulations*).

Further information can be found in the HSE's *Memorandum of guidance on the Electricity at Work Regulations 1989*[4].

Emissions into the atmosphere

Air quality and assessment is covered by a number of mandatory items of legislation including the Clean Air Act 1993, the Pollution Prevention and Control Act 1999, the Environmental Protection (Non-refillable Refrigerant Containers) Regulations 1994, and the Air Quality Regulations 2000. European Directives have driven much of this legislation, including the EU directive on substances that deplete the ozone layer. For facilities managers, the areas requiring greatest attention are in the installation and maintenance of air conditioning, refrigeration and firefighting systems.

Environmental Protection Act 1990

Building owners and operators now accept the need to protect the environment from indiscriminate disposal or leakage of waste. Facilities managers should ensure that not only is the company environmental policy in place but that implementation is achieved. Waste products should be accurately identified, transported by an accredited waste carrier and disposed of exactly as planned at approved locations. A responsible person should keep comprehensive records.

F-Gas Regulations

The EU F-gas Regulation[5] became law on 4 July 2006. This imposes obligations on 'operators' of this equipment from 4 July 2007. 'F-gases' include HCFs, which are the commonest refrigerants in use today. The regulation aims to minimise emissions of these gases, which affect global warming if they escape into the air.

'Operators' are defined as the people or organisations that have actual power over the technical functioning of the equipment. The legal responsibility for compliance with the regulation lies with the operator.

For stationary refrigeration, air conditioning and heat pump units over 3 kg charge (6 kg if hermetic), operators must:

— prevent leakage, and repair any leaks as soon as possible

— arrange proper refrigerant recovery by certified personnel during servicing and disposal

— carry out leak checks to the schedule shown in Table 16.1

Table 16.1 Schedule for leak testing under the F-gas Regulations

Quantity of F-gas in system	Testing requirement
3 kg or more*	At least once every 12 months
30 kg or more	At least once every 6 months
300 kg or more	At least once every 3 months; leak detection systems must be installed and, when in place, checking requirements are halved

* 6 kg if equipment is hermetically sealed

Note: where a leak has been detected and repaired, a further check must be carried out within one month to ensure that the repair has been effective

— ensure that only certified competent personnel carry out leakage checks

— maintain records of refrigerants and of servicing.

Regulatory Reform (Fire Safety) Order 2005, Fire Precautions Act 1971 and Fire Precautions (Workplace) Regulations 1997 (amended 1999)

Fire safety reforms have been implemented to simplify and consolidate existing fire safety legislation. The Regulatory Reform (Fire Safety) Order makes compliance easier by replacing existing legislation with a single fire safety regime applying to all workplaces and other non-domestic premises. Responsibility for fire safety is placed on the employer or 'responsible person' for the building who has to assess the risks of fire and take steps to reduce them.

Employers have a responsibility for carrying out fire risk assessments. They should ensure means of fire detection and means of giving warning are in place. Escape routes must be marked. Firefighting equipment should be in place and employees given instruction. Fire escape routes should be lit with emergency lighting. Records/log book should be kept of persons responsible, periodic reviews of arrangements and equipment and system tests. Further sources of information include: Building Regulations Approved Document B: *Fire safety*[6], CIBSE Guide E: *Fire engineering*[7], and HSE publications *Fire Safety: an employers guide*[8] and *Fire safety in construction work*[9].

Health and Safety (Display Screen Equipment) Regulations 1992

These regulations are mandatory and relate not just to the operators, computer monitors and visual display screens but also to work areas, desks, chairs, the work environment and the task. Regular and well-documented inspections by trained personnel are recommended.

Lifts, lifting equipment and escalators

If a lift has the capacity to carry passengers it should be treated as a passenger lift (as opposed to a goods only lift). Passenger carrying lifts are subject to the Lifts Regulations 1997 and the Lifting Operations and Lifting Equipment Regulations 1998 (LOLER). Facilities managers should ensure that appropriate and regular maintenance is carried out, that the statutory thorough examinations are carried out (normally every six months) and that the reports are kept for at least two years for inspection by health and safety inspectors. A lift log in which to record all events, including maintenance and breakdowns, is highly recommended. Escalators are not specifically required to have statutory examinations but the HSE guidance recommends that inspections be undertaken to meet the requirements of the Health and Safety at Work Act.

Lifting machinery and lifting equipment is subject to the Supply of Machinery (Safety) Regulations 1992.

Lightning protection systems

Every building having a lightning protection system should have records on file including 'as built' drawings and a log book in which all test dates and test results are recorded. Annual checks are recommended, refer to BS 6651[10].

Portable and transportable electrical equipment

Periodic inspection and testing is required for all portable and transportable electrical equipment, whether it is used on a construction site, as a maintenance tool or on an office desk. The frequency of inspection and testing should vary according to a deliberate policy and linked to the harshness of the task or the working environment. It would be normal for testing to be carried out by a competent person using appropriate test equipment. Details are given in HSE's HSG 107: *Maintaining portable and transportable electrical equipment*[11] and the IET's *Code of practice for in-service inspection and testing of electrical equipment*[12].

Management of Health and Safety at Work Regulations 1999

Much of the content of these regulations is 'absolute' and requires compliance. These regulations extend the employer's responsibilities as contained in the Health and Safety at Work Act. Employers are required to make an assessment of the risks to employees in the workplace (and others including visitors and members of the public, young persons and expectant mothers) and must keep records. If it is found that risks remain high, cannot be eliminated or if precautions are complex, a permit-to-work system should be employed.

Manual Handling Operations Regulations 1992

Avoidance is the key when considering the lifting of heavy loads and equipment. If lifting cannot be avoided, irrespective of the nature of the workplace, then the risk of injury must be assessed and reduced to a minimum. Compliance is mandatory and employee consultation should be a matter of course. The risk of injury is to be reduced as far as is reasonably practicable.

Pressure Systems Safety Regulations 2000

Pressure systems and equipment that contain fluid or gas under pressure can cause death or serious injury should the contents be released unintentionally. Each year in the UK there are about 150 dangerous occurrences recorded involving unintentional releases. The Pressure Systems and Transportable Gas Regulations 1989 have been replaced by the Pressure Systems Safety Regulations 2000, the aim of which is to prevent risk or injury from the release of stored energy.

Pressure systems are fully described in HSE Approved Code of Practice L122: *Safety of pressure systems*[13], but most commonly include compressed air systems and pressurisation units in heating systems, but may also include calorifiers and boilers depending on working pressures. Written schemes of examination and testing must be held on site and are normally drafted by insurance inspectors.

Reporting of Injuries, Diseases and Dangerous Occurrences Regulations 1995 (RIDDOR)

The Regulations relate to all accidents, injuries, diseases and dangerous occurrences in the workplace. The provisions and responsibilities of employers are extensive but, fortunately, are well documented in a number of publications. Compliance is mandatory. Near misses, where serious injury might otherwise have resulted, are to be included and authorities are to be notified quickly, usually by telephone in the first instance.

Other relevant legislation

There are too many Acts and Regulations to list here but comprehensive lists of legislation that apply to work and the workplace are contained in *Principles of health and safety at work*[14] and *Tolley's Health and Safety at Work Handbook*[15]. Further examples of UK legislation of which facilities managers should be aware include the following:

— Asbestos (Licensing) (Amendment) Regulations 1998

— Building Act 1984

— Building Regulations 2000

— Cinemas Act 1985

— Consumer Protection Act 1987

— Electricity Act 1989

— Energy Act 1983 and 1985

— Fire Precautions Act 1971

— Gas Act 1986

— Health and Safety (First Aid) Regulations 1981

— Noise at Work Regulations 1989

— Pollution Prevention and Control Act 1999

— Personal Protective Equipment Regulations 2002

— Utilities Act 2000

— Work in Compressed Air Regulations 1996

— Working Time (Amendment) Regulations 2003

— Workplaces (Health, Safety and Welfare) Regulations 1992

Appendix 16.A1 gives a summary of a compliance requirements for a selection of the legislation listed above including some non-statutory requirements.

16.2 Requirements for inspection and testing

There is a considerable amount of routine inspection, maintenance and testing which needs to be seen to be done in order to comply with statutory requirements. That is, maintenance should be evident and records kept of all work activity required by law. Some selected examples are given below.

16.2.1 Fire safety

The Fire Precautions (Workplace) Regulations 1997 were made under the European Communities Act 1993 and the UK Fire Precautions Act 1971. Responsibility for fire safety within a building lies with the employer, who is required to make an assessment of the risk from fire and keep a written record of this assessment. The Fire Service is able to offer advice and assistance in meeting this obligation and can provide guidance to avoid costly over-provision in this area.

Under the Fire Precautions Act there is a requirement for regular testing and inspection of fire alarm systems. This also includes the need to keep records of such tests. The same applies to sprinkler installations and fire extinguishers. Similarly, smoke extract systems, where they exist, need to be regularly tested to demonstrate their capability.

16.2.2 Gas safety

The Gas Safety (Installation and Use) Regulations 1998 were made under the Gas Act 1986. The regulations deal with safety, installation and use of gas fittings and cover gas storage, distribution, supply and use. Work on gas fittings and storage vessels may only be carried out by competent persons who hold a current certificate. The registration of competent persons is the responsibility of the Council of Registered Gas Installers (CORGI), the only body currently recognised by HSE. The regulations require employers to ensure that any gas appliance or system under their control must be maintained in a safe condition. Landlords are required to maintain gas appliances and their flues on an annual basis and provide tenants with a written record to this effect. Where inspections and supporting record documents are not to the required standard, technicians or their employers, can be taken to court and fined or imprisoned.

16.2.3 Water quality

Water quality inspections are based around the need to prevent any risk from *legionellae* bacteria. There is considerable guidance available such as HSE Approved Code of Practice L8: *The control of legionella bacteria in water systems*[16], CIBSE TM13: *Minimising the risk of Legionnaires' disease*[17] and BSRIA AG20/2000: *Guide to legionellosis — risk assessment*[18]. One important aspect, again, is the need to demonstrate that the inspection and testing regime is properly managed and the results are being recorded and acted upon.

16.2.4 Lifts and lifting equipment

The need for in-service inspection of lifts and escalators is essential and property owners and operators need to understand the difference between inspection and maintenance. Maintenance is the ongoing servicing (i.e. lubrication, cleaning and adjustment) whereas an inspection is similar to a motor vehicle's 'MOT' test, providing a 'fitness for purpose' certificate for a defined period into the future.

A person carrying out a lift inspection should possess such theoretical and practical abilities as to be able to identify defects and assess their importance. In general, in the UK, independent bodies of inspection engineers or insurance companies carry out inspections. The requirements for competence are described in the Lifting Operations and Lifting Equipment Regulations 1998 (LOLER).

The Safety Assessment Federation Ltd (SAFed) introduced its revised *Guidelines on the supplementary tests of in-service lifts*[19] in 2006. These have superseded the earlier SAFed *Guidelines for the thorough examination and testing of lifts* and HSE document PM7.

LOLER requires the planning, supervision and execution of lifting operations to ensure safety, the safe use of lifting plant, and periodic thorough examination by competent persons. The insurance companies recognised the value of guidance on inspection frequencies and provided indicative information shown in chapter 5, Appendix 5.A2, Table 5.A2.1.

16.2.5 Work equipment

The Provision and Use of Work Equipment Regulations 1998 require the nature and degree of risk associated with equipment and its use, and the means available to reduce those risks, to be identified by a competent person. Again, the insurance companies have provided recommendations, see chapter 5, Appendix 5.A2, Table 5.A2.2. Equipment owners and operators are required to determine the frequency of inspection.

16.2.6 Ventilation duct hygiene

HSC Approved Code of Practice L24: *Workplace health, safety and welfare*[20] states that: 'mechanical systems (including air conditioning systems) should be regularly and properly cleaned, tested and maintained to ensure they are kept clean and free from anything that might contaminate the air.' This has applied to all workplaces since 1996.

Guidance is available in HVCA DW/TM2: *Guide to Good Practice — Internal cleanliness of new ductwork installations*[21] and CIBSE TM26: *Hygienic maintenance of office ventilation systems*[22]. BSRIA has summarised reference sources and other guidance in BSRIA TN 18/92: *Ventilation system hygiene — a review*[23]. Ductwork is also covered by the HVCA's *Standard maintenance specification for building services*[24].

There are several recognised techniques for cleaning ductwork that are described in the above publications and are likely to be used by specialist duct cleaners to address particular situations.

16.2.7 Competency of staff

Building services maintenance is possibly one of the most regulated areas of work. There are many regulating authorities with which 'quality' service providers need to be registered to demonstrate their capability to carry out their work. Clients of these service providers, whether using direct employees or contracting in the service, need to be aware of the importance of using trained and competent staff. If there has been an accident or dangerous

occurrence, responsibility rests on the client and his/her professional team, to demonstrate that they have complied with their legal duties.

A competent person is one who, by virtue of training and experience, can perform specified tasks satisfactorily and safely.

Examples of regulating authorities are:

— *Council of Registered Gas Installers* (CORGI): CORGI registration demonstrates competency for work on gas installations. CORGI certification is provided to employers who register individual employees. The employee carries an identification card showing expiry date and classes of work able to be undertaken. Each employer has to apply for registration; employees do not transfer their registration to a new employer.

— *National Inspection Council for Electrical Installation Contracting* (NICEIC): the NICEIC is an auditing body for electrical contractors. The NICEIC does not certificate individuals. This is based on the requirements of the Electricity at Work Regulations 1989, under which employers must only employ competent persons to work on electrical installations.

— *Heating and Ventilating Contractors' Association* (HVCA): the HVCA has agreed with its members to institute a 'Quality Contractor' scheme, under which each participating company is audited every three years by an independent specialist monitoring organisation (e.g. BM TRADA) to check compliance with the scheme. This includes demonstrating that competent and trained staff are employed. This scheme became fully operational in mid-2003 and is intended to reduce the number of unprofessional contractors in the industry.

— *Trust Mark*: this is a government initiative introduced throughout the UK for domestic clients. Contractors wishing to be included are audited annually by an independent auditor (BM TRADA) and have to demonstrate compliance with criteria such as trained and competent staff. This initiative is also aimed at removing 'cowboy' installers.

Facilities managers need to be fully conversant with the requirements and legislation relating to staff competency. It is important to ensure that contractors or directly employed staff are fully trained and competent to undertake the work, not only to ensure that the installation is safe for the users but also that the employees are fully aware of the need for safe systems of work to protect themselves from possible danger. Examples of applicable legislation are the Health and Safety at Work Act and the Control of Substances Hazardous to Health Regulations 2002 (COSHH).

Clients also need to be aware of the environmental implications of work they undertake, particularly concerning the disposal of waste. They should also be aware of the implications of the Working Time Regulations 1998[25], since maintenance work, particularly arising from sudden and unexpected plant failures, can mean operatives are required to work long hours to return plant to normal operation.

16.3 Sources of maintenance guidance

The principal source of maintenance and operation information for a particular building should be the operating and maintenance (O&M) manual and 'hands on' equipment training provided at initial handover and following subsequent alterations and refurbishments. Information on the content of O&M manuals is available in BSRIA AG1/87.1: *Operating and maintenance manuals for building services installations*[(ref)] and BSRIA BG2/04: *Computer-based operating and maintenance manuals*[(ref)].

References

1   Directive 2002/91/EC of the European Parliament and of the Council of 16 December 2002 on the energy performance of buildings *Official J. of the European Communities* 4.1.2003 L1/60 (Brussels: Commission of the European Communities) (2003)

2   *A short guide to managing asbestos in premises* HSG227 (Sudbury: HSE Books) (2002) (http://www.hse.gov.uk/pubns/indg223.pdf) (accessed March 2008)

3   BS 7671: 2001: *Requirements for electrical installations. IEE Wiring Regulations. Sixteenth edition* (London: British Standards Institution) (2001)

4   Memorandum of guidance on the Electricity at Work Regulations 1989 HSR25 (Sudbury: HSE Books) (2007)

5   Regulation (EC) No 842/2006 of the European Parliament and of the Council of 17 May 2006 on certain fluorinated greenhouse gases *Official J. of the European Union* L 161/1 (14.6.2006) (Brussels: Commission for the European Communities) (2006) ('The F-gas Regulation')

6   *Fire safety* The Building Regulations 2000 Approved Document B (London: NBS/RIBA Enterprises) (2006) (http://www.planningportal.gov.uk/england/professionals/en/1115314110382.html) (accessed March 2008)

7   *Fire engineering* CIBSE Guide E (London: Chartered Institution of Building Services Engineers) (2003)

8   *Fire Safety: an employer's guide* (London: The Stationery Office) (1999) (http://www.archive.official-documents.co.uk/document/fire/index.htm) (accessed March 2008)

9   *Fire safety in construction work* HSG168 (Sudbury: HSE Books) (1997)

10   BS 6651: 1999: *Code of practice for protection of structures against lightning* (London: British Standards Institution) (1999)

11   *Maintaining portable and transportable electrical equipment* HSG107 (Sudbury: HSE Books) (2004)

12   *Code of practice for in-service inspection and testing of electrical equipment* (London: Institution of Engineering and Technology) (2001)

13   *Safety of pressure systems* HSE Approved Code of Practice L122 (Sudbury: HSE Books) (2000)

14   Holt A St.J *Principles of health and safety at work* (Wigston: IOSH Services) (2005)

15   *Tolley's Health and Safety at Work Handbook* London: Butterworths Tolley) (2006)

16   *The control of legionella bacteria in water systems* HSE Approved Code of Practice L8 (Sudbury: HSE Books) (2000)

17   *Minimising the risk of Legionnaires' disease* CIBSE TM13 (London: Chartered Institution of Building Services Engineers) (2002)

18   *Guide to legionellosis — risk assessment* BSRIA AG20/2000 (Bracknell: BSRIA) (2000)

19   *Guidelines on the supplementary tests of in-service lifts* (London: Safety Assessment Federation Ltd (SAFed)) (2006)

20   *Workplace health, safety and welfare. Workplace (Health, Safety and Welfare) Regulations 1992 (as amended by the Quarries Miscellaneous Health and Safety Provisions Regulations 1995)* HSC Approved Code of Practice L24 (Sudbury: HSE Books) (1996)

21   *Guide to Good Practice — Internal cleanliness of new ductwork installations* HVCA DW/TM2 (London: Heating and Ventilating Contractors Association) (1990)

22   *Hygienic maintenance of office ventilation systems* CIBSE TM26 (London: Chartered Institution of Building Services Engineers) (2000)

23   *Ventilation system hygiene — a review* BSRIA TN 18/92 (Bracknell: Building Services Research and Information Association) (1992)

24   *Standard maintenance specification for building services* (electronic database) HVCA SFG20 (London: Heating and Ventilating Contractors Association) (2004)

25   The working Time Regulations 1998 Statutory Instruments 1998 No. 1833 (London: The Stationery Office) (1998)

26   Hastings P, Pennycook K and Bunn R *Handover, O&M manuals, and project feedback — a toolkit for designers and contractors* BSRIA BG1/2007 (Bracknell: BSRIA) (2007)

27   BS 5839: *Fire detection and alarm systems for buildings* (6 parts) (London: British Standards Institution) (1988–2004)

28   BS 7671: 2008: *Requirements for electrical installations. IEE Wiring Regulations. Seventeenth edition* (London: British Standards Institution) (2008)

29   BS 5266: *Emergency lighting* (8 parts) (London: British Standards Institution) (1981–2007)

30   *Emergency lighting design guide* SLL LG12 (London: Society of Light and Lighting) (2004)

31   BS 6651:1999: *Code of practice for protection of structures against lightning* (London: British Standards Institution) (1999)

Appendix 16.A1: Compliance requirements

Table 16.A1.1 Summary of compliance requirements for a selection of items of legislation

Statute	Requirement	Implication	Means of compliance	Notes
Health and Safety at Work etc. Act	Employer to ensure health, safety and welfare of employees (all persons employed)	Employer to be fully conversant with responsibilities. Arrangements to be in place	Safe place of work and safe working environment. Health and safety policy to be written.	
Management Regulations	Risk assessments, employee training and co-operation between employees (and with temporary workers)	Appointment of competent person(s) from within or outside the organisation	Risk assessments and method statements. Comprehensive record system in place	
Gas Safety Regulations	Only competent and qualified operatives to work on gas systems	All gas fitters must be CORGI registered	Safe installation, maintenance and use of gas systems	
Lifting Operations and Lifting Equipment Regulations (LOLER)	Suitability of equipment to lifting task	Periodic thorough examinations by a competent person	Risk assessment required	
Provision and Use of Work Equipment Regulations (PUWER)	Provision of safe work equipment and safe use irrespective of age or origin	All activities involving work equipment are included	Implementation of schemes of inspection, thorough examination or test	
Fire Precautions Act	Fire risk assessments to be made and recorded	Few buildings are exempt	Provision of a framework for the control of fire safety	See BS 5839[27]
Electricity at Work	To prevent danger and injury from electricity in whatever form	Regulations apply to all places of work and all voltages	All electrical systems to be constructed and maintained to prevent danger at all times	Made under the Health and Safety at Work etc. Act 1974
Environmental Protection Act	Disposal of waste not to harm employees or the environment	Employers to be fully conversant with details of the Act	Written environmental policy, use of registered waste carriers. Documentation of waste disposal activities	

Table 16.A1.2 Summary of compliance requirements for some non-statutory guidelines

Standard etc.	Requirement	Implication	Means of compliance	Notes
BS 7671: *Requirements for electrical installations. IEE Wiring Regulations. Sixteenth edition*[28]	Regular inspection of fixed electrical installations	Health and safety	Inspection report signed by a competent person	
BS 5266: *Emergency lighting*[29]	Regular inspection and testing	Confidence in system operation	Inspection certificate signed by a competent person	Certificate format in BS 5266[29] and SLL Lighting Guide LG12[30]
BS 5839: *Fire detection and alarm systems*[27]	Regular inspection and testing	Confidence in system operation	Inspection certificate signed by a competent person	
BS 6651: *Lightning protection*[31]	Regular inspection and testing	Confidence in system operation	Inspection certificate signed by competent person	
Water quality	Prevent risk of *legionellae* bacteria	Inspection and test regime in place	Regime managed and records in place	See CIBSE TM13[17]

17 Health and comfort

Summary

Various factors are identified which, to varying degrees, come within the sphere of operation and maintenance responsibility and can exert an influence on the health, safety and well-being of the occupants of a building.

The first is indoor air quality. The influence of this on both external and indoor factors is discussed and the monitoring of air quality explained, with some of the key contaminant influences described in some detail. Air quality standards relating to health and safety are outlined.

Thermal comfort influences are dealt with, and the relationship between activity rates, clothing levels and ambient conditions are described.

The need for air distribution systems to supply fresh or purified air to work places is recognised and for duct and system cleanliness noted. Assessment of the potential effects of refurbishment works on the well-being of occupants is examined with factors such as noise, airborne contaminants and ventilation considered. Assessment schedules for air quality, air distribution installations and thermal comfort are recommended and outlined.

Health and safety law is based on the premise that elimination of hazards is much preferable to minimising the effects (the 'hierarchy of safety').

The progressive introduction of regulations to support the Health and Safety at Work etc. Act 1974[1] has led to increasing awareness by management of factors affecting the health, safety and welfare of the workforce. As well as the requirement to consider health and safety in operational procedures, a healthy environment must be provided in the workplace. Prominent in these considerations is air quality. Management should bear in mind not only contaminants that may be created by working procedures but also pollutants from the ambient environment that may be drawn into the workplace by mechanical or natural ventilation. The Construction (Design and Management) Regulations 2007[2] require designers to think about user comfort by the requirement to satisfy the Workplace (Health, Safety and Welfare) Regulations 1992[3], which include the internal environment.

Thermal comfort requirements under statutory obligations are very modest but management needs to be aware that productivity can suffer when temperature extremes are encountered.

Specific regulations cover the matter of cleanliness in ventilation systems in addition to the need for a supply of wholesome air to the workplace. As well as meeting these requirements, it is important for management to keep some form of written record of the measures taken.

17.1 Indoor air quality

Air quality within a building is influenced by external and internal factors. The ability to maintain satisfactory air quality depends on identifying the factors that affect air quality in a particular application, controlling or eliminating detrimental factors and promoting beneficial ones.

External factors include:

— vehicle traffic, including parking facilities

— building geography, urban or rural

— neighbouring land use, industrial or commercial.

Internal factors can include:

— occupant-related effects

— effects of furnishing equipment and building materials.

The primary methods of controlling air quality are:

— *elimination*: removing potential contaminants from the workplace

— *substitution*: replacing materials with alternatives that are less harmful

— *dilution*: the reduction in concentration of harmful contaminants through the introduction of less contaminated or uncontaminated air.

17.1.1 External factors

Ambient air pollution is generally caused by energy provisions for industry and by transport and its control in overall terms is, therefore, usually the responsibility of central or local government. External pollutants may be diluted by locating fresh air intakes away from pollutant sources. This normally involves siting ventilation air intakes at roof level, away from chimney flues, soil vents, standing water and cooling towers. Air ventilation intakes at ground floor level should be avoided wherever possible.

Where a ventilation air intake is unavoidably close to pollution sources, control measures must be implemented to remove or reduce contaminants to acceptable levels; CIBSE TM21: *Minimising pollution at air intakes*[4] gives detailed guidance.

17.1.2 Internal factors

The major sources of contaminants in the workplace are occupants, office furnishings and equipment. All may affect actual or perceived air quality. Occupants generate odours, skin flakes, bacteria and other bio-effluents. Office furnishings release solvent vapours including volatile organic compounds, such as formaldehyde, as does office equipment such as copiers which also release ozone.

All three primary methods of control are applicable to indoor pollution, i.e:

— eliminating contaminants by preventing the use of volatile solvents

— substituting where possible with water-based paints

— diluting dust and odours through the introduction of fresh, filtered air.

Ventilation systems with terminal recirculatory facilities may act as secondary contaminant sources as internally generated dust and microbes will, unless removed by regular filter replacement and cleaning, accumulate and be ejected back into the workplace.

Guidance on indoor air quality is provided in CIBSE Guide A: *Environmental design*[5] and CIBSE TM40: *Health issues in building services*[6]. Assessment of indoor air quality relies on the experience of engineers, building managers and air quality consultants to determine whether satisfactory ventilation rates are maintained, occupancy levels are within guidelines and housekeeping practices are effective.

17.1.3 Air quality monitoring

External contaminants may be assessed through visual inspection of fresh air intakes and their proximity to pollution sources. Local pollution data can be obtained from local authority monitoring stations. Specific contaminant sources such as generator flues, car park facilities and cooling towers should be monitored to determine any effects on the quality of ventilation air intake.

Petroleum or other fossil fuel-derived combustion products are the most common cause of deteriorating external air quality. Any fraction of vehicle or generator fumes may be sampled by an air quality consultant to determine whether infringement of World Health Organization (WHO) or Health and Safety Executive (HSE) guidelines has occurred. However, these pollutants are likely to cause an odour nuisance within a building before any one chemical component reaches unacceptable levels.

Where dilution to undetectable levels is not possible because of the siting of fresh air intakes or the need to maintain minimum fresh air supply rates, gas phase or absorption filtration should be applied to remove noxious fumes. Carbon monoxide cannot be removed by activated carbon filters, but most other harmful gases can.

Indoor contaminants cannot be exhaustively monitored without incurring excessive costs due to the low concentrations encountered and the large number of contributory substances. It is usual to monitor surrogate contaminants and, because of their association with other potentially harmful contaminants, arrive at an indication of relative air quality. Results may then be compared with similar property findings and World Health Organization or HSE standards to determine what standards are reasonably achievable, bearing in mind the nature of work, occupancy levels and ventilation system capabilities.

The following paragraphs cover the typical contaminants assessed.

17.1.3.1 Respired carbon dioxide

Ventilation is largely supplied to dilute body odour which is influenced by occupancy levels and the metabolic activity rate of occupants, see chapter 1 of CIBSE Guide A[5]. Respired CO_2 provides a useful indication of whether adequate fresh air is being supplied. Obviously, this can be determined only under normal occupancy conditions. Where occupancy levels are low, the room air volume itself may be sufficient to dilute respired CO_2. Under such conditions, monitoring may become an unreliable measure of odour dilution and more subjective methods may need to be employed. Analysis is normally carried out using colorimetric gas detection tubes or gas cells.

17.1.3.2 Airborne particles

Dust arises from human activity, deterioration of building and furnishing fabric, and work practices. Particles may be drawn in from the external environment by the ventilation system or generated in the workplace. The majority of dust is harmless to healthy adults although some particles may carry harmful chemicals arising from fuel combustion or pathogenic microorganisms shed by occupants. What proportion of dust presents a particular hazard cannot be readily determined. The total dust burden is measured, therefore, and assumptions made that the greater the dust burden, the poorer the air hygiene and the greater the likelihood that harmful contaminants are present. Analysis is normally carried out using a laser particle counter or by gravimetric (filtration) methods. If there is a suspicion of asbestos, this must be thoroughly investigated.

17.1.3.3 Noxious gases

Noxious gases may be introduced from outside the building through the ventilation system or generated within the workplace. Typical gases sampled for include ozone, formaldehyde, carbon monoxide, oxides of nitrogen and sulphur dioxide.

Volatile organic compounds are often sampled as part of detailed building investigations but, as they are unlikely to be present in significant concentrations, sampling to establish their presence and concentration can be expensive. Recognising that HSE standards are not likely to be breached in the indoor environment, and that no recognised indoor standards are available for these gases, sampling should be carried out only in exceptional cases. In most cases a visual inspection of a building should be sufficient to highlight any gaseous contaminant sources and to decide on means for controlling these.

Analysis of noxious gases is carried out using a variety of methods, normally involving a colour indication analysis tube or chemically impregnated paper. Infrared electronic detection systems are also available, but these often require regular calibration. Invariably the lower the detection limit required, the less portable and more costly the sampling device.

17.1.3.4 Microorganisms

Bacteria and fungi are always present in the indoor environment but, in most cases, not at levels to be significantly detrimental to healthy adults. Microorganism concentrations are largely a result of occupancy levels and served environment hygiene practices within the occupied environment. Temperature, humidity and fresh air ventilation rates affect their proliferation, and satisfactory control of these components should ensure that microbe levels are not detrimental to occupants.

Airborne microorganisms may be sampled by drawing air across a growth medium followed by laboratory incubation and analysis to allow enumeration and species identification.

17.1.4 Air quality standards

For the purpose of health, safety and welfare, exposure to any contaminant known to be detrimental to health or to cause a nuisance such that normal work activities cannot be pursued, must be eliminated regardless of whether or not any air quality guideline has been breached. Exceptions to this are where exposure to pollutants is unavoidable because they form a normal part of work practices.

Within the UK, the HSE publishes occupational exposure standards and maximum exposure limits for harmful substances[7]. These should be consulted in the event that elimination is not possible to ensure that control measures meet the stated criteria. The World Health Organisation (WHO) publishes air quality guidelines[8] based on observable health effects and includes a margin of protection for more sensitive individuals. These standards are recommended where it is not reasonable to expect exposure.

17.2 Thermal comfort influences

The amount of heat generated within buildings is higher now than in the past due to increases in occupant density and in the amount of electrical equipment and, especially, personal computers. Consequently, internal comfort conditions have become more difficult to achieve and control. Poor thermal control is largely responsible for the discomfort of occupants, both directly and through increased perception of poor air quality.

Comfort depends on occupant activity, clothing and ambient conditions including air temperature, air movement and radiant heat sources.

The aim of air conditioning is to control the thermal environment, largely through simple adjustments to air temperatures. The method by which air temperature is adjusted and the effect that this has on overall comfort control will depend on the form of air conditioning employed and its ability to provide a uniform thermal environment. Increased cooling demand may be met by increased cool air supply, which may lead to increased air movement and discomfort from draughts. Alternatively, the demand for greater heating may affect relative humidity resulting in detrimental physiological symptoms.

Heating, ventilation and air conditioning systems are designed and installed to meet predicted thermal loads and occupancy patterns for a particular building design. The ability of the system to maintain comfort is assessed at the commissioning stage by recording cooling and heating temperature and air volume flow rates during system regulating procedures. Air movement in the conditioned space may also be measured at this stage. Confirmation that design assumptions are adequate cannot be given until actual occupancy levels are realised and the full range of weather conditions experienced.

17.2.1 Pre-occupancy environmental monitoring

Time constraints often preclude a comprehensive thermal assessment of the building environment at the pre-occupancy stage; factors such as normal occupancy conditions, thermal load and weather conditions cannot be readily simulated to obtain the operational performance of a building throughout a complete annual cycle. Instead, commissioning and its resulting data have to be relied on at this stage and, for this reason, adequate time must be allowed for the commissioning process.

It must be assumed that any alterations to the intended use of the building will have taken due account of the original design capabilities of the structure and its engineering services.

17.2.2 Post-occupancy environmental monitoring

As part of routine maintenance, air temperature and relative humidity will be monitored, through either a building management system (BMS) or manual measurements. However, this does not take into consideration the effects of air movement, radiant heat sources and personal preferences.

The two primary means of determining whether satisfactory comfort is maintained are physical monitoring and personal evaluation by trained maintenance personnel, independent consultants and building occupants. A comprehensive assessment can be carried out in accordance with ANSI/ASHRAE Standard 55-2004[9] or equivalent. Where comfort control has been brought into question, experience, observations and communication with occupants to establish their views are all that is necessary to carry out a preliminary assessment.

The factors that affect comfort and the effectiveness of the air conditioning systems, together with the way they interact and how they can be manipulated, must be understood before any meaningful assessment of post-occupancy environmental monitoring can be carried out.

17.3 Air distribution systems

Air handling units should be operated in accordance with The Workplace (Health, Safety and Welfare) Regulations 1992[3], pursuant to the provision of a suitable volume of fresh or purified air. This requires that the highest appropriate standards of filtration be applied and that ongoing maintenance be based on reasonably practicable planned preventive measures, including hygiene.

Air handling units must be routinely inspected to ensure that deteriorating components, such as spent filters, are replaced as necessary and that other conditions likely to affect air quality — for example, water pooling within condensate drain trays or carry-over water on duct surfaces — are prevented or controlled. Minimum standards of cleanliness should be applied based on visual inspection and scheduled maintenance periods. Such routine inspections will be facilitated if the items to be inspected are located in easily accessible areas.

As standards of cleanliness are partly subjective, some components should be cleaned as a matter of routine. These components include air intake equipment prior to filtration, post-filter chambers, condensate trays, cooling coils during the cooling period and humidification equipment during the heating period.

Filter condition provides the most convenient indicator of other condition-related maintenance requirements, and full cleaning of all air handling unit components should be undertaken at least once a year to return these to optimum hygienic condition. Unexpected contamination should be investigated to establish its source and whether it constitutes a risk to occupants.

Risk assessments should be prepared for each air handling unit to identify specific maintenance requirements and to confirm that adequate air filtration is applied, as determined by minimum filter standards and air source evaluation. The risk assessments should take account of any harmful deposits that may build up in the system.

The effectiveness of ongoing maintenance should be periodically assessed and validated independently to confirm that satisfactory standards are being achieved. Annual inspection of air handling units is recommended, although representative units may be examined more frequently and their condition taken as indicative of similar systems.

Independent assessment is, to some extent, subjective, which is why attempts have been made to examine cleanliness based on the mass of dust and dirt deposition over a given surface area. One problem with this is that dirt often accumulates unevenly so that sampling from different areas will give different impressions of the cleanliness of a system. With this in mind, and assuming no other interests, an independent visual inspection is recommended. Representative photographs may be provided to assist in an objective evaluation of report findings.

17.3.1 Air distribution ductwork

New ductwork needs to be stored and installed in accordance with current standards of good practice, particularly to ensure the prevention of contamination. Independent inspections should be undertaken during installation and at the final inspection for deficiencies and defects. At the time of installation, adequate access should be provided to facilitate inspection of sensors and fire curtains, and to monitor cleanliness.

The handover of clean ductwork and high standards of ongoing maintenance should limit subsequent contamination of duct surfaces. Air handling equipment should be assessed at least once a year to provide an accurate indication of cleanliness. Representative areas of ductwork may then be examined. For an office type of working environment this would typically be on a five-yearly basis. Other ductwork systems, e.g. such as kitchen extract where a fire risk applies and laboratory/hospital supplies where cleanliness standards are even more critical, require more frequent examination. Where distribution systems are extensive, separate areas may be examined more frequently, providing an indication of the condition of similar duct runs; see also HVCA TR19: *Guide to good practice — cleanliness of ventilation systems*[10].

The cleanliness of supply ductwork systems is more serious than that of extract duct systems because of its more direct association with occupants; nevertheless, extract duct systems should be kept under review especially where air recirculation is operated.

Distribution ductwork systems with an unknown or questionable maintenance history may be affected by more significant contamination. More importantly, ducts or plenums may be of an age where the materials contain asbestos and are now deteriorating. The passage of supply air across damaged or unsealed asbestos tiles presents an unacceptable hazard.

For most applications, the ratio of air volume flow rate to the exposed internal surface area of the duct makes it unlikely that HSE exposure limits for airborne asbestos fibres[7] will be exceeded. However, an avoidable hazard remains and a failure to take reasonable control measures is likely to be poorly received by building occupants.

An asbestos register should clearly identify all asbestos materials. Damaged surfaces in contact with air should be replaced with non-asbestos alternatives as soon as practicable. All other asbestos should be sealed with a view to removal at the earliest practicable opportunity. Airborne fibre sampling should be carried out at supply diffusers to confirm compliance with current standards.

Other distribution network contaminants with no specific hazardous components should be assessed as to their likelihood of affecting air quality and the health and well-being of occupants of the conditioned space. Typical contaminants comprise a mix of organic and inorganic debris including vehicle-derived combustion products, vegetation, silica dust and recirculated dust such as skin flakes, paper and textile fibres. The effect of this contaminant mix is unknown although likely to contribute to at least superficial infection; it should, therefore, be prevented from accumulating to any significant degree.

Standards of cleanliness have been adopted by trade associations representing those involved in duct cleaning in an attempt to regulate the industry. It is advisable that specialist consultants who have no direct involvement with the physical cleaning of ductwork within the building be made responsible for determining the appropriate level of cleanliness for a particular situation. Illustrative photographs of existing conditions can help to provide an objective assessment of the initial state of the ductwork.

17.4 Modifications to existing buildings

An assessment of any major modifications and refurbishment should be undertaken to determine the effect on building occupants and maintenance staff. The headings below are indicative of the areas that should be addressed.

17.4.1 Noise nuisance

Can normal office work continue without interruption? If not, what precautions are necessary? Consider the following options:

(a)   out of hours working

(b)   acoustic barriers

(c)   relocation of local office staff for the duration of work

(d)   ear defenders for maintenance staff.

Monitor noise levels during the works and record sound pressure levels to confirm that preconstruction assumptions were correct. If noise levels exceed the control limits, review precautions and modify as necessary.

Account also needs to be taken of the noise that mechanical plant can make as part of an assessment in selecting the plant for a building. Noise is also a health and safety in design issue. There is no point in having clean air and unbearable noise.

17.4.2 Airborne contaminants

Which of the following contaminants are likely to be released into the air?

(a)   particulates

(b)   fibres

(c)   gases and vapours

(d)   microbes.

What concentrations are likely to arise? Who will be affected? What precautions are necessary to protect health, safety and welfare?

17.4.3 Personal protective equipment

Assess the type of protection necessary to prevent nuisance or adverse health effects. Office modifications are likely to generate dust which may constitute a nuisance to maintenance staff and building occupants in the locality of the works; additionally, some of the dust released may contain recognised hazardous materials (e.g. glass fibre or asbestos). Any activity generating dust will require the protection of maintenance staff, office occupants and equipment, including ventilation systems.

Dust, in itself, may cause irritation while associated microorganisms may be released in high concentrations, particularly during the renovation of old structures. Vapour migration from construction materials may occur during the works and for some time after the work is completed. Adhesives used in construction will have been assessed as safe for use although most will specify the need for ventilation to control concentrations and dilute odours. Precautions should be taken to protect construction workers and building occupants from inhalation, ingestion and skin contact with potentially hazardous materials. Protective measures can include ori-nasal masks, gloves and dilution by supply air ventilation or local exhaust ventilation.

Enclosures should be erected around the work area, or at access routes, to contain contaminants. Coveralls, eye and respiratory protection should be provided as necessary for anyone working within the enclosure. Gloves should be supplied to prevent skin irritation, particularly for eczema sufferers.

Monitor contaminant levels within and local to the enclosure to confirm effective control. If control levels are exceeded, modify precautions.

17.4.4 Ventilation

Ventilation systems offer a means of controlling contaminants, including collection and removal. Measures should be taken to ensure that adequate fresh or purified air is provided to dilute generated contaminants. Recirculating systems should be isolated within the work zone to prevent distribution of contaminants to other occupied building areas. Extract diffusers should be taped shut and terminal recirculatory systems isolated unless required for ventilation and comfort control. Terminal equipment should be examined before starting the works and after completion to assess the need for filter replacement and unit cleaning.

Where extract ventilation has been isolated, local exhaust ventilation may be required to prevent pressurisation of the work area. Exhaust ventilation will also help consequent contaminant dilution. Contaminants should not be exhausted into the atmosphere without an assessment of the discharge point to confirm that it is safe to do so.

Treatment (filtration) of the exhaust may be necessary depending on property boundaries, the discharge point and height, and the prevailing wind direction. See also CIBSE TM21[4].

17.4.5   Who is to carry out safety assessments?

For the majority of refurbishments and modifications, familiarity with the hazards through day-to-day experience should be sufficient to identify the effect of work on the building environment and occupants and to recommend the appropriate control measures and precautions. Monitoring the effectiveness of precautionary measures may require the assistance of a competent person, such as an occupational hygienist or air quality consultant to provide independent assurance that the health, safety and welfare of occupants is protected. It is important that his/her recommendations be acted upon.

17.4.6   Notification and record keeping

Notification of construction work should be made in writing to building and office managers. Records of the safety assessments, together with noise and air quality analysis results, should be kept within an on-site building log identifying assumptions made and precautions implemented.

17.5   Recommended assessment schedules

17.5.1   Air quality monitoring

Initial assessments are recommended at handover, prior to occupation, to confirm that satisfactory standards of air quality have been achieved and that system ventilation operation is unlikely to be detrimental to the health of occupants.

Ongoing assessments are carried out under normal occupancy conditions and should be carried out within one year of handover to confirm that satisfactory office and air distribution system hygiene standards are being maintained.

Routine monitoring should be carried out at the building facilities manager's discretion and on the basis of initial assessments. It is recommended that air quality indicators are routinely reviewed to assess seasonal variations, confirm the validity of initial assessments and demonstrate a commitment to the maintenance of satisfactory working conditions. Reviews of air quality may be carried out quarterly together with assessments of the air distribution system and thermal comfort. The actual frequency will be a balance between building size, age and budget constraints.

17.5.2   Air distribution system

Initial assessments are recommended during installation works to confirm that ductwork and equipment is delivered to site in a satisfactory condition of cleanliness and that storage arrangements minimise the entry of dust and contaminants. Installation proposals should be reviewed to confirm that adequate access has been allowed to facilitate maintenance and inspection. An intermediate inspection may be carried out at first fit and a final inspection as part of defect and deficiency inspections.

Ongoing assessments are recommended on an annual basis to validate the efficacy of planned preventive maintenance. The actual frequency of assessment should be based on the number of air handling units using, say, a three-monthly inspection while ensuring that each unit is inspected annually.

See also HVCA TR19: *Guide to good practice — internal cleanliness of ventilation systems*[10].

17.5.3   Thermal comfort

Initial assessment cannot determine the effect of occupants and equipment until normal occupancy conditions are realised. Likewise, the effect of solar gain and weather conditions cannot be assessed by carrying out a one-off spot check. Instead, commissioning data must be relied on.

Once the building is occupied, building maintenance personnel should record air temperatures and relative humidity levels as part of ongoing routine assessments. Occupants' comments as to satisfaction with working conditions should be monitored where appropriate and compared with BMS data and manual temperature readings to ascertain the likely cause of any complaints.

Periodic independent assessment is recommended to validate routine monitoring. Where dissatisfaction cannot be readily attributed to monitored conditions, assessment of the thermal environment should be undertaken. This should include a visual assessment of the workspace, together with measurement of air speed, draught, radiant heat gain, air temperature and humidity. Where occupant complaints are concentrated within one section or department it may be appropriate to review the relevant work practices and management techniques.

Routine monitoring at an appropriate frequency should be carried out to confirm satisfactory sensor calibration. Independent validation of control sensor settings may be carried out to identify discrepancies. Special investigations should be carried out in response to an exceptional level of complaints (e.g. in excess of 15–20% of occupants).

17.5.4   Modifications to existing buildings

Initial assessments should be carried out local to the construction enclosure to determine the air quality prior to the commencement of work. Where routine monitoring is an existing part of control strategies, data will already be available.

Ongoing assessments should be carried out at the earliest period during renovation work to determine the effectiveness of preventive measures and confirm the maintenance of satisfactory air quality throughout the remainder of the workplace.

References

1   Health and Safety at Work etc. Act 1974 (London: Her Majesty's Stationery Office) (1974)

2   Construction (Design and Management) Regulations 2007 Statutory Instruments 2007 No. 320 (London: The Stationery Office) (2007)

3   The Workplace (Health, Safety and Welfare) Regulations 1992 Statutory Instruments 1992 No. 3004 (London: Her Majesty's Stationery Office) (1992)

4   *Minimising pollution at air intakes* CIBSE TM21 (London: Chartered Institution of Building Services Engineers) (1999)

5   Environmental criteria for design (ch. 1) in *Environmental design* CIBSE Guide A (London: Chartered Institution of Building Services Engineers) (2006)

6   *Health issues in building services* CIBSE TM40 (London: Chartered Institution of Building Services Engineers) (2006)

7   *Occupational exposure limits* HSE EH40 (Sudbury: Health and Safety Executive) (revised annually)

8   *Air quality guidelines for Europe* (Copenhagen: World Health Organization) (1987)

9   *Thermal environmental conditions for human occupancy* ANSI/ASHRAE Standard 55-2004 (Atlanta GA: American Society of Heating, Refrigeration and Air Conditioning Engineers) (2004)

10   *Guide to good practice — internal cleanliness of ventilation systems* HVCA TR19 (London: Heating and Ventilating Contractors Association) (2005)

Bibliography

Workplace health, safety and welfare. Workplace (Health, Safety and Welfare) Regulations 1992 (as amended by the Quarries Miscellaneous Health and Safety Provisions Regulations 1995) HSE L24 (Sudbury: HSE Books) (1996)

Management of health and safety at work. Management of Health and Safety at Work Regulations 1999 Approved Code of Practice and guidance HSC L21 (Sudbury: HSE Books) (2000)

How to deal with sick building syndrome HSE HSG132 (Sudbury: HSE Books) (1995)

General ventilation in the workplace. Guidance for employers HSE HSG202 (Sudbury: HSE Books) (2000)

Harrington J M, Gill F, Aw T-C and Gardiner K *Occupational health* (Oxford: Blackwell Science Publications) (1998)

The Control of Substances Hazardous to Health Regulations 1999 Statutory Instruments 1999 No. 437 (London: The Stationery Office) (1999)

The Control of Asbestos at Work Regulations 1987 Statutory Instruments 1987 No. 2115 (London: Her Majesty's Stationery Office) (1987)

Environmental design CIBSE Guide A (London: Chartered Institution of Building Services Engineers) (2006)

Loyd S R *Guidance and the standard specification for ventilation hygiene* BSRIA FMS1 (Bracknell: Building Services Research and Information Association) (1997)

Indoor air pollution — an introduction for health professionals EPA 402-R-94-007 (Washington DC: US Environmental Protection Agency) (1994) (http://www.epa.gov/iaq/pubs/hpguide.html) (accessed March 2008)

Hansen D J *The work environment: indoor health hazards* (vol. 3) (London: Taylor & Francis/CRC Press) (1994)

BS EN ISO 14001: 2004: *Environmental management systems. Requirements with guidance for use* (London: British Standards Institution) (2004)

BS ISO 14004: 2004: *Environmental management systems. General guidelines on principles, systems and supporting techniques* (London: British Standards Institution) (2004)

BS EN ISO 19011: 2002: *Guidelines for quality and/or environmental management systems auditing* (London: British Standards Institution) (2002)

18   Training

Summary

An organisation's personnel are recognised to be its greatest asset and the training of staff needs to be planned and managed. The achievement and demonstration of individual and corporate competency is discussed together with the need to have a formal training policy.

Reference is made to the importance of identifying particular training requirements and more general training needs such as coverage of health, safety and quality management. An organisational plan and a dedicated budget are proposed for the training activity.

Means of providing training are highlighted and the importance of a suitable training environment is identified.

The need to 'confirm' training by some form of certification in order to evaluate the results and to keep records of training individual personnel is identified.

The greatest asset of any organisation is its employees and developing their skills is a sensible investment. Employees need to replace or refresh existing skills throughout their careers in order to maintain their market value. In turn, well trained and committed staff are better able to contribute to the future success of the organisation.

Training is a management tool that enables a company to attract and select the best qualified personnel and to retain them. A prospective employer which is able to demonstrate clear career opportunities and objectives, and that promotes development training, will always be in demand.

A commitment to training is essential to the success of an organisation. Training should be a strategic priority in the management and future development of businesses. Training is a long-term investment, but an area that has traditionally suffered from cost-cutting in many organisations seeking higher levels of profit. Unreserved commitment from senior management is essential to developing a culture where training is properly valued throughout an organisation. The HVCA includes a requirement for a training policy to be in place supported by records of employees' skills and competencies as part of their membership assessment scheme.

Many professional institutions, and CIBSE is no exception, require their members to keep themselves up to date in their technical, professional and managerial knowledge by undergoing continuous professional development (CPD).

18.1   Management

The organisation of training cannot be left to chance; lack of consistency of purpose will result in failure.

Organisations should begin by identifying the most important operational requirements or problems to highlight training needs. They must then plan and initiate the training, which may be from in-house resources or by a specialist training provider. The selection of an outside specialist may require a small-scale trial to assess the suitability, effectiveness and cost. Once a satisfactory source or method has been identified, the training should be implemented. There is then an ongoing role in evaluating the effectiveness of the training. The cycle is one of learning and ongoing improvement. What forms of training do and do not work for that organisation are learnt systematically through an iterative process.

Emphasis on short-term profits must be countered by demonstrating the effectiveness of training and the benefits to the organisation.

18.2   Competency

Within the building services industry there is an increasing requirement for designers, engineers, technicians and tradesmen to be able to demonstrate and prove competence. It is particularly important that those involved in an operation or process that is inherently hazardous are competent to perform the required tasks safely. The maintenance function is also responsible for the provision and management of internal comfort conditions for the building occupants and the business critical engineering support services which allow the business to function.

Employers have a responsibility to do all that is reasonable and practicable to ensure that correct and appropriate training is provided to ensure that employees are competent to undertake their roles.

The Management of Health and Safety at Work Regulations[1] define a competent person as 'a person who has sufficient training and experience or knowledge and other qualities'. BS 3811[2] defines it as 'a person who by virtue of training and experience can perform specified tasks satisfactorily and safely.' BS 3811 defines 'competence' as 'the ability to perform a specific activity or range of activities satisfactorily and safely by virtue of training and experience.' Proof of competence is enshrined in health and safety legislation and much of that legislation applies to the building services industry. The need to demonstrate or prove competency applies as much to the designer and engineer as it does to the technician and tradesman. Training at every level should be focused, organised and delivered to meet that requirement.

18.3 Training policy statement

The organisation (internal or external) charged with the responsibility for operating and maintaining a building needs to identify a policy that provides a clear statement of what it is seeking to achieve by way of training and development. The policy statement should identify the technical, health, safety, quality and performance standards relevant to the operation and maintenance function.

The aims of the training strategy should be to:

— support and develop the business aims of the company

— identify the resources for training

— identify the benefits that will result from training

— enable managers and staff to contribute towards the achievement of business targets.

The training strategy should also set out key business targets and communicate these to staff, including the:

— importance of training within the company

— relationship between training needs and training

— importance of personal commitment to self-development.

18.4 Identification of training needs

18.4.1 Training needs and the building

To achieve the working or living environment, buildings utilise building engineering services to control that environment within appropriate limits. Buildings contain an increasing amount of advanced technology that controls not only the internal environment but also the business processes carried out within the building. Those responsible for operating and maintaining the building need to acquire and develop the appropriate technical and managerial competency.

In order that a building can be managed successfully, all the factors that contributed to the original decision to construct the building have to be understood:

— business objective

— building design concept

— method of construction

— building services

— financial objectives

— facilities management

— environmental and social issues

— core business process.

The skills and knowledge required to manage, operate and maintain the building services economically and effectively must be identified and suitable resources applied to carrying out that function.

The information contained within the operating and maintenance manuals, the record drawings, the commissioning records and the health and safety file, provide a comprehensive picture of the building. This set of data can then be used to develop the skills analyses and training outlines for both the building occupier and the engineering and maintenance personnel.

The service organisation must use this information when structuring the operation and maintenance function.

18.4.2 Assessment of training needs

The training needs assessment is used to compile a comparative inventory of the knowledge base and skills possessed by an individual operative against a specified competency outline. The difference between the specified requirements and the actual measured ability is the training required.

The use and provision of job descriptions for each of the core competencies within an organisation identifies the:

— key responsibilities

— levels of authority

— duties and demarcations

— qualifications.

If these basic competencies are established for each post, a training matrix can be created for the core posts within the organisation and this can be used as a comparator to assess training requirements for specific jobs.

The establishment of a training matrix has the additional benefit of providing a basis for reviewing the existing structure and future restructuring of the service organisation and also provides an employee selection criterion. There is no financial case for employing staff who do not satisfy the criteria identified within the job description; to do so will only increase the overall training costs.

Additional training needs will be required to meet particular project and organisational requirements. These may include:

— professional and technical qualifications

— trade skills

— management skills

— specialist process skills

— understanding of health and safety procedures and legislation

— understanding of environmental issues

— understanding of facilities management.

Health and safety is a subject that has increased in significance in recent years, as have quality and risk management.

18.4.2.1 Health and safety

The subject of health and safety is a major element of staff training. The establishment of safe systems of work for all the operation and maintenance functions is a statutory requirement. Staff have to be trained to understand the requirements of the legislation that apply to the tasks they are required to carry out and to recognise the possible risks to health in carrying out those tasks. Risk assessments need to be in place which identify the potential hazards, while implementation of safe systems of work should eliminate or reduce the risk.

Where the risk remains significant and the hazard cannot be eliminated, control measures need to be implemented. If the risk is life threatening, control measures should extend to more prescriptive arrangements such as permit-to-work procedures. Staff involved in these areas of work need to be trained specifically to understand and assess the risk, be able to meet the requirements and be certified by the organisation as competent to carry out specified tasks.

There must also be a health and safety plan (an extension, in effect, of the construction phase health and safety plan) that will plan, action, monitor and review all health and safety activities on a regular and continuous basis. Information and training has to be provided to ensure that all concerned understand the need for the procedures and how they are to be applied.

18.4.2.2 Quality management

Customers have an increasing expectation of service and performance. Engineering staff involved in the operation and maintenance of a building need to be provided with the appropriate skills in:

— customer awareness

— quality aims and objectives of the business

— quality management procedures

— performance criteria and measurement techniques

— individual responsibility for quality

— continuous improvement cycle.

18.4.2.3 Risk management

Those responsible for the management and operation of the maintenance function need to identify and understand the factors that represent the greatest risk to the continuity of the core business process. These should be formally documented and translated into procedures and work practices to eliminate such risks. The engineering management staff has to be trained to undertake the task of quantifying the risks and to prepare operation and maintenance working procedures that keep the risks to a minimum. The resulting information, understanding and working procedures then have to be conveyed to the operational staff.

18.5 Training plan

Training has a cost and this has to be accounted for financially. Each business unit or department within an organisation needs to identify:

— how the training will meet the business targets

— the resources that will be allocated

— the investment value within the annual business plan for the forthcoming financial year

— the method of measurement of the benefit achieved.

Training plans are subject to change. A process for the review of the training plan should be in place to ensure that:

— training is prioritised to meet the changing needs of the business

— actual commitment is made in accordance with the training plan

— training is delivered according to business or project needs

— any additional or new training requirements are identified and scheduled

— regular reviews of expenditure on training are undertaken.

Regular reviews of the training activity is essential to ensure that training meets both the short and long-term targets, that training remains effective and that there is a continuing commitment from all levels of management.

18.6 Means of provision

Having assessed the training needs, the method and resources to deliver that training have to be identified. Training can be delivered through:

— universities

— further and higher education colleges

— independent training organisations

— internal courses utilising expertise available within the business or the original design team

— distance learning courses

— cross-training

— multi-media/interactive training products

— trade organisations and professional institutions (e.g. CIBSE Professional Learning)

— equipment or product manufacturers

— seminars and conferences.

The choice of training method and provider will be based on the effectiveness and value for money required by the individual company. Where a business is centralised in one building, training is easier to deliver than in an organisation that has a number of offices spread over a large geographical area.

18.7   Environment

The training environment is a major factor in the effective delivery of training. Important elements affecting the effectiveness of training are:

— furniture comfort

— lighting levels, ventilation, temperature and humidity control

— quality and quantity of course material

— teaching equipment and facilities

— course tutors

— delegate class numbers

— a sympathy with and understanding of the requirements of individual delegates.

The effects of these elements are well understood by professional training organisations, but the same standards must be achieved in the delivery of any internal or site-based training. These, plus any additional personal variations, should be confirmed prior to any training commitment.

18.8   Certification

The certifying authority is an important issue in the selection of training courses, particularly where proof of competence is required. It is desirable that the certification is provided by a national or industry recognised authority.

Where there is no certifying authority, certification from other bodies may be accepted but should, generally, be restricted to:

— registered training organisations

— trade associations

— reputable manufacturers of plant or equipment relevant to the business.

18.9   Evaluation

Having provided the training, there needs to be evaluation to assess its effectiveness and to ensure that:

— skills acquired by the employee are adequate for the task or process to be carried out

— training has met the employee's training need

— training has met the overall business aims and objectives.

It is essential to prove measurable benefit as a result of providing training. The criteria for demonstrating the actual cost effectiveness or operational benefit of the training should be detailed and set out when the training programme is still at the approval stage.

18.10   Records

Good training records are essential to prove the competence and development of each individual employee. Ideally, the records should be:

— easily accessible

— available at all times

— reviewed on a regular basis

— kept up to date.

The training records have another important and valuable use; that is to provide statistics on the training carried out by the organisation. For example:

— number of person days of training carried out in any one period

— types of training provided

— cost of training provided.

These statistics should be made available to employees and customers, maximise the value of the training achievement.

References

1   The Management of Health and Safety at Work Regulations 1999 Statutory Instruments 1999 No. 3242 (London: The Stationery Office) (1999)

2   BS 3811: 1993: *Glossary of terms used in terotechnology* (London: British Standards Institution) (1993)

Index